You have come as a breath of fres
epoch maki

Professor B N

I found your book a joy to read. Many of the concepts you discuss
I've been interested in for years. For the lay audience, this book
will be a wakeup call about vibrations and electromagnetic
energies and I hope that students who read it will want to pursue
research in the many areas that need more study. You wrote an
excellent book and I hope it reaches a large and diverse audience.

Magda Havas

Talk of vibrations and energy is not acceptable in medicine. At
least that's what I learned in medical school. Scientific inquiry
is mainly funded by pharmaceutical companies studying drugs.
So, they aren't about to study vibrations and energy. Even though
medicine has to admit that placebos work better than drugs, they
pass that off as "unscientific." What are we left with? A society
that's educated by TV commercials pushing drugs and an inability
to take responsibility for our own health. I see in Matthew's book
a way for people from many different specialties to come together
and explore the many common sense truths that he exposes.

Dr Carolyn Dean

This book is long overdue, and being so easy to read will
make a large impact.

Ian Dejongh

Fantastic chapter... especially the link between water and vibrations, vortex and dynamisation, blood and diseases... Wow... This book is the 'missing link' so many people all over the world were expecting. This is no fiction, this is not only science, this is mind-opening!

Christian Callec

"This is a highly original and well-written book full of intriguing and thought-provoking information. The author's personal journey into science leads the reader down some fascinating highways and byways and offers up new ways of thinking about old issues.

Peter Argent"

A fascinating fresh look at a technology long forgotten. I can't wait to get to the next chapter.

Steve Krattiger

Wonderfully thought-provoking book. I am sure this book will open our minds, and that is what we need in this world, more than anything else. But why, I wonder, is science so blind

Alex St Clair

Scientists already acknowledge that they can't explain everything and how some things work. They also recognise that there is a force outside of what they know which makes things work. Challenges to scientific theory which includes past overlooked evidence such as this one will hopefully increase global sharing of knowledge and research and working together to look after the global community which is long overdue.

Jenny Waldie

A great inspiration!

Pamela Wheeler

Absolutely enthralling. Can't wait to read the rest of the book

Robert Mak

Thank you for writing about little-known scientists and their work - so sad that their work has fallen into near-oblivion.

Rosemary Mattingley

It's disappointing that science has turned away from this concept and have run in the wrong direction - taking the easier way out.

Ep Conway

Just a note to thank you again for your extraordinary efforts in this book, and offer our unqualified encouragement..

Odin Townley

The idea of vibrations interacting with each other is so obvious, yet seems to have eluded many of the scientists of our time.

Gill Graham

The book is a wonderful new addition as it carefully tries to bring new concepts and emphasises their importance after a careful study of many wonderful works.

Prof. Dr Khalid Mahmood Khawar

Very easy to read which will appeal to a larger portion of the population. Thank you.

Cath Andison

I was aware of some of the influences of the moon and planets on biological systems, but you show many studies of how much more influence there is. It is interesting how "science" is so dogmatic and belief oriented about certain things and prides itself on being open minded when in fact it is so closed.

Walter Jaworski

I applaud your bravery. It is not easy to tackle conventional science and allopathic medicine at this point in time without being attacked and even having a license removed. I loved your introduction. It caught my attention immediately and I really hope that many people read the book as it seems to me that 80% of people blindly accept whatever they are told and either do not research further for themselves or find different and possibly better solutions for their problems. I can verify that your statement that universities encourage research of only recent papers and texts is correct. This is very sad. We have lost so much knowledge over the years due to those in authority using the 'witch hunts' of all those who had herbal and healing knowledge for their destruction. Alternate therapies are denigrated publicly and there is even a movement to have them banned by law.

Cheryl Orian

Brilliant, refreshing and fascinating. Love it.

Justine Balaam

I loved the chapter on plants. Gardening will never be the same.

Sara Rasmussen

We owe you a debt of gratitude for making this
knowledge available.

Harry Vaughan

Absolutely refreshing read and succeeds in drawing
attention to the important work and research of an important
neglected scientist

Amelia Blass

It's books like this that, when read by the masses, will bring some
light into the area of alternative treatments. Thanks for doing
this Matthew!

Rob McIntyre

The world could be a much better one for everyone if we all
opened our eyes and mind. Thanks again for helping us doing it!

Rebecca Tuge

Congratulations on the book. You have pulled so much research
together it seems impossible for anyone to be able to discredit it

Valmai Hamlin

This is amazing. I'm so glad that you are sharing this information with the world. The next step is getting everyone to wake up and seek this information.

Bobby Flick

The more I read the more excited I am about your book. I really hope that you get this out to a wide audience. Sadly, so many people don't read and just accept what they hear on the TV or through the media.

Kevin Trundell

It's my lucky day finding a link to your book. The reading of the intro chapter was brilliant

Linda David

It's about time a book like this came along...Such a good read... couldn't put the book down!

Laura Bordin

I can't stop reading this book, it is so enlightening, combining many things I have considered but not understood.

Ruthsmith

This is such an informative book and very clearly written. Every single thought and idea is direct to the point. Perfectly laid out. Thanks for taking your time sharing this to your readers.

Joanna Hargreaves

Your explanation is so simplistic that even children can understand. Great, now we will have an easy to understand reference.

Constance Tracy Tayler

Wow. This info has some amazing implications.

Walter Martin

No longer do I have to keep many books around to read up on, just one.

Karen Robinson

Thank you Matthew for shaking some trees, so to speak

Charles Pienaar

A chatty, informative read about a deadly serious subject : Our health.

Tony Moody

This is a ground breaking book with a refreshing perspective.

Barry O'Donnell

You put into words all the concepts I've been screaming about for years!

Rosemary Kaessick

PUBLISHED BY
LLOYD'S WORLD PUBLISHING 2011

CONTACT: MATTHEW@BLINDEDBYSCIENCE.CO.UK

ISBN 978-0-9568656-0-1

BOOK DESIGNED BY THINKLATERAL
WWW.THINKLATERAL.COM

DEDICATION

This book is dedicated to Andrei Danila and
everyone like him who work too hard.

BLINDED BY SCIENCE

CONTENTS

INTRODUCTION

THE GERM OF AN IDEA

The real beginning for me, the initial seed of an idea for this book, bizarrely came from a tree. I am sure I have a pretty average knowledge of trees amongst a generation of other city-dwellers. I can recognise some trees, but very few of them. I know they grow leaves in the spring, which fall off in the autumn, although I know some trees keep their leaves all year round. I know I really love standing next to big trees, and for some reason I always find myself gravitating towards them while in the local park. I like trees, but besides climbing them as a child I don't think I have ever thought much about them. Until that day. The day that someone, for whom I had great respect, casually told me to go and touch a tree as it would improve my health.

Well, you can imagine my look of complete incredulity. It was probably one of the most ridiculous suggestions I think anyone had ever made to me – that I should go to the park, stand next to a tree and touch it. Just the thought of it was ridiculous. I am sure I had touched trees before, certainly while climbing them as a child, but I couldn't remember noticing any physical effect it had on me, either positively or negatively. You can understand therefore that I had no intention whatsoever of complying with my friend's wishes and being made to look an idiot in the park, leaning against a tree, getting better. I mean, for how long would I have to do it – one minute, twenty minutes, God forbid an hour? And which tree would I touch? A big one, a little one? He hadn't given me an instruction manual.

It came as no surprise to me that I didn't take him up on his idea, but what did surprise me enormously, however, was that my nineteen-year-old son took up his suggestion. Watching the result of him touching a tree completely changed my opinion and in fact opened my eyes to a whole new world. I mean, if a tree can affect us, what does that mean? The implications seemed to be huge – so much so that I wanted to investigate further and see what scientific evidence might lie behind this.

But I have moved on too quickly, without telling you what happened to my son that fateful day. To cut a very long story short, my son was suffering from severe chronic fatigue. Up until the point he became ill, he had been a straight A student who loved playing football. As a parent, you try all of the accepted medical routes, which in the case of chronic fatigue are very limited, most avenues taking you to psychiatrists. But as both my brother and my father are Professors of psychiatry, I knew there was no solution there – chronic fatigue is a physical problem, not a mental one. So what did we have to lose when we turned to "quackery science" as a method of treatment?

We were forced into this position when we were told by the doctors and complementary medical practitioners that they had run out of options and there was nothing more that could be done. It was my wife who suggested we try even the "crazy" ideas, for what did we have to lose? I remember that discussion vividly. We were sitting at our kitchen table feeling incredibly depressed when I turned to my friend sitting next to me and said, "Look how low we have sunk – we are actually going to try the services of a healer."

Now one point I have to make is this: women seem to be much more open to taking on new ideas than men. I am not sure I would have been brave enough to seek out the help of extreme alternative ideas, but it seems that women are much more likely to do so. Well done them! Anyway, whatever weird and wonderful things the healer, Lloyd Geddes, did are not relevant to this book, as the main thing to know is my son got better and was cured by Lloyd within six months. Three months into his treatment with Lloyd, my son became well enough to begin talking to us on the telephone. At this stage, though, we could still not be in the same room as him as it drained his energy levels too much. So we thought it would be a good idea to rent a cottage in the Norfolk countryside for a week, where he could sit outside in the garden (we don't have a garden at our flat in London), which might help his recuperation.

You have probably guessed by now that there was a tree in the garden. Just an ordinary old tree. It didn't look particularly interesting to me. But one morning I saw my son, dressed in just his dressing gown, go up to the tree and touch it. We had both been present when Lloyd had told us that there are benefits from touching trees, but it seems that my son was the only one who thought there was something in it. So I watched him for five minutes or so from the small kitchen window in the rented cottage, and then he suddenly stopped and walked back to the house; it was all over.

At this point, although the two of us were together in the rented cottage, he still was not well enough to talk to me, so I was not able at the time to ask him, firstly why he had done it, and then, once he had done it, whether there had been any effect on him. During that week, I only observed him doing it once; he never went back to the tree, or even near it again. Oh well, I thought, there is nothing in that idea, then. But how wrong I was.

It was in fact not until a month or two later, when he had got well enough to begin speaking to us, that I mentioned the time when we were away and I saw him touching the tree. I asked him about it, and he told me that he had to stop touching the tree that one time as it had literally made him feel physically sick. Now, to me, previously, I probably would normally have dismissed this as psychological stuff, it must have been all in his head, but the one nagging doubt was this simple fact. The only part of the healer's treatment that made my son feel sick was when he treated his liver, and this he tried to do as little as possible during his recovery; however, occasionally he "pinged" his liver, causing sickness sensations. So I thought, could a big tree really "ping" his liver in the same way the healer did? Was it really possible that a tree could in any way affect our physical well-being? I had to know more, and Lady Luck was on my side.

Lady Luck in this case was the fact that I live very near to the biggest library in the world, the British Library. It is a mere ten minutes' walk from my home. As I had become the permanent carer for my son, I had given up full-time employment, which meant I had plenty of time to pop into the library as often as I wanted to. It didn't take long to discover the fact there was nothing seriously written on "tree-hugging". It appeared to be just an idea that came from the 1960s and was associated with the use of LSD. When people took the drug, it seemed to stimulate something within their brain that allowed them to see lots of different colours emanating from the trees and plants, but pretty much that was all. So I started looking elsewhere in the library, searching with strange queries to see what would turn up, to see if maybe there were in fact studies on trees and their behaviour that could be relevant to my enquiries.

To say that my journey of research took me to places that I did not know existed is an understatement, as you will discover in the following chapters. As my journey unfolded, I made one fundamental rule – that all of my ideas must come from medical and scientific studies, not from opinion or hearsay but from proper studies. This was not a problem as there were millions of available research documents for me to choose from, and reading the bibliography of one article would always lead me onto further ideas. However, I have not made any judgements on any particular experiment, as scientists seem to do. I have not said that the size of the trial was too small to be of value. I take the opinion that if an experiment took place and ten people out of ten were cured, then that experiment worked; I don't think that the research should be dismissed because only ten people took part in it. Also, I have not dismissed research conducted more than twenty or thirty years or so ago, as often happens. In fact, all I require is that the work has been conducted by a scientist in the field of research, and that it has subsequently been published.

What I have found most unusual, however, is how biased Western ideas are against others from different cultures. Why should Western scientists have a monopoly on the truth: a study done in Russia by trained scientists in the 1970s should be just as acceptable as similar studies in the West. But it is very sad to report that, as you read this book, it will become obvious that this is not the case amongst research scientists. Most of the authoritative work conducted by Nobel prize-winning physicists in Russia into the effect of electromagnetic fields on the human body has been completely dismissed as incorrect and has been ignored. Only in Russia did they ban the microwave cooker when it first came out. What did they know that we don't? If it's going to affect my health, I feel I have a right to know.

One of the greatest disappointments, I believe, is the lack of progress that has been made in scientific attitudes over the last hundred years. In researching this book, I expected that science would operate on the basis of change, one piece of science helping to build up another piece of science so that each bit led to an advancement of knowledge along the road. But in many cases this is not what happens. In fact, I have read scientific papers written in the past few years that replicate papers written fifty years ago. Why would this be necessary? Why repeat the same research?

To give a simple example, a lot of people currently believe that some forms of cancer, such as pancreatic cancer, are in fact viruses. In order to cure the cancer, one form of treatment suggests that if you can calculate the frequency of the virus, you can blast it out of existence by hitting it with the same frequency – the virus will literally explode and disappear. This is in fact not a new idea but a very old one, discovered in 1935, but it highlights what I have found out while researching this book – that there are many major discoveries that have been completely ignored and passed over. Only today, in 2011, have scientists started treating pancreatic cancer by using ultrasound waves, harnessing a vibration to destroy the cancerous cells, the very same principle that was discovered nearly eighty years ago. If only scientists had not been restricted by dogma, ego and politics, we might already have had cures for specific cancers and many lives could have been saved.

The best way to understand why this happens is to analyse the industry of science as a whole, to see how research is funded, who receives funding and how topics for research are chosen. We also need to examine which scientific papers are published, who are the people who peer review them and what are the effects of the research once the paper has been circulated and read. In order to understand the scientific community, we might best adopt the expression that power stays in the hands of the few. Why else would revolutionary cures for cancer have been ignored for seventy years, or methods to increase crop production by the use of magnetic and sound waves been dismissed as nonsense?

The last great medically trained man who actually stood against the establishment was Culpeper, who lived as long ago as 1616–1674. No-one since then has really stood up against the medical profession. His story makes fascinating reading. He had to challenge the establishment whose members attempted to block his knowledge being spread freely to the poor who could not afford to pay doctors' fees. He was the Robin Hood of the medical establishment, translating Latin text into plain English and showing people how they could go into the woods and pick flowers that would cure them. This was a free alternative to visiting a doctor, which provided the same service but in Latin terminology. In one of his many comments, Culpeper wrote:

> "This not being pleasing, and less profitable to me, I consulted with my two brothers, DR. REASON and DR. EXPERIENCE, and took a voyage to visit my mother NATURE, by whose advice, together with the help of Dr. DILIGENCE, I at last obtained my desire; and, being warned by MR. HONESTY, a stranger in our days, to publish it to the world, I have done it".

The book in question was called *The English Physician*, and it was brought into life because of what Culpeper thought of as the unfair medical establishment. Culpeper had been apprenticed as a doctor but, due to his mentor running away with his money, he was not able to finish his studies to become a doctor. In the context of medical politics of the time, Culpeper decided he would not continue with his studies but would set up in opposition to the medical establishment, which he felt charged an unfair amount for its services.

At this time, in order to become a doctor, it was necessary to learn Latin. All of the medicines were catalogued using their Latin definition rather than their English one. In order to be prescribed the correct medicine, it was necessary to obtain its Latin name, which was not accessible to lay people at the time. Culpeper felt that this was an injustice and took it upon himself to write a book containing no Latin, so that it would be possible for the commoner to treat himself independently. But, more importantly, Culpeper chose to fill his book solely with herbal medicines that were easily available locally, so that it was no longer necessary to go to the doctor and pay lots of money for treatment. It was now possible to go out into the gardens or woods and just pick the herbs that satisfied your illness. Culpeper has been called "The first herbalist", which for most people in India, Asia, Africa, South America and parts of North America would surely be insulting, as they have followed a herbally based medicine since many thousands of years prior to the publication of Culpeper's book.

Sadly, Culpeper's ideas seem to have been overshadowed by the modern-day drug industry. I am not sure why, but when I walk past a Chinese medicine shop, I am very dismissive of the notion that anything sold within it could make me better. I have the same impulse when I walk past all herbalist shops – I would never entertain the idea of going inside and purchasing any of their herbs. What has made me think this way? Why do I think that a herb could not function as well as a drug created by Western pharmaceutical companies? I think it is because I have been brought up to believe from the media that Western science is superior, that you should always trust your doctor and the drug industry as they are there for your best interests. How blinded I am!

I feel sure that most people who are reading this would not dream of using a herbalist. If you asked people in the street who they would prefer to be treated by, a herbalist or a doctor, most people would say a doctor. But what they don't realise is that the job of a doctor is to prescribe drugs, drugs that have mostly originated from plants. Two historically very popular drugs – aspirin and quinine (an antimalarial agent) – come from the bark of a tree. In fact most drug companies today are looking to plants for new discoveries of the next generation of medicines that they hope will cure illnesses. If drug companies had consulted ancient herbalist books years ago, they would have discovered very quickly that a good many answers were already there. The problem for the drug companies is how to synthesise the chemical in the plant so that it can be reproduced in tablet form. There is no profit recommending that patients just take samples directly from the plant even though they are aware it might have curative properties.

One example that I came across to emphasise this point is a plant called Quebra Pedra (*Phyllanthus niruri*) or "stone blaster". This plant has been tested in a scientific experiment and been shown to cure gall stones in 95% of patients. You would assume, therefore, that doctors would recommend this to patients suffering from gall stones, as just taking this herb in tea can get rid of gall stones within two weeks. But sadly this is not the case; doctors prefer that the patient either takes drugs that are not always effective or, more commonly, has an operation to remove the stones. This is neither sensible treatment nor clever economics.

So why are there not herbalists in every high street selling plants of all descriptions to combat illnesses? Why is it only recently that we have been able to buy herbal supplements in specialist shops? There are now more and more Chinese herbalists in most major towns and cities, but their products are based on Chinese rather than English herbal medicine. The plants and trees available to the Chinese are quite different from those available in Europe, but why are there not many English herbalist shops, in this their native country?

The idea that herbs grown in the wild could make you well was a readily accepted part of life not that long ago. For many millions of people living throughout the world, this is still the case, but in Western medicine the idea that herbs are the solution to illnesses is constantly ridiculed. This is ironic since most drugs are chemically derived from plants, the very ones that Culpeper was referring back in 1652.

Before writing this book, I never at any time felt that my rejection of herbalism and my faith in pharmaceuticals was wrong.

Why would I question everything that I had been led to believe was true? Western medicine, with its double-blind studies and its peer-reviewed papers, was obviously the best way for science to progress, and only truth and good science would come out of it. Sadly, this is not what I have found to be the case. Yes, lots of good science has been developed, but so has lots of bad science, with years and years having been wasted on repeated studies and wasted opportunities. I hate to say it, but millions of people's lives could have been saved if scientists had been open to new ideas and had not closed ranks, just as they did back in 1652.

In my research for this book, I have read hundreds upon hundreds of papers on science. As I said above, one recurring theme seems to be that today's scientific papers rarely give much credence to scientific studies that were conducted more than thirty years ago. This might be due to access, as it is often hard to get hold of a published paper that is out of print or a book that is hard to find. It is mostly only papers that have been published in the last twenty years that have been put online. If you are a scientist who is looking to develop a new area of research and wants to investigate whether a similar line of enquiry has been developed before, all of your research would take place online unless you had access to a great library. This would significantly restrict your level of research, and you would not know if the study had previously been conducted. I also believe that it is common practice not to look at studies that were conducted more than forty years ago in the belief that if it was important, it would be common knowledge in textbooks today. This is a misguided point, as I have discovered a great deal of lost science in books written as long ago as 1910 that seems to have been completely forgotten.

Another current problem in research is that science has become incredibly specialised. Scientists develop research in their specialist areas, attend conferences within this line of work and read magazines that concentrate on their subject, and this then becomes more and more a niche area of research. Very rarely can you discover a completely different part of science crossing over and awakening new ideas in other specialised areas. I have not seen any scientific paper on animals that refers to the biology of plants or vice versa, which is a tragedy, as you will discover in later chapters. Chemists and physicists are not good bedfellows, and neither are biologists and biochemists, but they should be. Out of all academics in science-based subjects, physicists appear to be more open to change than other disciplines. This is not the case in biochemistry or medicine, where ideas that are over a hundred years old have only just been accepted into Western medical practice.

An example of this is the discovery that electrical stimulation of bones helps them to heal, which was originally discovered in 1812 by Dr John Birch of St Thomas' Hospital, London, using electric shocks to help heal a non-union of the tibia bone. This discovery was again reported in 1860 by Dr Arthur Garratt of Boston, who stated in his electrotherapy textbook that in the few times he had needed to try it, this method never failed. Electrical treatment was not, however, put to modern use until the 1980s, and today it is still not completely accepted and used as a primary treatment. Two hundred years have elapsed since this technique was first discovered, so what else might have gone unnoticed?

One book I have read, *The Body Electric* by Dr Robert Becker, an American orthopaedic surgeon, contains so much useful information on the general state of the science that I am going to quote verbatim the final paragraph in his book of 347 pages, which is packed full of medical data and scientific experiments about regeneration and the use of electrical stimulation. It is a book that makes you sit up and take notice of some fascinating and ground-breaking experiments that Dr Becker conducted into the possibility that our bodies could self-generate to repair damaged tissue just like the salamander, which can regrow its limbs if they are cut off. The science Becker conducted should have paved the way for major breakthroughs in the development of science and by now have made available the facility to repair damaged heart tissue by the simple use of electromagnetic forces. This, however, is his depressing conclusion:

> *"I've taken the trouble to recount my experience in detail for two reasons. Obviously, I want to tell people about it because it makes me furious. More importantly, I want the general public to know that science isn't run the way they have read about it in the newspapers and magazines; I want lay people to understand that they cannot automatically accept scientists' pronouncements at face value, for too often they're self-serving and misleading. I want our citizens, non-scientists as well as investigators, to work to change the way research is administered. The way it's currently funded and evaluated, we're learning more and more about less and less, and science is becoming our enemy instead of our friend".*

This extract was written in 1985, and as far as I can make out very little has changed. In his introduction to the book, Dr Becker explains that his primary target is the biochemistry industry, which he feels has thwarted the development of alternative ideas. If the techniques do not fit the chemical concepts – even if they do seem to work – they will be abandoned as pseudo-scientific or downright fraudulent. If you want to find a textbook example of this, all you have to do is look at the homeopathic industry, which appears to work but is based upon chemistry that makes no sense to the biochemist. I will show in later chapters that the scientific principles behind homeopathic medicine have been completely misunderstood, both by traditional and homeopathic scientists.

A good example of an area of science that needs to be reassessed is seasonal affective disorder (SAD), in which sufferers experience symptoms of depression at different times of the year. I don't know about you, but I am fully aware that I am not as happy on miserable cloudy days as I am on glorious sunny ones – a very common and obvious reaction. When the sky is darker, and less light is reaching us, I would guess that most people feel more depressed. But are we in fact clinically depressed or just feeling a bit low, a bit sorry for ourselves? And if so, why? What is happening on these cloudy days to change our emotions?

The answer is so obvious that it should be common knowledge, but the failings of science to understand this simple phenomenon lie at the very heart of the book. What is light if not energy, and what does our body need to sustain itself – energy? Traditional science suggests that we get our energy only from our food, but this seems patently wrong. Does it not seem absurd to assume that our bodies would not help themselves to free energy? I would argue that our bodies clearly recognise this and have been developed so that we can absorb energy from light. Plants do this and, as you will see in later chapters, if plants do it, it is likely that animals and humans do it too.

How can we prove this simple idea? I would suggest that we could simply go to a doctor and get our energy levels checked. But hold on a minute, there is no medical test for our body's energy levels – if you went to your doctor, they would just look at you blankly when you requested an energy test. Science, it appears, seems to have ignored this whole area of research. So until science catches up with common sense, SAD research will be left up to psychiatrists, who are looking for the answers in completely the wrong place.

We know a lot about medical biology, such as about the genetic code, the nervous system, the blood, muscle movement, respiration and other observational aspects of biology. But we understand virtually nothing about hunger, thirst, sleep, growth and healing. We know nothing about the way our body regulates its metabolic activity in cycles with that of the Earth, moon and sun. And we understand virtually nothing about consciousness, choices, memory, emotions, creativity, learning and personality. Mechanistic chemistry will never have answers to these issues, so we must develop other sciences that help us to understand them – but as long as we remain fixated with biochemistry, we will never find answers to all of these issues.

We are at the moment in a scientific cul-de-sac. Scientists have been giving us snippets of knowledge that do not add up to provide us with a complete visual picture of how things are and how things interact. We are stuck. We need to take a step back and free our minds from what we have been told. We need to look at the science around us to get a picture that is whole and complete. To liberate our instincts, we need to use our own common sense. We need to go back to the beginning because we have to unravel what we think we already know and then build on that knowledge and see life afresh.

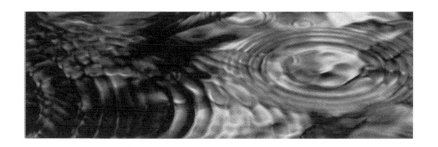

INTRODUCTION TO

VIBRATIONS

" *When you have eliminated the impossible, whatever remains, however improbable, must be the truth*".

SIR ARTHUR CONAN DOYLE

I am a sceptic, a real sceptic. It takes a lot to persuade me one way or another. If I believe something to be true, then unless someone can prove otherwise to me, either by experiment or through a logical argument, it is very difficult to move me away from my entrenched opinion. I think this is probably true for most people. In my own case, it took my son's illness to shift me away from my stubborn position on complementary forms of health treatment, and I think it takes such an awakening in most people before they are persuaded there is an alternative option. Why would you change the opinion you have held for most of your life unless you had a personal experience that caused you to change your mind?

I have no intention of just telling you my story and hoping you will be persuaded by it. My idea is to take you on the journey of discovery that I made while spending one and a half years in the British Library researching this book. I will introduce you to many unsung scientists from the past three hundred years who have all provided small pieces of science that, when looked at collectively, provide a truly remarkable story – one that I hope, at the very least, will open your mind up to the possibility that we have all been led down the proverbial garden path and that some of what we have all dismissed of as quackery does in fact have scientific validity after all.

I am full of optimism that you will be impressed by what you read simply by the reaction of my father, who read the draft of this manuscript. He is a renowned Professor of medicine who has written hundreds of different research papers covering issues from obesity to bipolar disorder. When I asked his opinion on my first two chapters, he was left somewhat speechless as he said he had never come across any of my research and therefore could not offer an opinion as he had no expertise on which to base one. He wanted to read the whole manuscript before he would offer his views. When he had read it all, he said that the book made fascinating reading and he was now no longer a complete sceptic. As far as I was concerned, if I could shift the opinion of someone who was firmly entrenched in the biochemical theory of life, by even a small amount, then my job was done.

I have written eight different chapters, all of which are interrelated. It is not necessary to read them all in sequence: you can dip in and out as you wish. All that I would recommend is that you first read this chapter and the next, on water, as these will hopefully provide you with some incredible new ideas. Then feel free to use those ideas on the chapters on the moon and sun, magnets, bees and birds, technology and plants as, and how, you want. When you have digested all of the information, feel free to join in the discussions on my website and put your own opinions forward.

MY DISCOVERY

I believe I have discovered a great missing part of the scientific jigsaw that provides a new and very simple unifying theory. The piece of the puzzle that seems to have been ignored for so long is this simple fact – that everything vibrates. I know this sounds ridiculously simple, but let me explain why this point is so important and why, when you have read the following chapters on water and the moon, you will wonder why you have been deprived of this knowledge until now.

The idea that vibrations play such an important role took me a long time to work out; it did not come to me straight away. But once I understood this very simple principle, everything else fell into place. Simply put, everything vibrates, absolutely everything, from the nucleus of an atom to the molecules of our blood, our organs, our brain, light, sound, plants, animals, earth, space, the universe; they all have one thing in common – they all vibrate. This fundamental principle should be the basis of all science as it is the one principle that unifies everything, and if you can understand vibrations, everything else becomes clear. Throughout this book, vibrations, whether they are in the form of sound, light, electricity, magnets or gravity, will be shown to be the number one factor that underlies the unexplained phenomena that Western science fails to understand. Without an understanding of this science, we have been guided down the wrong path, to reach where we are today. Most of us have had a very poor scientific teaching in the way that life works, for if it were better, we would all look at plants, the solar system and our health in a completely different light.

In isolation, this may not really be such a big deal. I am pretty sure that some people are thinking that this is very common knowledge and it is well known that everything vibrates. I am sure this is true, but what they do not know is how vibrations interact with each other – this is the piece of the jigsaw that even makes me smile in anticipation while writing. Maybe I get excited every time I explain my ideas just because I drink too much coffee. Or maybe you will think it is not coffee that I'm drinking too much of when I tell you that vibrations are bouncing around us everywhere, but it is the unique properties of *water* that provide the other amazing piece of the jigsaw; and one is not interesting without the other.

Water; what on earth can I be talking about? Since when has water been said to be of interest in terms of anything other than hydration? – we drink it when we get thirsty. But no, water also has a unique property: it has the ability to shape-shift. Water is never just one thing but a chameleon, changing its properties in different situations. What causes water to change and take on these new shapes is, amazingly, all to do with vibrational waves. If we combine the idea of vibrations with the unique properties of water, we arrive at some outrageous new possibilities.

As all living organisms contain water, and water can soak up and retain different vibrational waves, water will change when it is stimulated by a new vibration and maintain that new vibrational level. Obvious vibrations of which science is aware that change water are those caused by sound and light: if you put sunlight onto water it heats up, and when you play music against a puddle it moves as a result of the sound vibrations. These are two basic ideas that will hopefully give you a simple understanding of how different vibrations can affect objects. But what about all the billions of other vibrations that are out there? What effect do they have on water? Vibrations caused by other living objects that also vibrate. How about a tree – what sort of vibration does that give out – or an elephant? Because they are made up of living mass, they have to vibrate. This is one of those scientific truths that is undeniable. But how big are the vibrations they emit, and how do they affect each other? This is where it all starts to get a bit scary.

Imagine this scenario: if our bodies are made up of water and water changes when it comes into contact with different vibrations, could this not mean that our bodies will change the way in which they behave when in contact with a big new vibration? What big vibrations are there which are capable of influencing the water within us? The pretty obvious ones are the giant vibrations called gravity coming from the planet we are standing on and the gravitational vibrations of the sun, the moon and the planets. As I will show in later chapters, science has shown that they affect our biology, but until now no-one has understood why. The answer lies in the amazing properties of water.

If it is true that the gravitational waves of the planets affect us, what else could be changing the vibrational properties of water and thus affecting our biology? Could a tiny little vibration also cause change? And how about this idea: could the person next to you be changing the way your body behaves? If they give out a different vibration from yours, which by definition they *will* as the combination of cells in their body is not the same as in yours, how will the water content in your body react – will it be positive or negative? As nonsensical as it might seem, could the idea of love be based on a compatible vibrational chemistry between two people? Could instant likes and dislikes be based on vibrations as well? Who knows? I certainly do not intend to develop these ideas in this book as there is no science to back them up, but I have put them in to show the endless possibilities that vibrations offers us to look afresh at the way in which we interact. Vibrations open up a whole new way of looking at life and, as I hope to show in the later chapters, they all affect the way in which we go about our daily lives. Some of this is positive, but some of it is alarmingly negative.

Scientists have long known about vibrations and how they can induce change in objects. The first significant discovery was made in 1787 by Ernst Chladni, whose book should be part of every child's science education as it could encourage interest at a young age in physics and music. Chladni was a Hungarian musician who liked to build unusual musical instruments. When Chladni heard about a scientist's use of powders on a floating table, he took it upon himself to create a series of experiments. These turned out to be so significant that Napoleon himself personally financed the translation of Chladni's book from Hungarian into French.

So what were these experiments? Very simply, Chladni placed a small pile of very fine sand on a small metal plate and then stroked his violin bow along its edge to create a vibration. The results of this experiment are now referred to as Chladni patterns. Depending upon the specific vibrational note played, a pattern would emerge, and as he changed the speed and intensity of the stroking, a different pattern would be seen. I have included some of the patterns here, and you can see that they are really remarkable. The logic of the patterns based on just these few different vibrations would imply that the range of patterns is almost limitless.

These patterns are amazing to look at as they are such a varied bunch. But what is of more interest to this book than just this fascinating concept is that when two or more sound frequencies are combined from two sources, the patterns created are again unique. One sound produces one pattern, but two sounds produce a completely new one. If this knowledge was available over two hundred years ago, why have we not considered the possibility that vibrations affect the mass of whole living objects and not just a pile of sand on a vibrating plate?

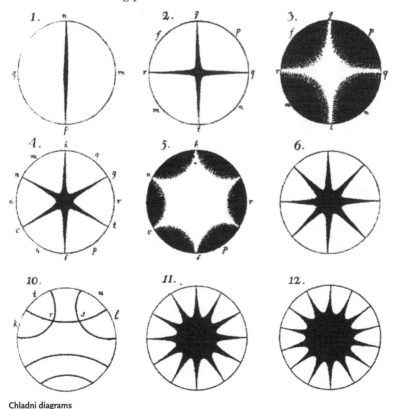

Chladni diagrams

In 1967, Swiss scientist Hans Jenny published a book called *Cymatics*. This took Chladni's ideas a stage further as Jenny showed what happened when various materials such as sand, spores, iron filings, water and viscous substances were placed on vibrating metal plates. Jenny made use of crystal oscillators and an invention of his own called the Tonoscope to set these plates and membranes vibrating. The advantage with using his Tonoscope was that he could determine exactly which frequency and amplitude/volume he wanted. Jenny found that if he vibrated a plate at a specific frequency and amplitude, the shapes and motion patterns characteristic of that vibration appeared in the material on the plate. If he changed the frequency or amplitude, the pattern changed as well. If the

Hans Jenny

frequency increased, so the complexity of the patterns increased, the number of elements becoming greater. If, on the other hand, Jenny increased the amplitude, the motions became more rapid and turbulent and could even create small eruptions.

Imagine talking into Jenny's Tonoscope and watching the patterns of sand dance in front of you on the vibrating plate. The tone produces a pattern based on not only the sound, but the pitch

Two patterns created by different vibrations

as well. As the voice is raised or lowered, the patterns change, so that an exact visual representation of our voices can be made on a table full of sand. Since the invention of the Tonoscope, deaf people have used it to practise learning to speak even though they cannot actually hear the sounds that they are emitting – by comparing the shape of the sand pattern with that of a hearing person, they can adjust their speech until the correct shape in the sand is obtained.

Jenny also showed the effect of sound vibration in three dimensions by using a very fine powder, Lycopodium. When sound is applied, the powder starts to move and form many small mounds that all seem to be alive and moving. These mounds move against each other and also from within, so that the powder is constantly

moving from the bottom to the top. If the amplitude of the vibration is greatly increased, the powder changes into clouds of dust; photos of this look like slow-motion close-ups of machine gun fire into sand – the powder seems literally to be exploding.

Pattern formed in Lycopodium

So if it is possible to change

the patterns of sand on a vibrating table, might the same thing occur with fluids? If it did, this would further the idea that water in living organisms could change due to external vibrations. It was not hard for me to find evidence of a large number of experiments showing that water behaves in exactly the same way as sand in response to external vibrations. Faraday conducted experiments back in 1831 which showed that when a large drop of water was placed on a vibrating plate, beautiful patterns, which he called "crispations", formed on the surface. Numerous other researchers have also shown that water reacts in this way.

Jenny also experimented with fluids of various kinds. He produced wave motions, spirals and wave-like patterns in continuous

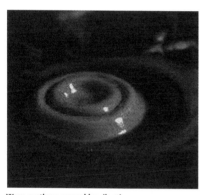

circulation. He also showed that it was possible to produce vortices in fluids by the use of specific frequencies within particular fluids – a fact that will become more important later in the book. This is fascinating as vortices are an integral part of nature. They crop up everywhere, and the fact that sound plays a role in creating

Wave motions caused by vibrations

them is developed in great detail in Chapter 2. So it is very clear that water is affected by vibrations.

What proof is there that our bodies do in fact contain vibrations? One person who over 80 years ago expounded a scientific basis for vibrational waves was a man called Georges Lakhovsky, a Russian émigré who moved to Paris and subsequently became a French citizen. His book *The Secret of Life* is a typical example of proven science that was dismissed by contemporary scientists for reasons I cannot understand. However, I will not for now go into his discoveries on cures for cancer, but will instead highlight his underlying theory of the effect that gravitational waves have on the cellular structure of living organisms. In order to explain this further, I have to get a bit technical, although I'll try to make it as simple as possible.

Lakhovsky talked a lot about oscillating circuits. These are electrical circuits that produce a vibration if a current of electricity is put through them. From such a circuit, energy is given off in the form of vibrational waves, and by using certain apparatus, an inductance coil and a condenser, the vibration can be raised to any vibrational value. This is a really important fact and one that needs to be digested thoroughly. *An electrical circuit produces vibrational waves*, and as all living organisms contain an electrical current, all living organisms must give off electrical vibrations.

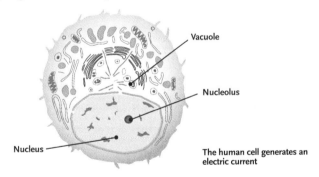

The human cell generates an electric current

Take the example of the human cell, which has a cell wall enclosing the cell's cytoplasm, vacuoles and other constituents lying around its nucleus. This nucleus contains a nucleolus, genetic material and twisted filaments. The nuclei act as individual electric circuits endowed with the equivalent of condensers and an inductance coil (filament), and consequently have the capacity to vibrate, the size of the vibration being dependent on the values of the filaments and condensers. The waves given off are thus electromagnetic in origin, by virtue of the nature of the circuits.

From the constitution of the cells, it can be said that each cell is capable of being the centre of vibration. As our bodies contain billions of different cells, no two cells are likely to be vibrating at exactly the same frequency, partly due to the constant activity taking place within the cell, but also because of the specific characteristics of different tissues. Every cell of every individual tissue of any particular species is characterised by its own vibration.

The eminent American surgeon Dr George Crile wrote in his book *The Phenomena of Life* that electrical energy plays a fundamental part in the organisation, growth and function of the protoplasm – or cytoplasm as we now call it. Crile has a similar interpretation to Lakhovsky for how the cells produce electrical currents. There is no disputing the fact that our bodies produce electric currents at the cellular level, which means that every cell produces its own unique vibration and proves that our bodies do in fact emit vibrational waves.

WE ARE ALL UNIQUE – VIBRATIONALLY

It only recently dawned on me that everyone is very different biologically. When you think about this, it is not very surprising, yet I had not thought about this possibility at all. I have always taken medicine and assumed that it affected me in exactly the same way as it affected the next person, but I have come to the conclusion that this is blatantly impossible.

If you analyse the human body and list, for example, its component parts down to the smallest amino acids, sugars and fatty acids, there are probably tens of thousands of different mechanisms in process all working together to produce one person. All of these processes are interlinked: if you change one process, it will have a knock-on effect elsewhere, but exactly where and how this effect will take place is very difficult to ascertain, as any doctor will tell you. A pain in the chest area could have an infinite number of causes, which is why doctors often fail to find the cause of a symptom without undertaking many different tests whose objective is to rule out as many possibilities until only one is left – and hopefully that will solve the problem. Much of the time, however, it is just a question of luck whether they find the answer in the first test or the last, or even at all.

Our bodies are incredibly sophisticated living organisms with an unbelievable capacity to adapt to anything that might change us. In order to see how we adapt, let us imagine that two people have been created out of nothing (excuse the biblical reference) and have been located on an isolated piece of desert with no external stimuli as a fully grown man and woman. And let us say that these perfect specimens are the base level of perfection – they are the perfect humans for whom absolutely everything within their body is in complete equilibrium. What will happen after day one? Firstly, in order to live, they will need to have access to water and then food. On their island is a natural pool of fresh water, and next to it are wild vegetables and fruit. Firstly, the water will be drunk, and as this is pure water, it will not affect any of their equilibria as their bodies have been programmed to expect clean water and therefore anticipate it and react accordingly. And it's the same for the food: the body has been pre-programmed to digest the food and break it down into its component parts.

So the first two people are still in perfect equilibrium. Nothing has made them change, and even when the woman gets pregnant and produces a child, her body will still be in equilibrium as it is pre-programmed to reproduce. The baby, on the other hand, is a new being and will have different balances within its body as it is made up of genes that come from both the woman and the man. Its DNA will be different, its fingerprints will be different, it will have a different natural equilibrium from that of its parents. It will be the same perfectly healthy individual with everything working in perfect equilibrium, but on a slightly different vibrational level from its parents.

Later, when the child grows up, he discovers that there are adjacent islands to explore, and there he finds new fruits and food that his body has never tasted before. The food will, when ingested, set off reactions within his body for which it was not pre-programmed. However, this is not a problem as his body will immediately adapt to the change and set itself on a new equilibrium level that allows it to function efficiently. If eaten regularly, this new diet will reset the child's body to a new level, but it will still work efficiently.

The amazing concept to understand is that the new change does not happen in days, weeks or even months, but that the body reacts immediately. The food that is ingested will have an immediate effect on the body, and whatever changes occur will be dependent upon how quickly the change is transferred throughout the body. This is a really important point as I am sure most of us assume that any change is slow, but that is a bad reflection on how we perceive our body. We must always assume that our body is a complex organism that constantly reacts to change almost immediately. We react to being too hot, too cold, to pain, to emotions and to a lot of obvious things almost immediately. And we should also assume that we react to a change in water, food or electrical stimulation just as quickly.

The child soon discovers a partner and produces another child who grows up on the new island. Again, this child will have a different equilibrium and vibrational level from its parents. This sequence of change obviously goes on for ever and produces the billions of different people who are alive today, every one having a different level from the others.

But why is this relevant? Simply because it means that we all react to the same external stimuli differently, and that there is not one panacea for us all. If one person suffers from eating mushrooms, it does not follow that we will all suffer. If one herb cures one person of gall stones, it does not mean that it will cure everyone. This is the problem that we have today, and it is a major problem as our attitude towards our health is based upon finding one drug or treatment that will cure everyone. This is a fundamental impossibility.

DO ALL LIVING ORGANISMS REACT IN THE SAME WAY TO NATURAL ENVIRONMENTAL VIBRATIONS?

Let us go back to the beginning, when the earth had just formed and was cooling down sufficiently for life to begin, so that we can answer this question. The universe, that dark mass of space, looks empty but is in fact full of amino acids floating around, and these amino acids are bombarding our planet all of the time. The sun is emitting light onto us and giving us heat, the moon is rotating around the planet, and we are in an evolved solar system of our planets revolving around the sun. All of the planets, both near and far, generate gravitational waves of energy, whether strong, such as those from the moon that move the tides, or weak, as from distant planets such as Uranus and Jupiter.

At the right point in our planet's evolution, the millions of amino acids that had arrived on the planet suddenly found an environment conducive to life, and single-cell organisms were created. This is one theory of the beginning of life itself but it is not important whether it is the correct one – I am just using it as an example of how life might have been formed. Over the next few millions of years, the organisms developed, but still they all had the same external factors that affected their growth: heat, light, atmospheric conditions and gravity. As the planet changed and the organisms evolved into plants, which were the first developed organic (carbon-based) objects some 350 million years ago, these plants developed patterns of behaviour that would adapt to those four variables. Remember that gravity has been around for all of that time and that all of the life forms would have been developing with this constant pattern, more so than with any consistency of heat and atmospheric conditions. It has been suggested that the atmosphere was three times richer in oxygen millions of years ago, which is the reason dinosaurs were able to grow so big. Plants were also enormous, but today, due to the different atmospheric conditions, plants are not capable of growing as large.

The point here is that nature adapts very obviously to measurable changes in atmospheric conditions, but we seem oblivious to the point that nature has also adapted to the unobservable changes, those of the gravitational pull of the planets. For some unexplained reason, scientists seem to have ignored this effect and very rarely refer to it in any scientific studies. I am not sure why it has disappeared from our psyche as ancient civilisations such as the Egyptians, Greeks, Romans and Celts were all clearly believers in the planets and the fact that they had an effect on our lives. Somewhere in time, our belief system seems to have steered us away from the logical and has tried to tell us that the gravitational pull of the planets has no effect on our health or behaviour. The simple logic of the evolution of life should make these scientists sit up and take notice, irrespective of the hundreds of studies that have been done on plants and animals to show that they have a direct relationship with the cycle of the moon and the planets.

It seems undeniable, therefore, that if all other living organisms are affected either directly or indirectly by external gravitational forces, we as humans will also be affected in some way. But the question of how we are being affected and to what degree seems rarely to have been investigated.

VIBRATIONAL DISHARMONY – THE CAUSE OF ALL ILLNESS?

This is a very contentious point but it needs to be addressed – what do you think would happen to a rogue cell that for some unexplained reason started to vibrate at an incorrect frequency? Would it have a domino effect; would all of the good cells start to vibrate at the rate of the bad cell? Would the bad cell be changed back to a good cell by simply being next to the good cells? Could an external stimulus increase the rate of change of the bad cell or alternatively reset its vibration back to that of a good cell?

Surely there are lots of scientific papers that have studied this phenomenon and should be able to tell us exactly what happens and how we can fix it. Sadly not. This whole area of science has been largely overlooked as it does not follow the normal chemically based solution of biological problems. It seems very strange to me that there are not a lot of contemporary studies dealing with vibrational issues. The two major works here appear to date from the 1930s, and in both cases they cured numerous patients with cancer using their own version of vibrational medicine. So why are we not delving further into this area? I have asked several scientists this question and they do not have an answer except that maybe it has not been investigated until now because it has been dismissed in the past.

Maybe, however, the reason is that scientists have discovered it without actually recognising it and what it means. This is the avenue I had to take to study the matter further, otherwise it would seem ridiculous that one logical idea about the behaviour of organic matter could be so easily researched yet have been ignored by the scientists who are supposed to be looking after our welfare.

VIBRATIONS AND CURES FOR CANCER

The most depressing of all the research I have undertaken was investigating the hidden science behind one of the greatest discoveries in medical development that few of us know about. Every day, I think about the millions of people who could have been helped and cured from illnesses ranging from cancer and typhoid to influenza and tuberculosis, all needless deaths that resulted from science's decision to ignore unique discoveries that have been proven in trials to work on humans. Sixteen patients with incurable cancer were all completely cured under strict scientific study conditions. Yet everything about the study and its amazing results has been almost completely destroyed.

We all have a debt to pay the inventor of the cure, a man with a name to remember, Royal Rife. His parents must have had a

Newspaper headline from 1936

good sense of humour to give him the first name of Royal, but maybe they sensed greatness to come. One of the most significant parts of this story is that it ties in with everything else I am talking about in this book. The key part of Rife's discovery lay in the use of vibrations. Just as J.C. Bose (see Chapter 7) measured the different effects of outside stimuli on plants using his own invention of the "crescograph", so Rife used his own invention to produce the results he was interested in. It was this invention that allowed him to develop his unique tools for curing almost all illnesses.

What was so amazing about this machine was that it could look at live viruses under the microscope without having to kill them: modern electron microscopes can only look at dead viruses.

Rife used light as a source of magnification and was able to see different viruses as a colour, each different colour representing a different vibrational frequency. The reasoning was that if you could determine the colour of the virus, you could destroy it by blasting it with a large number of light waves that were of that specific frequency.

Even if I did not know anything about Rife's work, I

The Universal microscope 1933

know, having looked into so many scientific papers and studies, that most viruses can be cured by the use of vibrations. How do I know this? Quite simply because logic tells me that it must be the case, based upon all the information that I have gleaned from studies relating to plants, animals and lunar cycles. What baffles me most is the fact that I know this yet the so-called major scientists of this world seem to have chosen to ignore it or have purposely dismissed it for reasons that only they know. I could suggest that money and power were the two most likely reasons for this "ignorance", but that would be a separate book in itself.

I am not a conspiracy theorist, and I do not believe that everyone is conniving to undermine our knowledge and hide the truth from us, but in this instance, I feel ashamed to have to admit that I have no other conclusion than to say it has been a collective unconscious decision by doctors and scientists throughout the West not to look at this major form of medicine as it is not drug-related but product-related. Medical care without drugs would create a great big hole in the cosy Western world of medicine, hospitals would be empty, doctors would be without work, drug companies would spiral out of the stock exchange, and corporate profits would be non-existent. Maybe these are the very reason why a simple machine has been left ignored – it would open up a huge can of worms for doctors. Which person who has spent ten years training for a job would want to see a machine put them out of business? Not many I would guess, even if it meant saving the lives of millions of people.

Yet in some areas of science, machines that use vibrations are very common. The MRI scanner and the ultrasound machine are very popular in medicine. How do they work? The MRI scanner uses the different vibrational frequencies of chemicals in our bodies, and ultrasound uses sound vibration, to reproduce a three-dimensional image of our insides. So the physicists know about vibrations and have utilised the vibrational signal to develop sophisticated machinery.

Just as I had started to write this book, I finally heard of a trial study taking place that was incorporating vibrational medicine. The machine in question was being used to cure patients of prostate cancer by giving them a treatment of vibrational waves, exactly of the type that had been developed seventy years before by Royal Rife. However, the machine that was being used was the ultrasound machine, a machine that had been around for thirty years before someone decided to test it out on cancer. Isn't it a bit strange that it took someone so long to get round to this area of science? Maybe it will soon be realised that you can cure a wide range of illnesses other than prostate cancer using sound waves. In fact, maybe someone will eventually look to develop a human vibrational table and with it use the ultrasound machine to cure all sorts of vibrational problems.

I hope we don't have to wait around too long for this. The prostate cancer trial is, at the time of writing, currently being conducted, and it will take at least 5 years before the technique might be fully used. My biggest fear, however, is that those who are conducting it will not understand the basic nature of vibrational medicine and will not adapt the ultrasound frequencies differently to their many different patients; instead, they may just adopt one frequency, which might be the wrong one for many patients. As each person has a different frequency, the cancer might have adapted its frequency from a different vibrational position and might be vibrating at a different frequency dependent upon the patient. I hope that the study acknowledges this fact, otherwise the results will not be as good as they should be.

SUMMARY

Many people really enjoyed the film *Avatar*, a recent worldwide phenomenon, despite the unsatisfactory storyline, which implied that there was some sort of unifying energy that pervaded everything. This is similar to the "Gaia theory", which says that everything in nature is intricately connected to everything else. At the time of watching the film, I had already started my research for the book and had already been educated in the idea that this, in fact, could be a scientific probability if looked at it from a less spiritual point of view.

This idea that there was a unifying energy I translated as the fact that all life vibrates, and therefore all living organisms are affected by each other. But living organisms are affected not only by other living organisms, but also by forces that exist both on this planet and not on this planet. Living organisms are affected by the gravitational forces of the moon, the sun and the planets, as well as the gravitational pull of the earth. So in one respect I felt that *Avatar* was right: the so-called spirit of the trees and animals can affect us, and we can feel it directly, but only through the science of vibrations.

Then I discovered that plants can react to changes in not only normal vibrations, such as light and sound, but also what I call non-normal ones, such as intent and emotions. These emotional vibrations are somehow produced by our bodies and are transmitted so that any other living organisms that are capable of absorbing them will do so. Plants are one of the few organisms that can be scientifically tested for this, and in some very strange experiments described in Chapter 8, you will see how this has in fact been proved.

So this book did not ever mean to attempt to provide support for the theory of Gaia, but it in fact provides lots of evidence to provide me with a stronger belief that this is likely to be more right than wrong. As a sceptic, it pains me to write this, but, based upon all of my research into hidden scientific discoveries, I have to admit that I believe a lot more now than I thought imaginable a year ago that everything is interlinked.

This is not a book that offers any sort of conspiracy theory. It does not attempt to lay the blame for our ignorance on the doorstep of any single company or group of organisations. This is a problem that is embedded within our psyche. I am the first to acknowledge that I have been blinded by science and have had no time for alternative ideas. I was certainly not consciously part of any conspiracy theory, but I believe this way of thinking has been so indoctrinated into our society that it is almost impossible to drag ourselves out of it.

Why would we possibly believe that the moon and the sun play any part in our health? This is the stuff of quackery. So is the idea that plants are anything more than pretty to look at. Who would have guessed that they are as sophisticated as animals and can communicate with each other in ways we had never before imagined. Why would you know that plants are 100% behaviourally the same as animals or that trees grow in weekly cycles related to the moon and the planets, that water retains the vibrations of everything that it come into contact with, that your computer can increase your diabetes level, that cures for cancer have been ignored and that sex on a full moon increases your chances of a successful pregnancy? In fact, who would have contemplated the idea that your house plant is as emotionally attached to you as your pet dog! I know this sounds like nonsense, but the further into this book you read, the more you will see how obvious all of this really is, and why, when you put down the book at the end, you will have a completely different approach to everything around you.

INTRODUCTION TO
WATER

" *Running water is more beneficial, as it is made finer and more healthy by the mere agitation of the current* ".

PLINY 23 A.D.

Why have I written over fifty pages explaining the properties of water? What on earth, you might think, is there to write about? It was only by chance that I came across the possibility that water plays a fundamental role in the way in which all living organisms interact. It took a great deal of work to come up with all of the material within this chapter, unearthing many old books with hidden scientific facts, reading hundreds of articles and constructing lots of cross-references from lengthy bibliographies. Only after all of that research work was accomplished did I realise that water was an incredibly significant player in biological processes.

I only started to think about water when I was researching the chapter on plants and I discovered that biodynamic farmers, while attempting to create excellent manure, did very strange things to water. I could not stop myself from wondering why it was considered necessary to stir water in a bucket so fast in one direction for thirty minutes and then in the other direction for another thirty minutes. How can stirring water clockwise and counterclockwise be of any use in farming? The practice of stirring made no sense to me whatsoever. So, over the coming months, any reference made to water in any of the books I read piqued my curiosity, and by piecing smaller and smaller parts of the jigsaw together, I finally managed to find the answers to why stirring was so important. And this was just the starting point. Once I got my teeth into the subject, there was no stopping me, and I started to investigate everything I could find about water. This led me on a journey of discovery that has changed my attitude to science more than any other discovery I have made.

How would you feel if I were to tell you that the moon can affect your lymphatic glands because of water, or that the person next to you can affect your mood because the water in your body picks up their vibrational waves? And how about this for an amazing idea: might your houseplants be as emotionally attached to you as your pets, so that when you are upset, your plant is too? I don't blame you if you think these ideas are complete nonsense as I would expect that to be a normal reaction. These ideas are so far removed from the way we have all been educated that it is easy to dismiss them as the rantings of an insane man.

What will surprise you, I hope, is that scientists have proved all of the above points to be true without necessarily being aware of it. Let me give you a perfect example of a scientific experiment that was performed in 2010 and looked into the properties of a popular sugary drink, which proves this idea. This particular experiment investigated the energy benefits of a famous-brand sports drink in order to assess the length of time it took for the drink to increase the stamina of cyclists. In the first instance, the cyclists were asked to swill the drink around in their mouth and then, without swallowing any, to spit it out. In the second condition, the cyclists drank it. What the scientists discovered when they analysed the results from brain scans and muscular functionality tests was the body had reacted in the same way to both experimental conditions: the mouthwash was just as effective as swallowing. This defied all known laws of medicine. How was it possible that the body could react without any chemical input? The scientists had no option other than to conclude the body must have a yet to be discovered set of neural pathways linking the taste buds in the mouth to every muscle in our body. The scientists had to invent this far-fetched answer based on what they already knew or it would imply there was a gaping hole in their knowledge of human biology.

The results of this study are typical; scientists are only ever looking for chemical solutions to provide answers. If the results do not fit the hypothesis, it is often the results that are considered strange rather than the theories. In the case of the sugar drink, there is a very simple solution, one that has nothing to do with a biochemical mechanism but has to do with the very remarkable properties of water, and the answer lies in vibrations. I attempted to highlight the properties of vibrations in the Introduction and to explain how important they are, and now I can show that the combination of vibrations and the properties of water provide a simple and logical answer to the energy drink conundrum.

I will show the science behind this idea later in the chapter, but for now you will just have to accept this fact – that water retains the vibration of everything it comes into contact with. If pure water in a stream comes into contact with a chemical substance, the water will absorb not only the chemical atoms, but also their unique chemical vibration. If you then remove the chemical atoms, the chemical vibration remains. The pure water looks exactly the same under a microscope as it did before, yet it will now have a brand new vibrational pattern. In the energy drink experiment, the water in the blood that fills the tongue, the throat and the upper and lower mouth recognised not the new chemical atoms but the new vibrational pattern of the energy drink, and it was this different vibrational pattern that was instantly transferred via the water to the muscles.

PROOF THAT WATER RETAINS VIBRATIONS

Over a ten-year period, three English scientists proved in experiments that the vibration in water is both the cause and also the cure of illnesses. They set out to show that, with patients who were incredibly sensitive to specific chemicals, it was possible to reproduce a similar reaction using just water that has been given specific vibrational frequencies. One of the patients had such an extreme reaction to a fungus mould that she would pass out immediately when the fungus touched her skin. But she could be reawakened when touched by a much diluted solution of the fungus.

In an interesting discovery, the researchers found that this reaction could be reproduced by giving patients a very weak electromagnetic stimulation. Using a frequency generator, the patient became unconscious with a vibrational signal of 3 Hz and awoke using a vibrational frequency of 10 Hz. Now this is where the experiment gets very exciting. In a double-blind study, the scientists used water that had been exposed to both these different frequencies and discovered that this treated water had exactly the same effects as the chemical reaction. The subject receiving water that had been treated directly by an electromagnetic vibration both passed out and woke up when the treated water contacted her skin. These experiments were repeated over several months to prove that the water retained the electrical vibration for lengthy periods. This experiment proved not only that water could retain the vibrational input from an external source, but also that it was the vibration and not the chemical stimulus that was of importance.

The ramifications of this discovery for all of us are totally horrendous. I am seriously worried about our long-term health if this science is to be believed. It means that if we drink water from anywhere other than a natural spring or stream, the likelihood that the water has at some point been in contact with pollutants implies that we are, in effect, drinking the ghost of that pollutant, whose vibration might very well affect our body as badly as the original chemical itself. This is scary stuff. In order to change the water back, it would be necessary to somehow provide it with the correct frequency that would reinstate it to its healthy parameters.

What is even more frightening to discover is that drinking vibrationally changed water affects directly the behaviour of our blood. An experiment conducted in 2010 by Beverly Rubik, showed that drinking water that had been treated by specific vibrations of the order of 7.83 Hz, 14.3 Hz, 20.8 Hz, 27.3 Hz and 33.8 Hz (The Schumann resonances) caused our blood to change. When seen under a microscope minutes after drinking the zapped water the vibrational treatment "decreased the formation of red blood cell rouleau and aggregates, diminished protein linkage of the cells, and produced less clotting than blood from subjects drinking control water." This is great news for patients who need their blood thinned without the use of medication, but horrific news for the rest of us who use mobile phones which broadcast using frequencies very similar to those used in Ms Rubik's experiment 2 Hz, 8.34 Hz and 30–40 Hz. It is also bad news for those people who drink polluted water that has been in contact with chemicals that emit these frequencies.

WHY DON'T WE KNOW THIS?

How can water behave like this and yet we know nothing about it? One scientist who has been banging his head against a brick wall trying to get the message out to the masses is a man called Vladimir Voeikov, a scientist at the Moscow State University. He has conducted a range of experiments into the properties of water and has found that it is able to absorb and reproduce vibrations as part of the biochemical process. What is even more interesting is that his experiments showed that this effect of water was not limited to human biology but instead covered all biology – every living organism that has a water content has the ability to react to different vibrational signals and affect its biological processes at the same time. Voeikov compares water to an antenna that collects every vibrational signal. These vibrational signals could be anything that gives off a vibration and, as everything gives off vibrations, from the nucleus of an atom to the largest planet, Voeikov's statement is very, very important.

But what does this mean for science? This basic principle has huge ramifications because everything vibrates and because of the nature of vibrations – one vibration can have an impact on another through water. If you think this is a very strange concept, how about the idea that if you stand in front of a music speaker, it is the water rather than anything chemical in your body that recognises the vibrational sound wave, and it is the water that instantly transfers the vibration around your body. If you then stretch your imagination to the limit, you can also say that as water can pick up on every vibrational wavelength, it is possible it can pick up on emotional vibrational signals that are being given off by friends, on signals emitted by the gravitational forces of the planets and, yes, I hate to say it, on the vibrational signals of trees and plants. It pains me to have to admit it, but there is science in the concept of tree-hugging after all.

Images from Hans Jenny, Cymatics, 2001

If you need visual proof for yourself that water reacts to different vibrations, all you have do to is type "Water Sound Images" into an internet search engine and see Alexander Lauterwasser's amazing slow-motion film of a close-up of a water droplet. In this film, Lauterwasser did nothing more than play music to the water. The astonishing footage shows beyond doubt that water is directly affected by vibrational waves. The film literally shows the water dancing to the music – as the notes change so does the pattern of the water droplet. As our body is made up of 73% water, it is pretty scary to think that our blood could be literally dancing to music in our blood vessels. This might even explain why we like some music over others; it is the vibrational pattern of the music and our body's reaction to it that is the most important factor.

If this is just too much too fast, I completely understand, but as you will read in the following chapters, there is a good deal of science that supports these outrageous theories. It just took a lot of work to join up all of the dots and finally work out the great missing pieces of the scientific jigsaw that offers up a completely new way of looking at the way in which living organisms work, both individually and collectively.

I hope that, by the end of this book, you will never look at water, the moon, your body, plants and trees in the same way again.

PROPERTIES OF WATER

If we look at the basic properties of water, what do we know? Well, water makes up about 70% of our mass, so in essence we are mostly a water-based organism. And that is pretty much all most of us know – that we are mostly made up of water. Water makes up 99% of the total number of molecules within our body, while the part that is of interest to scientists – nucleic acids, proteins, hormones, vitamins and so on – makes up only 1% of our molecular make-up, yet takes up almost 100% of our research. It seems to me that if water were not important, we could reduce our bodily content by up to 50% and nothing much would result. Far from it, however, as if our water content is reduced by only 1–2% as a result of dehydration, we suffer severe symptoms, as anyone who has experienced dehydration knows only too well. So water cannot be the passive player in our biological make-up but must instead play a significant role, as any small change produces significant side effects. We can all live for a long time without food but only a few days without water.

Let me put this into some scientific perspective. Water is unique, and some scientists have even described it as "abnormal".

These are just some of its unusual properties:
- It is the only natural thing that exists in three forms: water, ice and gas.
- Its density rises the hotter it gets.
- Its surface tension is abnormally high.
- Its specific heat is abnormally high.
- The latent heat of ice fusion is, except for ammonia, the largest known.
- Water changes in structure as it rises in temperature.

Are the properties of water unique for a reason? Have living organisms chosen water to be fundamental to their growth for a specific purpose? Does water behave in a way that we need for every organism? There are no developed living organisms that do not require water to sustain life. So water is a very, very important factor, and yet we know virtually nothing about it. There is very little research that helps to explain what water can actually do other than the obvious fact that it comprises two hydrogen and one oxygen atom. Imagine, though, that water had a set of remarkable properties that have yet to be explained, ones that help to provide answers to most of the unknown questions about how our bodies work.

As I mentioned, my interest in water was first stimulated by my research into biodynamic farming. This is a new and alternative method being increasingly used in wine growing as it is possible to see the measurable results in the quality of the wine being produced. More and more leading wine growers now have part of their crop produced by this method. What exactly is biodynamic farming? In essence, it is a way of creating a large number of bacteria in the soil to nourish it, and utilising the lunar cycle and the cycle of the planets as a calendar for timing the sowing of the seeds, the pruning of the plants and the harvesting of the grapes. Biodynamic

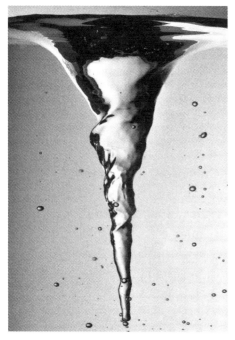
Water in a vortex

farming was "created" by Rudolf Steiner, who came up with a unique sequence of steps that were required in order to produce better crops without the use of fertiliser. Having spoken to journalists who write about the wine trade, no-one knows why it works, just that it does. As far as they are concerned, it does not matter why as long as it produces a better quality of wine.

So what has this got to do with a chapter on water? Well, one part of the process in the sequence involves water. In order to make sure that the bacteria multiply in the soil, it is necessary to create good-quality manure, and this is achieved by burying cow horns with cow manure in the ground and then, after several months, taking this compost and diluting it in water so that it can be sprayed onto the crops. In order to dilute the manure, the water used has to be spun in a very specific way.

Firstly, the water has to be spun in one direction for half an hour fast enough to create a vortex (like water going down a plug hole), and then after another half an hour the water is spun in the other direction, creating another vortex or whirlpool. Without this step in the process, the biodynamic farming method will not work in the most productive way. Why not? What does water do when it is in a vortex, and how can this spinning of water make any difference to anything? This was a major question for me as I could scientifically explain everything else about biodynamic farming except this. Some of the answers were, however, discovered by a man called Viktor Schauberger.

VIKTOR SCHAUBERGER

Viktor Schauberger is a fascinating character, an individual who made observations in his native woods around Austria. He was not well schooled but derived his education from nature itself. This did not, however, stop him becoming a rich man from his revolutionary new method of transporting chopped trees down from the mountains using water chutes. In the 1930s, Schauberger's ideas met with considerable scientific opposition, probably because his practical discoveries completely contradicted the known laws of physics as well as common sense.

At the time, it was necessary to use pack animals or barges in order to transport trees downhill, as heavy wood did not float and could not be sent floating downstream by itself. What Schauberger observed in nature was that the density of the water was the most important factor, and this density changed when the temperature rose or fell. Archimedes' Law suggests that as the density of wood is heavier than that of water, wood will not float, but this does not take into account the fact that the density of water is lighter during the day and heavier during the cold nights. Schauberger's discovery proved that, in order to transport logs down a chute, you just had to do the operation at night when the water temperature was colder. This simple discovery made him a millionaire, and his log chutes were used in many different countries for the next thirty years. I am including this case as it shows that although it is not a scientifically proven theory, it is a practical idea that bypassed contemporary scientific thought and is to my mind eligible for inclusion in this chapter. It is what I call practical science.

One of Schauberger's many other observations in nature was the fact that a trout can stay motionless within a fast-moving stream and will, when startled, swim away from danger by swimming upstream against the oncoming flow instead of swimming downstream with the motion of the water. Would not the fastest escape be to swim with the flow, downstream? So why would the trout act this way? In order to test his theory that it was the temperature of the water that was the important factor in the trout's behaviour, Schauberger ordered a group of men to pour one hundred and fifty gallons of heated water into the river one hundred metres upstream of the trout and watch what happened. The temperature change in the river would have been minimal, but the trout's change in behaviour was significant. The trout was unable to hold its steady position; it thrashed around for a time before giving up and disappearing downstream, presumably to an area where the temperature was normal. Only later did the trout reappear.

Schauberger was the first person who applied for patents to make artificially pure water from dirty water. He then built an apparatus which strove to refine water back to its purest state. He took sterilised water from the River Danube, added small amounts of metals, minerals and carbon dioxide and then let the mixture undergo a "cycloid spiral motion" in darkness while allowing its temperature to fall towards water's biological zero, which is 4°C. The process was Schauberger's attempt to copy nature's cycle. What is the most noticeable point is his use of the cycloid spiral motion or, to put it another way, the spinning or vortex pattern, like the water going down the plug hole or the spinning used in biodynamic farming. Where did he get this observation from? It was clearly one of the fundamental parts of his apparatus, one that he observed in nature: "in the river the water is thrown hither and thither, spins, reels on itself, as the rope in the hands of the ropemaker. It forms whirlpools, eddies, spiral-forming current, where the water rotates on its own axis and condenses."

Is it a coincidence that both Schauberger and Rudolph Steiner, the "inventor of biodynamic farming", have the spinning of water as part of their innovations? Both of them are Austrian, and both were expressing their concerns over the damage we were doing to nature. It is a guess that Schauberger would have heard about

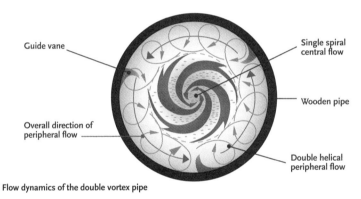

Flow dynamics of the double vortex pipe

Steiner, who died in 1925, when Schauberger would have been forty years old; in fact, they might even have met each other. I believe this is fairly likely because Schauberger refers to the same ideas as Steiner proposes in his biodynamic farming methods but refers to them simply as "close-to-nature farming". Schauberger's description of his traditional farming techniques is very similar to Steiner's biodynamic farming method.

At the end of his career, Schauberger, aged 67, was invited by Minister Kumpf to work in the technical college in Stuttgart alongside Professor Franz Popel, the resident expert of water resources at the college. It is alleged that the purpose of the exercise was to show

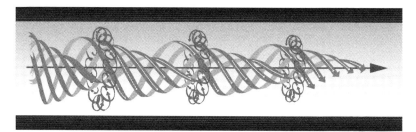

The small outer vortices act as ball bearings for the large inner vortex

that Schauberger's claims were unjustified; he was still treated with scepticism by the traditionalists, of whom Popel was a leading member. At first, Professor Popel refused to work with Schauberger as his claims went against the known laws of mechanics, but the Minister insisted he carried out the experiments, allegedly because he wanted to finally discredit all of Schauberger's ideas.

The first experiments were based on the characteristics of water motion. After the experiments had been conducted, Popel analysed the results, whereupon his opinion completely changed. He discovered that a straight glass pipe, which had smooth walls, actually caused greater resistance than a spiral pipe that Schauberger had invented, a pipe with fins. This went against all of Popel's previous ideas on the flow of water. The addition of the fins created two different patterns within the pipe, the first a set of small spiral motions towards the outside of the pipe, and the second a larger spiral motion in the middle. The small spirals acted as a lubricant for the larger one, similar to the action of ball-bearings.

Schauberger suggested that if we are looking to adapt any ideas that will enable us to improve the health of water, one simple change we can easily apply is to make the water spin in a vortex within a pipe that is channelling it. If you can imagine a river in full flow after a few days of torrential rain, you know that water does not move in a nice smooth flowing pattern; it rises, falls, crashes, spins and spirals all the way down the river. If you imagine water in a pipe, you might think, as most scientists do, that this is the most efficient method of transporting water, but Schauberger showed that this is not the case. In order to transport water efficiently and healthily, you need to move the water around so that the water spins in the middle of the pipe, which reduces the level of friction at the outer walls. His solution was a series of vanes placed on the walls of the pipe that simply created a pattern of double vortices so that the water was spinning in two separate paths, just like the double-helix pattern of our DNA.

I hope that Schauberger over time receives many more plaudits then he has until now. I have only touched upon some of his ideas. One that I mention here briefly is his invention for unlimited energy from water. I will admit I do not understand most of the physics behind his ideas, which is why I do not devote more to this topic, but he put forward experiments in which he developed the idea that water has different energies and that this is a fundamental principle that has simply been ignored, but one that explains so much about the laws of nature. It is this energy change that allows water to move so freely.

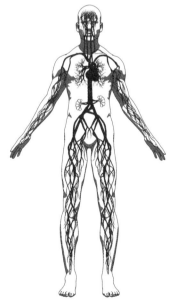

Blood flow around the body

As a consequence of Schauberger's idea and the fact that my radiators at home were not working and required the services of a plumber, I could not help think that something in our understanding of water was missing. In my flat I have ten radiators, three of which were not getting hot. It transpired that some of the pipework was blocked by sediment, which stopped the water from flowing smoothly through the system. The other seven radiators, however, worked fine. In order to fix the problem, a special stronger pump was required to flush out the system and clear away the old sediment. It seemed to me that this was a very similar problem to the way in which our body works; it is simple plumbing.

The heart pumps blood around the body, and we are taught that it is the pressure created by the heart that pushes the blood freely around the veins and arteries. This is not an idea that sits comfortably with me, having had so many plumbing problems and new boilers over the years. The body has miles and miles of veins and arteries, and I am not sure whether the heart is a large enough pump to be able to move so much blood around by its simple movements of contraction and expansion. If I were to put water in a balloon and squeeze it, how far would I be able to push it when it split off into millions of different channels? If the heart is pushing the blood, for example, to the outer reaches of the body, how can the pressure be large enough in all of the little veins without something oiling the blood's path?

Blood is very viscous. It is much thicker than water and flows more slowly than other fluids, so something must be helping it move so freely around the body. I believe that there must be something else happening, which Schauberger discusses in his books related to positively and negatively charged ions. He argues that there must be a relationship to these electrical charges to assist the movement of blood around the body and maintain the body's blood pressure. I wish that scientists would go back to the drawing board, reassess the function of the heart and set up an experiment to see how far blood actually moves when there is no electrical impulse in the body to stimulate movement. I don't think that it would move very far at all. Therefore the electrical charge created by the water in relation to the electrical charge of the blood vessels and walls of the arteries and veins is, I believe, hugely significant and requires much more analysis by experts in physics and biology. All they have to do is open one of the many books written by Schauberger in the 1930s to kick-start this fascinating area of research. It could result in many heart and blood problems being cured simply by utilising electrical stimulation.

NATURE MOVES IN A VORTEX

If there is an advantage to water creating a vortex, it seems likely we would find this everywhere in nature. If nature knows about vortices helping to restore the vibrational equilibrium, where can we find them? Obviously, this can be seen in running water, where little eddy currents appear in every river and stream. But where else can it be found? It was not hard to discover that these shapes are found everywhere; everywhere, that is, except the one place that you would expect to find them – the blood. Why would this be? Why have doctors for the last one hundred years taught the fact that blood flows in a unique way. Why would nature place vortices in every part of nature but not the one most obvious place? It made little sense to

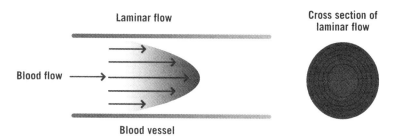

Laminar flow

Cross section of laminar flow

Blood flow

Blood vessel

Laminar blood flow

me. It took me a long time to realise that one of the most accepted parts of medical training seems to be completely wrong: blood does not flow in a unique way; blood is like everything else in nature – it flows in a vortex.

HOW HAVE DOCTORS GOT THIS BASIC PIECE OF SCIENCE SO WRONG?

In almost every medical school around the world, doctors are being told that blood flows in concentric circles throughout the body, a movement referred to as laminar flow. The diagram above shows the classical interpretation of this flow.

So let me ask you this question: try verbally to describe this type of flow without the use of the word "laminar". The diagram above sets the scene, showing blood flowing at different speeds within the arteries and veins, fastest in the middle and slowest at the outside. On the right of the diagram above is a cross-section of this flow, and it suggests that the blood flows in concentric circles. The reason I first questioned this principle was when I attempted to describe it and I found myself asking how I could describe flow in concentric circles as there were no words in my vocabulary that allowed me to do it. So I looked hard at the diagram and suddenly alarm bells started to ring very, very loudly. I could not believe what I was seeing:

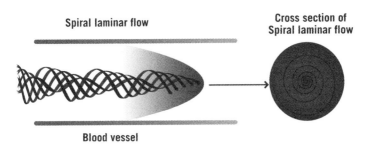

Spiral laminar flow

Cross section of
Spiral laminar flow

Blood vessel

Spiral blood flow

how was it possible for blood to travel in concentric circles? Where in nature is there laminar flow in concentric circles?

If you add a vortex to the laminar flow diagram then blood flow makes a lot more sense. It seems blatantly obvious that the blood is moving in a spiral, and if this is true, it has major consequences for the medical establishment. If they have always thought that blood flows in concentric circles, the following idea must be completely incorrect:

> *The orderly movement of adjacent layers of blood flow through a vessel helps to reduce energy losses in the flowing blood by minimizing viscous interactions between the adjacent layers of blood and the wall of the blood vessel.*

In fact, almost everything that is written about the blood flow will then be wrong.

What does this mean for science? If blood is flowing in a natural vortex and comes across an intrusion, how will the blood behave, and what consequences does this have for our health? If you look at the following diagram of blocked arteries, it is not too hard to imagine that the blood will not be flowing smoothly, and the natural vortex will be affected. If the blood is not following its path in a vortex, what are the consequences of this? What relationship is there between the blood and the walls of the artery – does the vortex create pressure on the artery walls? Does the vortex give the artery walls energy? Does the blood lose its energy at the point of interference, and does the artery wall get weaker and weaker the longer the intrusion stays in place? Will it be like a piece of rust on metal that slowly gets bigger and bigger as it eats away at the artery lining because it is not being healthily nourished by the vortex? I do not have any answers to these questions, but I am very confident that there should be a whole new area of research into the incredibly important issues that this issue raises for our long-term health.

SPIRAL BLOOD FLOW

As I was so astonished that blood could be moving in a vortex, I felt I had to check thoroughly that this idea had been overlooked. It came as a surprise to me that the concept that blood could flow in a vortex was suggested as long ago as 1991, but, it was proposed, this flow was limited to the heart area. Later papers went even further, making suggestions that blood flows in a vortex in other areas of the body. One highlighted the importance of blood flow and suggested that "the absence of spiral flow has been associated with carotid

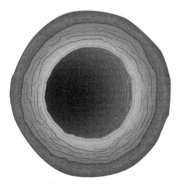

Healthy and blocked arteries

arterial disease." If they know this, why are the old ideas of laminar flow still very much in place?

I could find only a few research papers that discussed this spiral flow, and one of these made for depressing reading. A Scottish surgeon had discovered that the spiral flow was significant in the success rate of operations replacing damaged artery walls in the knee area. If the surgeon operated on a patient and replaced the arterial wall with a smoothly shaped graft, one third of the operations resulted in failure, often leading to amputation. With this surgeon's discovery of a new design for the graft that spun the blood, he discovered that the success rate was 90%, with no ensuing amputations. He concluded that spiral flow "confers advantages over other flow patterns in reducing near wall kinetic energy, turbulence and pressure differences in complex branching systems", three very important factors medically.

In 2004, a group of Japanese scientists discovered that blood not only moves in a spiral, but moves in both clockwise and anti-clockwise spirals in different parts of the body. Their findings reported that "clockwise spiral blood flow exists in the human abdominal aorta from birth" (and why wouldn't it?), and second, that anti-clockwise spiral blood flow and the severity of an injury are related. Clockwise blood flow, on the other hand, reduces the likelihood of injury. Researchers in England in 2003 similarly described a link between spiral flow in the heart and health: "Healthy patients are known to have high prevalence of spiral flow while patients with vascular disease commonly lack spiral flow". Furthermore, "the loss of spiral blood flow has been associated with the presence, severity and progression of the build-up of a waxy plaque on the inside of blood vessels".

Fascinating stuff; I just wish more people had read these studies. Not only is it agreed that blood flows in a spiral, but it does so in two directions, each having a relationship with a person's susceptibility to illness. If this information had been recognised more widely and students of medicine had been taught these basic facts in their textbooks, I am sure we would be further down the route of knowing more about how to cure illnesses that are related to damaged blood flow, such as many heart-related illnesses and circulatory problems.

WHAT ELSE MIGHT THE SCIENTIST HAVE GOT WRONG? – MASARU EMOTO

A Japanese researcher who has looked into the properties of water is Masaru Emoto, who wrote a fascinating book called *The Miracle of Water*. Emoto discovered, by taking photographs of crystals of frozen water exposed to certain external elements, that the water behaved differently and differently shaped crystals were formed. His early experiments looked simply at water that had come from different sources, such as tap water, chlorinated water and spring water. The difference in the crystals was so dramatic that it forced him to carry on with his work to discover what else might affect the water that we drink. He found that water from a spring produced beautiful regular hexagons, while water from the lower course of a river or from a dam hardly achieved a complete crystal. One of his most shocking images came from chlorinated drinking water as this produced very badly deformed-looking crystals, indicating that all was not well in the water that we drink daily.

I have not mentioned all of the external stimuli that Emoto used to produce different shapes of crystal, as I did not want to put you off straight away and dismiss this concept as hocus pocus. In essence, what Emoto did was expose the water to different frequencies of sound and then observe the patterns that the water created from those frequencies. In Chapter 1, I showed that, as long ago as the 18th century, sand exposed to sound waves on a vibrating table was

©Dr M Emoto

A water crystal

shown to produce a myriad of different shapes depending upon the sound frequency to which the sand was exposed. It was proved that objects are directly affected by the vibrational element of sound waves. So is it too much of a leap to replace the words "sand" with the word "water" and come to the same conclusion? If you play different frequencies of sound wave to water, this will produce different shapes that you can measure when you freeze the water that has been exposed to these frequencies. This makes perfect logical sense to me. In fact, as I am sure I have mentioned countless times already, I believe that everything reacts to vibrational waves.

So what does Emoto show in his book *The Miracle of Water*? His photographs clearly show that water is changed by vibrational stimulation – even the minutest change in the vibration changes the shape of the crystal. The problem, however, with this excellent research is that it is undermined by his other conclusions in his book, which have opened him up to ridicule. Let me explain how Emoto creates the different vibrational patterns. In one series of tests, he speaks a single word onto water that is contained in a Petri glass. This one word that is spoken obviously has a vibrational wave frequency as it is in essence a sound wave, and sound waves are easily measurable. So the individual word creates a unique pattern, and therefore I understand that this one sound wave could then create a unique frozen crystal.

However, in later tests, Emoto uses not only individual words, but expressions as well to create hundreds of differently shaped crystals. In his experiments, he uses words such as love, anger,

77

giving birth, happy home, mother's milk, nuclear power plant, cellular phone, tenderness, you inspire me ... I think you can begin to get the message from the types of word that he was speaking into the water. Many of these clearly have an emotional content, and I think that the biggest problem I have with his conclusions is that he states that the word itself, such as the "love" or "anger", contains

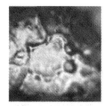

Water Molecule, Before Offering a Prayer

Water Molecule, After Offering a Prayer

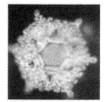

Thank You

You Make Me Sick, I Will Kill You

Love and Appreciation

©Dr M Emoto

Water crystals under different external stimulations

an emotional character that the water picks up on. So if you say the word "love", the water produces a beautifully shaped crystal, but if you happen to say any negatively emotive work such as "anger", or an expression such as "I can't do it", the crystal produces broken and unformed crystals.

The problem is not whether Emoto's general principle of the effect of vibrations is true; the problem is that if it were true, this really would be the missing piece that would help to explain every part of my book. It would help to explain why plants can pick up on emotions, how acupuncture works by transferring vibrations around the body, how being positive helps you recover more quickly from illnesses; in fact, it provides answers to a myriad of previously unexplained problems. If water is the conduit for the vibrations in plants, animals and humans, this is a major step in our development of

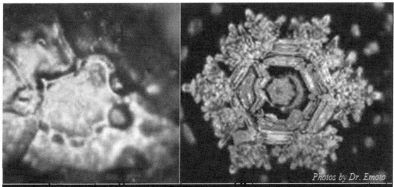

Photos by Dr. Emoto

The photo on the left is of an ice crystal frozen from severly polluted water. The photo on the right is the same water refrozen after having been blessed by Dr. Emoto. One can plainly see that we do have the ability to not only heal ourselves, but our Earth as well.

understanding how everything works. It is a major piece of the jigsaw.

We cannot use Emoto's images as any sort of proof as there is not a constant to work from, but we can use his images of crystals from water that has been exposed to mobile phone signals, television signals and microwaves, or water that has been left next to a computer for several hours. These images use specific and constant vibrations that can be found everywhere, and it is these that produce so many of the negatively formed crystal images in Emoto's book.

These pages of photographs provide image after image of

deformed crystals. All of the crystals have parts missing, or crystals are developing in the wrong areas, and in some instances no crystals are actually formed at all. The water exposed to the electromagnetic field of a mobile phone produced no crystals at all on freezing; neither did the water heated in a microwave oven. Why would this be? When water freezes, its atoms connect and form the nucleus of a crystal, and the crystal becomes stable once it has the structure of a hexagon. Once it has achieved this hexagon, the crystal starts to grow and reaches its natural potential. However, if for any reason something stops the atoms forming a hexagon in the first place, the crystal will not develop. Or if the atoms are affected in a way that the crystals only partially form, you have to ask yourself: what is affecting the water atoms to make this happen?

The results cannot be coincidental. When you go through the hundreds of pages in Emoto's book and look for pictures in which the crystals have been deformed, these always result from negative words, expressions that have been deemed to be negative, or harmful vibrational waves such as microwaves. It should come as no surprise that the Petri dish exposed to mobile phone frequencies or a microwave oven produced no crystals, as these two devices have been suggested to have a negative effect on our bodies' health.

In his early experiments with water, one of Emoto's assistants asked him to try playing music to the water and then assessing the changes in the crystals. What was most surprising was that the crystals produced in this way were some of the most beautiful crystals that he photographed. Beauty is, of course, in the eye of the beholder, but scientifically one would say that the crystals were all perfect without any deformities. Emoto's methodology was very simple. He placed a small bottle of distilled water between two loudspeakers and then played a variety of different types of music. The water was then frozen, and photographs were taken of the resulting crystals. He theorized that the water would absorb the vibration of the sound and retain this information. Now, this is a really, really, important point, and one I would like you to remember. If you listen to music, it is not as simple as the music entering your ear and you responding with enjoyment for that moment. The music actually changes your physical biological make-up by creating different crystals within the water content of your body. At least, that is what Emoto would have us believe.

I personally dislike the conclusions at which Emoto arrives as they provide the scientists and journalists with ammunition for ridiculing his ideas. But I cannot get away from the photos; these, and not Emoto's conclusions, make up the evidence that is of interest to me. They are evidence that vibrational waves affect the consistency of water, which I feel is a monumental piece of evidence, a major discovery, one that should be analysed for years to come. This one piece of evidence opens up a gamut of possibilities for more science research.

And other scientists agree with Emoto. In fact, many scientists believe that water is not just the sum of its chemical parts. In an article from 2008 by Elia and colleagues, remarkable results were obtained. Elia discovered that when water was excited by an externally supplied energy, the electrons within the water produced vortices that aligned them to the ambient magnetic field, including that of the Earth. Because these vortices are cold, they cannot decay, so the vortices can last many months or years. In a further study on water, Elia concluded that "water without doubt has an extended and ordered dynamic involving the whole body of the liquid. It is much more complex than the normal idea of a banal and chaotic cluster of molecular balls."

Dr Wolfgang Ludwig took the research one stage further by measuring the frequency of water itself. He has conducted many experiments showing that water has more than one frequency. How is that possible if scientists say that water has only one "composition"? – simply because its structure varies infinitely. Through his work at the

University of Freiburg, Ludwig set out to assess the "dielectric constants" (DCs) of water, which in layman's terms means the measurement of a material's ability to store an electric charge. What he found was that for all liquids apart from water, this ability, the DC, was constant, but in water it varied depending upon the external conditions the water had been subjected to. For example, the DC of water changed if it had been boiled and cooled very quickly compared with water that had been boiled and slowly left to cool.

Another incredibly important study that Ludwig conducted involved the vibrational frequency of one of his samples of water. This sample had been distilled twice before it had been tested, so he thought that it would be very clean and therefore have a normal frequency. It turned out, though, that the frequency of the water matched that of water that had become heavily polluted, at 1.8 Hz. But how can clean-looking water have the same vibration as dirty, polluted water? The answer can only be provided by the idea that the water has absorbed frequency of the dirty state and maintained it over time, irrespective of how many times it has since been chemically filtered. If this is the case, it provides even more evidence that water has unique properties and confirms the possibility that vibrations play a significant role in our biology.

HOMEOPATHY

I have sympathy with the biochemist's apprehension about homeopathy. How is it possible that a solution that contains no chemical atoms of any consequence causes a chemical reaction? It makes no logical sense whatsoever. Most people, including myself up until a year ago, would agree. But this is just like one of those intellectual games that people play, where the answer to the problem is based on very unusual and illogical clues because all the facts are not evident. As soon as all the facts are known, it is easy to discern the reasons why some homeopathic medicine works.

Let me give you one example of one of these intellectual games: by utilising a completely different area of science, a mathematical impossibility can be overcome. Imagine you are in a building with only two rooms in it. In one of the rooms, there is no furniture, just a chandelier hanging from the middle of the ceiling, and in the far corner of the room is a doorway. This door leads to another room that is also empty of furniture, but on one of the walls is a box that houses three switches. You are told that one of those switches turns the chandelier in the next room off and on and it is your job to discover which switch it is. The problem of course is that the door between the two rooms is closed and you only have two attempts at turning the switches to be able to prove which switch works.

Without going into too much detail, the only solution to the problem that proves every time which switch works lies with utilising a unique approach, one that has nothing at all to do with mathematics. It is like trying to solve a biochemical problem using physics. The answer is actually very simple. If you turn on one of the switches in the room and the door is closed, you cannot see whether or not the switch has worked. But if you leave the switch on for a minute, return it to its previous position and then open the door and walk into the room with the chandelier and feel it to see if it has become warm, you will immediately know if that was the correct switch. The answer is obvious when you are told it but impossible if you don't look for alternative ideas.

This is the same with homeopathy: you have to learn a different area of science to understand how it works. The impossibility of homeopathy is understandable if you think that everything revolves around biochemistry, but there are other factors of science that have to be taken into account, of which a fundamental one is vibrations. If you understand vibrations, homeopathy is very simple and works scientifically.

According to Emoto's crystal theory, water has infinite possibilities in terms of the patterns of crystals that it makes. Perfectly clean water without any pollutants will, it is suggested, produce beautiful crystals all shown to be of perfect shape. If we add a chemical to the water, this addition will cause all of the water's crystals to take on a new shape. If you then take out the chemical content, the crystals that have been formed do not return to their former shape but in fact stay in their new shape – and it is this new shape that is the reason why homeopathic medicine makes logical sense. It makes not the slightest difference how much you dilute your starting sample as the crystal shape of the solution will already have been formed. As soon as the chemical is added to the water, all the water takes on the vibration of that chemical.

What I have discovered is that this science, which is often referred to as that of dilution, is not new and was proved many times in the early 1900s, particularly by J.C. Bose and Lilly Kolisko. (You can read a whole chapter on Bose later in the book.) Bose analysed the behaviour of plants by giving them different levels of poison to see how this would affect their growth rate, and discovered the principle that the greater the dilution of the poison, the more positive an effect it would have on the plant. However, Bose only attempted a few experiments in order to prove his theory, and did not take the concept as far as a dilution of many billions of times. This was left to Kolisko, who, in 1923, conducted experiments on seeds by soaking them in diluted quantities of poisons. She called this area of science "smallest entities", work in which she had gained a large amount of knowledge through her experiments.

In one experiment, wheat seeds had undergone treatment in a seed bath containing quicksilver (mercury) chloride starting with a dilution of 1 in 10 and progressing to a dilution of 1 in 100,000,000,000,000,000,000,000,000,000. The wheat was immersed for two hours in these various dilutions and then grown in the field until fully matured. The seeds that had been exposed to the smallest dilutions completely died as if they had been poisoned by the quicksilver chloride (which of course they had), and the seeds that had been soaked in a solution of 1 to 1,000 parts water achieved normal growth. However, the seeds that were exposed to solutions equivalent to 1 part quicksilver to 10 million parts water or above all achieved increased growth with improved wheat content. In effect, this was a proof of the principle that dilution can benefit the growth and presumed health of plants.

Fast-forward now to the 1990s, when another scientist took this concept of dilution a stage further and discovered that water was the unique factor in the dilution effect. If you read about the history of the French doctor who made the assertion that water retains vibrational waves, Jacques Benveniste, you would think that he had threatened the very existence of Western medicine. In a documentary about Benveniste made in 1994, soon after his assertions had caused such a medical storm, documentary-maker Tony Edwards concluded that for some reason the medical establishment chose to stitch him up.

I read Benveniste's letter of reply in an issue of the journal *Nature* that was published a few weeks after the original document, and I have never read an article containing so much suppressed anger. I can see why he felt he had been stitched up; it would be like two buffoons who knew nothing about science coming into a laboratory and performing with a live musical band in front of experiments in which sound plays a vital role. He concludes his reply with the following words:

I now believe this kind of inquiry must immediately be stopped throughout the world. Salem witch hunts or McCarthy like prosecutions will kill science. Science flourishes only in freedom. We must not let, at any price, fear, blackmail, anonymous accusation, libel and deceit nest in our labs. Our colleagues are overwhelmingly utmost decent people, not criminals. To them, I say: never, but never let these people get in your lab. The only way definitively to establish conflicting results is to reproduce them. It may be that all of us are wrong in good faith. This is no crime but science as usual and only the future knows.

So what was it that caused such fear in the scientific community? Maybe it was because the idea that water could have some sort of "memory" was so unbelievable to Sir John Maddox, the editor of *Nature*, that he had no other choice but to dismiss the concept out of hand. Call me old-fashioned, but isn't it the purpose of science to be open to new and challenging ideas and welcome such scientific experiments?

I have to admit that I have been biased in my time against homeopathy, purely because of the media campaign against it. I believed that reducing an element down to a level smaller than that of an atom did not make sense. No-one ever explained to me that it was nothing to do with this whatsoever. The power of homeopathy is not related to the chemical nature of the water. The fact that there is only an atom left of the substance that has been placed in the water is a complete red herring. The important factor is that the water absorbs the vibrations.

As far as I understand it, water does not have a memory, and this is a completely incorrect way of describing it. If we said fabricated steel also has a memory, springs have a memory, any sheet metal that has been bent into another shape has a memory, it does not mean that the sheet metal can remember its life when it was flat, just as it does not mean water can remember how it was before the additive was put in it. The very notion of memory should be taken out of all of the correspondence to do with water as it implies something completely incorrect. Water does not have memory as we know it. Water is able to change its vibrational properties, that is all.

I am not claiming here that homeopathic pills work – all I am suggesting is that the science behind the concept is very logical and agrees with all of the science I have uncovered. However, I do have one major problem with homeopathic medicine: how do you transform a vibrational pattern from water into a pill and still retain the same vibration? I would guess that studies looking into the effectiveness of homeopathic treatments would have very mixed results if they analysed both water- and pill-based homeopathic medicine. I would assume that the vibrations of the water-based treatment would be more effective than those of a pill, for which I believe the vibrational content would be so far removed from its water one as to be almost redundant. I am open-minded on this point, and if someone from a homeopathic manufacturer explained to me how they transfer vibrations from water to solids without changing them, I could be persuaded that both forms of treatment were effective. For now, however, I can only say that water-based homeopathic treatment makes complete logical sense to me, but not treatment in pill form.

GEORGIO PICCARDI

Between March and April 1955, Professor Piccardi conducted three hundred pairs of experiments in order to test his assertion that water behaves differently depending upon its physical state. He concluded that his "experiments reveal something highly unusual;

agitation or turbulence seems to be capable of determining the effect of the water". But most importantly. he makes the proposition that:

> *Perhaps it is even by means of water and the aqueous system that external forces are able to react on living organisms.*

In 1962, Piccardi wrote: "Why is it that natural water drunk at a spring is more effective from a medical point of view than the same water bottled and aged?" Why is natural water so different from a medical point of view in spite of the fact that the difference in chemical composition reveals nothing in particular? He talks about these facts as if they were common knowledge back in 1962, but the science behind this opinion seem to have been lost to us since then. So why are all of Piccardi's important findings buried in a book that was published almost fifty years ago, ideas that should be in mainstream science today? If it is true that water is the conduit for many of the unexplained activities that occur in our bodies, this should be investigated with the utmost urgency. The possibilities for improving our health cannot be overstated.

If water is so important, imagine the effects that poor quality water may be having on us already. If water can retain all of the bad vibrations that scientists have suggested, might it be possible for these vibrations to start to have an effect on us the moment we drink a glass of water from the tap? The water enters our body through our mouth and will start to affect everything that it comes into contact with. The bacteria within the stomach and intestines will be vibrated to a different equilibrium level and will change their status, possibly producing bad bacteria that have a knock-on effect elsewhere within the body.

This one idea that water can affect bacteria in the gut is far-reaching as the bacteria is part of the first port of call for all food that enters the body. If we assume that "you are what you eat" and that the food that enters your body starts to be digested within the stomach, the body is set up to release all the good constituents of the food and discard the bad contents as waste, and bacteria play a major part in this. The vitamins, proteins, minerals and energy supplied by the food then enter the bloodstream and are taken around the body to supply the parts that need them. Imagine if the bacteria within the gut were not operating correctly because of the bad water being drunk. This would be a nightmare scenario as it could imply that, in order to stay healthy, we would all have to drink fresh natural mineral water, of which there really is not enough to go around.

WHY DO WE DRINK? – FEREYDOON BATMANGHELIDJ

I know why I eat: because food gives me energy. But I have no idea why I need to drink. I have asked myself this question many times, and the only answer that I come up with is because I am thirsty, which is not really a very satisfying answer. Why am I being told that I need to drink two litres of water a day in order to stay healthy? What would happen if I didn't? I, like most people, do not drink that amount of water as it is too much of an inconvenience, plus the fact it means I have to be constantly aware of where toilets are located. When I drink lots of water, it just goes through me very quickly, so I assume that my body does not need it in the first place. I falsely believe that if my body needed it, it would retain the water, and the less I went to the toilet, the better. It turns out that this is incorrect and in fact I could be doing myself a serious amount of physical damage by not drinking enough water.

It came as a great surprise to me that this knowledge has only very recently been brought to the fore. If it had not been for one man in particular, in 1992, writing a book explaining and proving the damage that we were doing to our health, we would all still be blissfully unaware that being partially dehydrated causes illnesses such as arthritis, ulcers, high blood cholesterol, asthma and allergies.

Fereydoon Batmanghelidj only discovered this fact through a twist of fate. He had the misfortune to be practising medicine in Iran at the time of the Shah's overthrow in the 1970s. As a consequence, he was thrown into prison. During his time there, he noticed that many patients were being diagnosed with peptic ulcers, and that medication, of which there was a major shortage, failed to relieve their symptoms. As Batmanghelidj was a doctor, the prisoners turned to him for help. The only medicine he had was water, and he suggested that one particular prisoner should take it to alleviate his symptoms. To both their surprise, drinking the water relieved all the symptoms of pain within only ten minutes. On completing a course of rehydration, drinking water six times a day, the ulcer completely disappeared.

Three years later, on release from the prison, Batmanghelidj escaped to America, where he carried on his research into the benefits of being hydrated and discovered that this fundamental philosophy had been misunderstood. Doctors had completely ignored the fact that we need to be hydrated for our body to function properly, and that dehydration will cause the onset of symptoms. This is not strange as water regulates every single feature in our body. Water is in every single cell, so any change in its equilibrium level will affect the cell's behaviour. When the body is partially dehydrated, the body rations the water using its own drought management system. Extreme symptoms of dehydration are, however, not what you would expect. I am sure you would imagine that if the body needed water, we would get thirsty. Sadly, this is not the case – the most common symptom is in fact pain.

I can talk from experience here. Having spent many holidays on the beach, I know that my body never told me that I was lacking water until my head started to explode with pain. This was always way too late to stop it from ruining my evening. Why did my body not tell me during the day, while I was sitting on the beach, soaking up the sun's rays, that I needed to top up my bodily fluids? All it had to do was tell my mouth, create the thirst sensation, and I could have still enjoyed my social life in the evening. Instead, I just suffered severe pain. If my headache's were caused by a lack of water, could it not also be true that other pains are also caused by a lack of water and can therefore be cured simply by topping up our bodily water levels?

This begs the question, then, what is thirst if it is not our body's response to a shortage of water? Strangely, the scientific relationship between thirst and drinking is very weak, indeed almost non-existent. The same is true of hunger and eating. How strange that science claims to know so much about our body yet does not even understand the two most fundamental aspects of life, eating and drinking. We all know that when we are hungry we should eat, and when we are thirsty we should drink, but no-one knows what exactly the triggers are for this. I know a bit about hunger because my father wrote a book called *Why We Eat*, which was aimed at doctors who distribute appetite suppressants. While he was writing the book, I chatted to him about hunger and was astonished that current science had absolutely no idea why we get hungry. It is obviously the same with thirst. If it were just a trigger for being dehydrated, we would get thirsty much more often. It appears that science is probably looking the wrong way when trying to find the answer to this problem, and I don't believe it will ever find the answer if scientists are just looking at the observational side of science.

I would imagine that thirst and hunger are triggered when the body has a disequilibrium in, say, its natural energy level, or when its vibrational frequency has changed in a specific area of the body. This would then trigger a response in the mouth or stomach depending on the message that was being sent. This message is not sent via the neural pathways but on the vibrational waves of water. This is purely a guess on my part, but it is one that I feel should be investigated further.

Just as I have suggested a very strange idea to solve a problem, science itself has looked at an unusual one in order to help women in labour. If you are pregnant and are about to go into labour, you might be surprised, when crying out in pain for a large shot of pethidine, to be told you are not going to receive any medication but are instead going to get an injection of water into your lower back area. I am pretty sure not many women would be pleased to be told this, for what good could water be in pain relief? But you would be surprised to know it is very effective. Studies have proved that "sterile water injections provide good pain relief, particularly for low back pain during labour". According to Batmanghelidj, the reason for this is very clear: the pain is caused by dehydration. He writes a chapter on lower back pain in his book *Your Body's Many Cries For Water*. In his chapter on rheumatoid arthritis, he concludes that lower back pain "indicates that the lower back joint is not fully prepared to endure the pressure until it is fully hydrated". Lower back pain, he declares, can be cured by water.

If this is true, I can see no logical problems with it providing the solution to the issue of pain in childbirth. It is a question of providing the joints with enough pressure to sustain the extra requirements that pushing a child out of the womb involves. Drinking large amounts of water during childbirth would provide this, but as far as I remember at my sons' births, this was never suggested. So a quick fix is to provide an injection of water into the lower back area. A very cheap and effective solution to the pain in childbirth without any side effects.

I had naively assumed that the doctors who utilise this method would be aware of the reasons why it works and had seen Batmanghelidj's book. However, having read a study that analysed the success of this method of pain relief, I was brought back down to earth. The researchers who wrote the article concluded that "to our knowledge, there is no study with the primary aim of investigating the underlying mechanisms of action underlying sterile water injections". Oh yes, there is. Just look at the bibliography in Batmanghelidj's book and you will find there is lots of evidence. Why do a study when several have already been done? So here is my recommendation to the midwifery community: I recommend that all women drink sensible amounts of water during child birth to relieve pain. Common sense tells me that if injecting water into the lower back relieves pain, so will drinking it.

What I did not expect to find was that injecting water not only reduced the pain, but also significantly reduced the number of Caesarean sections that were performed. In a meta-analytical review (this is the authoritative statistical scientific jargon for reviewing a collection of studies, which is often used to prove a theory) of sterile water injections, the researchers concluded that injecting sterile water was so effective that a large study should be mounted to validate their findings. "Such a study would be ideally a double blinded placebo control design ... ." Then what? I thought that a meta-analysis was supposed to prove something conclusively one way or another. It appears, however, that the researchers were so astonished by their findings that they needed more studies to provide proof that the conclusions they had come to were correct. Once such studies had been done, I would assume that another meta-analysis would have to be conducted to confirm the findings, and the whole merry-go-round of trials and studies would continue until the simple idea that drinking water can relieve back pain in pregnancy and reduce the number of Caesarean sections was generally accepted.

One more consideration from Batmanghelidj is related to drug trials. If water relieves the pain from illnesses, this can pose a problem in many different drug experiments. He surmises that, when taking a pill in a clinical drug trial, the patient happens to utilise a glass of water to help swallow the pill, and the very action of ingesting the water could be a factor when measuring the success of a particular drug. Maybe the water itself is playing an active role that could affect the trial. Batmanghelidj theorizes that water has its effect before the biological substance is absorbed into the blood. He also suggests "that the high cure rates with placebo in controlled studies reported up to now were not without good reason. Any interpretation or comparison of medication against placebo should be reconsidered due to the body's response to water as a natural medicine". Drug companies take note. In order to get the most accurate results in clinical trials, human guinea-pigs should take their medication dry, so as not to provide any false-positive results.

WATER AND ENERGY

To complete the picture of how amazing water is, I had to read books on quantum physics and the role of electrons and ionization. I am going to spare you the details as they are far too complicated for a book of this nature. The science that I am going to refer you to, however, was started by Bernard and Alberte Pullman in 1963 with their book on quantum biochemistry. This was then taken to a new level by Albert Szent-Györgyi, who, building on the Pullmans' discoveries, started a new science that he called bioelectronics. Within this new area of science, he chose to look at how the body worked from an energy perspective as he believed that the cell is the same as a machine – it needs energy to make it work. This was the basis for a new way of looking at biology. On the one hand you have the molecular biochemists, and on the other the bioelectronicists; Szent-Györgyi believed that these were two different, indeed opposite, ways of looking at the life of the cell. And you cannot come to an understanding of how the cell works unless you understand both these issues.

What was so interesting for me was that Szent-Györgyi discussed the properties of water in his book, and because my radar was very much on high alert to unusual properties of water, I read this section with great interest. I have translated his physics into an easier form of visualization because the technical jargon is very confusing. So I am going to talk about atoms and electrons in a way that I can make into a simple mental picture, which I find works really well.

One of the smallest objects is the atom, which is often portrayed as a round circle, (the electrons) with a dot in the middle (the nucleus). Imagine now a person (the nucleus) standing in a field with a very long rope and a ball at the end of it (the electrons), and then imagine the person starting to swing the ball around and around in a giant circle – this is the equivalent of a textbook diagram of an atom, a circle with a dot in the middle. You can think of the energy of the atom as being the amount of energy that the person uses to keep the ball swinging round. What is of interest to scientists is how much energy is needed for this and how much energy would be required for the person to swing the ball so fast that it would leave the rope and go off into the distant field, town or even universe. The further the better, it seems: a question that scientists always like to ask is how much energy would be required for the ball to be flown into infinity.

Now back to water. In one of his descriptions of energy, Szent-Györgyi talks about problems with understanding certain energy issues in biology. When analysing the simplest of all atoms, that of hydrogen, the energy required to swing the ball (electrons) around is smallest when the hydrogen atom is mixed with an oxygen atom to form water. So now we have to imagine two people in the middle swinging two balls, and the combination of Mr hydrogen with Ms oxygen creates an equilibrium in which swinging the ball requires the least amount of energy out of every combination of people standing in the middle. You can't get a more efficient form of swinging the ball on the long rope than that of water. As water is technically two hydrogen atoms to one water, you would actually have to imagine three people in the middle but I am not going to be too picky on that one!

One more unusual feature of water is that the amount of energy required using the people in the middle to allow the ball to break free from the rope and send it into infinity (known as the ionization potential) is the largest known amount of energy in nature. So water has this incredible facility in that it is in fact the lowest energy point of nature, with nothing below it in terms of energy and nothing above it in terms of strength amongst all biological substances. Even someone like me who knows nothing about physics would sit up and take notice of this fact as it means, yet again, that water is unique, and the more we investigate it the more impressive it becomes. Could water be unique in this area for a reason? Could water have a role not only in vibrations, but also in energy within all biological systems?

It was only discovered in January 2010 that there was "ultrafast energy transfer between water atoms" that had hitherto been unknown, and it has been suggested that this has "far-reaching consequences for biological systems", although exactly what those are were unclear in the article. But taking this discovery a stage further and incorporating all that I have shown on water so far in this chapter, could one take an intuitive step and question whether water maybe plays a far greater role in our bodies' energy transfer than had previously been imagined? I know that the idea of water being the conduit for the body's ability to receive vibrations was pretty much unheard of before now, so might the major idea that water has a twofold role, one of vibration transfer and another of energy transfer, not be so farfetched? Sadly, I have not found any scientific papers on the relationship between energy transfer and water in the human body to confirm or deny this, so I will just have to leave this question open for the moment.

Water does play a role in the present biochemical interpretation of how energy is transferred around the body through a chemical called ATP and intracellular components called mitochondria, but there is nothing that looks at alternatives to this idea that place more emphasis on the water content than on the red blood cells themselves, even though nearly 90% of the blood is made up of water. This is a great shame. I believe that science so far has ignored two fundamental aspects of water: its vibrational capabilities and its ability to generate and transfer energy. If water has the ability to do both of these things, this opens up a completely new area of science that provides such simple solutions to many issues that have stumped scientists until now.

A SIMPLE SOLUTION

I am not sure whether it is just coincidence, but twice I have been inspired while being on holiday sitting next to fresh running water. The first time was on holiday in Northern Spain, where the ideas about the beginning of life appeared in my head out of nowhere (see the next section). The second time was in Majorca, where I was sitting on a jetty with my feet dangling in the fresh Mediterranean water and an idea that was so extraordinary just popped into my head. If was so simple that I did not know why I had not thought about it before; if it were true, it would completely change the way in which we perceive energy and all of its New Age hippy connotations. What on earth, I always asked myself, are energy healers? What energy are they referring to? When people discuss their energy levels, what exactly is an energy level? While sitting by the water in Majorca, it occurred to me that it was all about vibrations.

What was the idea that suddenly occurred to me out of the blue? It was simply the fact that the levels of frequency could also be considered as potential levels of energy, so that the greater the frequency, the more energy would be available. As discussed earlier in the chapter, water can have different frequencies, measured as the number of hertz (Hz) it generates. The smaller the number of hertz, the lower the frequency it is generating per second. A microwave has a frequency per second millions of times more than that of a sound wave, which can be anything from 20 to 20,000 Hz. I had thought that all frequencies had the ability to generate energy, for example light, but microwaves generate energy that can simply be measured in the form of heat, and heat is in fact a very good way of determining the level of energy generated.

I am not sure whether you can exactly equate different frequencies with different energy levels, but I am sure you can equate frequencies with potential energy, which for my purpose is all that I need – the lower the frequency the lower the potential energy, and the higher the frequency the higher the potential energy. There must for water be an equilibrium frequency, a vibration at which it is perfectly balanced. Any variation away from this level would mean that the water would need to have an increase or a decrease in its vibration to achieve its natural vibrational level.

As an example, I previously reported that a sample of polluted water had a frequency of 1.8 Hz. If, for argument's sake, natural spring water has a frequency of 8 Hz, this would imply that the polluted water was lacking in vibrational energy by a value of 6.2 Hz (8 – 1.8 = 6.2). So how could the water get this extra energy? If left to its own devices, I would argue that nature would restore it through movement. Polluted water will at some point enter the climatic cycle; it will evaporate, form clouds and come down as rain, during which it will be unburdened of the chemical pollutant vibration. However, I believe there are many opportunities within that cycle for water to restore its vibrational energy levels, and not just when it is cleaned by evaporation and rainfall. I believe the spinning movement of water while in a vortex can do the same thing.

In the case of the biodynamic farming we talked about earlier, the spinning of the water is giving it more energy, and this energy helps it to achieve its objective in generating bacteria that nourish the soil. Water creates such vortices in streams and fast-moving rivers, I would argue, so that water can achieve its natural energy levels, and in order to restore water's energy levels, it is simply necessary to stir it. The same I believe happens in the blood, a vortex motion helping to maintain the blood's energy levels.

Imagine if you mixed polluted water that had a low energy level of, say, 1.8 Hz with water that had been stirred for twenty-four hours and had a higher energy level of 10 Hz. What would happen to the water? Wouldn't the polluted water grab the extra energy from the stirred water? Water would always be striving to obtain its natural level of 8 Hz and would attempt to grab the missing energy from whatever source it could – in this case, the stirred water. A new energy equilibrium position would be achieved depending on the different proportions of the two types of water that were mixed together. Energy would flow from the stirred water to the polluted water.

Imagine this was taking place in your body. The polluted water would grab as much vibrational energy from wherever it could in order for it to attempt to regain its natural level. And this energy would have to be taken from somewhere. The resulting disequilibrium is, I suggest, one that we all recognise – tiredness. The polluted water is pulling any spare energy that you have, and unless you replace it, the only consequence will be for you to feel tired as your body is naturally short of vibrational energy.

The same effect would, however, occur with the water that had been stirred for twenty-four hours, and I believe the effect would depend on how healthy you were in the first place. If you were a normal healthy person with a natural frequency of 8 Hz, your body would have too much energy and would try and get rid of it. I have no idea how it would achieve this, just that it seems logically obvious that it would. If, however, the body could not get rid of this excess energy, it might very well enter into an equilibrium level that was disadvantageous for the efficient workings of the body, and tiredness might also ensue.

If natural vibrations are the answer to energy, this highly significant discovery should be embraced more fully in our understanding of human interactions. Depressed people are more likely to have a lower hertz value and will suck the hertz out of happy people. This is probably the reason why depressed people have generally been shown to socialise with other depressed people, and when we talk about friends bringing you down, what we really mean are friends bringing down your natural hertz levels.

THE BEGINNING OF LIFE AND LIFE ON DISTANT PLANETS – "WATER GIVETH"

I have read a lot of theories on the reasons why life began on this planet, but none of them seems to acknowledge the role of water. I would like to put forward my own new idea of why life began, and as a consequence of this theory I propose that not all distant planets with a water content will have life on them.

My second spontaneous idea, just like the one I described in the previous section, was so obvious that I could not understand why I had not thought of it before. I happened to be on holiday in Spain and was escaping from the midday heat in a forest in the hills just north of Madrid. I was lying next to a beautiful stream in which the water was cascading down from the mountain. I took a few photographs of the water in the hope that I would be able to capture some images of vortices being created as it bounced around the rocks. At this moment, I was wondering how important these vortices were to the behaviour of the water and how water was affected by its environment. Looking at one of the mountains, I had an idea that water behaved like it did because of the environment in which it found itself, Earth, a mountainous landscape, where the water in the rivers goes through many different journeys of change. The water is dropped from the clouds in the form of rain, which then collects in small streams, joining up to form even bigger ones, charging down the steep slopes of the mountain, eventually running into flatter, calmer conditions further downstream, then forming larger rivers, and eventually flowing out into the relative calm of the oceans.

My thoughts turned to the changing properties of water and how it is different between the spring at the top of the mountain and when it is flowing sedately as it becomes a river. Could it be possible, I thought, that this pattern of change would be important to the creation of water that is vibrationally healthy enough to sustain life? If we did not have any mountains and water just fell to the ground into lakes and oceans, would water have vibrational properties that could sustain life? If not, I logically concluded that the natural shape of our environment was a factor in developing water to the stage at which it could sustain life. Could I not make an imaginative leap that would allow me to suggest that the most important factor in the creation of life on earth was when water finally developed the correct vibrational pattern to sustain life, and this was the most important reason why life on earth evolved? As soon as the water became evolved, so amino acids could develop into single-celled structures that could then double and quadruple in size until more sophisticated life forms were created.

If this were true, life on our planet developed because of several factors being in place at the right time. I would argue that the landscape had to be mountainous, the temperature had to be right, the environmental gaseous conditions had to be such that water could form in sufficient amounts for amino acids could multiply, and the gravitational forces of the earth and the planets had all to be at the correct levels. Only when there was harmony between these variables could water develop to the point at which it allowed life to form.

Logically, it follows that life on other planets might not be as abundant as we think. Just because water is found, it does not mean that the formation of life will definitely occur every time. The circumstances have to be right, and water has to have an environment in which it can develop the right vibrational pattern before life can begin. I would therefore argue that of course life exists on distant planets, but maybe not in the numbers that we all think. And it will only occur on planets that have a mountainous terrain and not a flat one.

THE DINOSAURS' EXTINCTION – "WATER TAKETH"

If the argument above is true, it is logical to assume that water can take life away as well as give it. If water became very unstable, this change might be so significant that cellular organisms would fail to develop. How could such a cataclysmic event happen? The only event that could be so significant would be one that completely affected the balance of nature, and in the case of Earth's history, there is only one such event – the great meteor that hit the earth and wiped out the dinosaurs.

This idea was suggested to me by the book's cover designer, Steve Lodewyke, who became interested in the idea that water could have been a factor in the evolution of life on Earth. As he was fascinated by the anomalies of the extinction of the dinosaurs, he suggested that my ideas about water might play a significant role in helping to fill in the gaps. The current thinking is that the meteor that hit Earth millions of years ago caused the extinction of the dinosaurs. This is a very good argument, but there are a few aspects that do not make sense. If all of the dinosaurs were wiped out very quickly due to the effects of the meteor on the food supply, there would be no argument. The problem arises because the dinosaurs lived on after the event for thousands of years and came to a long, slow death rather than a quick one. How does this fit in with the theory of the meteor?

The argument that I have always understood was that the meteor sent so much dust into the atmosphere that it caused the earth to be in total darkness for years, thus affecting plant growth and with it the lives of all of the herbivores that lived on the plants at that time. If the earth was in darkness, surely all of the larger animals would have died out very quickly as there would not have been enough food to go round? The only animals that would have survived would have been the smaller creatures that did not require very much food. A twenty-ton dinosaur would have to eat a lot of leaves to keep it alive, but a mouse would, by comparison, require very little. But how long would it take for all of these large dinosaurs to disappear if there was very little food? I would argue not very long, probably just a few generations. If after one hundred years they were still surviving, it is likely they would continue for another five hundred years. There would be no reason for them to become extinct based on just the food supply. But in fact, many dinosaurs lived for thousands of years after the meteor, so food cannot have been the exclusive reason for their extinction. Some dinosaurs survived and still exist today, chickens and sharks being two good examples of living dinosaurs. So why did they survive? Could the answer have anything to do with the properties of water?

I believe, with Steve, that there is some logic in assuming that it was a combination of the meteor and the properties of water that combined to cause the extinction of the dinosaurs. I believe that this cataclysmic event had such a huge effect on the environment that all of the Earth's water came into contact with new pollutants, atmospheric differences, electromagnetic changes (as the earth would have shifted its orbit due to the force of the meteor), temperature shifts and the unavailability of light. Water would be one of the first factors to be affected, causing it to change its vibrational pattern.

What effect would this new vibrational equilibrium have on living organisms? This is purely speculative, but I would argue that the new vibrational level would affect the larger animals in a similar way to humans today – they would get seriously fatigued. A twenty-ton dinosaur that was used to grazing all day for food would not, due to the changed water, have enough energy to forage all day. The water would be slowly draining it of energy. This would not cause the dinosaur to starve, but over the longer term the species would slowly die out. The reason that smaller animals adapted could be for twofold: firstly, they did not need so much food so being fatigued did not affect them quite as much, and secondly, their life-span was so much shorter that they could have evolved more quickly and adapted to the change. A dinosaur that lives for one hundred years might take twenty generations or even fifty to change, which could amount to thousands of years. If it did not change within that time, it would die out. Smaller animals that live just for a few years would have evolved much more quickly – for them fifty generations could occur in only two hundred years, giving them a chance to adapt.

This is all purely speculative on my part, but it does offer a new and exciting addition to explain some of the inconsistencies in the current models for the extinction of the dinosaurs.

WATER PRODUCTS

If you believe anything that I have written about the properties of water, I beg you not to go out looking to buy water-based products that allege to restore water back to its natural levels. I have yet to find one product in the field of water that provides any scientific evidence to prove that it is effective. Many of them make amazing spurious claims about how they can do this, that and the other, but not one of them has any proper science to back it up.

If so many people are developing machines that restore dirty water back to its original state, they have to provide proof of how they do it, but as yet I can find no scientific paper proving these machines work in a way that I find convincing. This is not to say, however, that the machines do not work to change the properties of water, but I am not yet convinced. Strangely, what convinces me more is not allegations of success by people who are marketing a product, but more the success of an industry that has taken on a technology and run with it, producing tangible results. I am of course referring back to biodynamic farming. It seems much clearer to me, from observing nature, that it is not necessary to introduce any electrical stimulus into water to restore its properties as this concept is not found anywhere in nature. It is much more likely that the simple solution of creating a vortex will have that effect.

So are there simple machines that spin water in a vortex? Yes, but lots of them make such spurious claims that it offends me to even mention them. In biodynamic farming, there are instructions to say you must spin the water in two directions for up to one hour in order to get the properties right in the water. I am not sure whether there is any difference between one or two hours of spinning as there is no research that has looked into this difference. But the machines I found do not make any claims in terms of how long they should be used for – some suggest that just a few spins will have a positive effect. Some are left on all the time, but this sounds particularly bad as too much spinning might create an abundance of energy in the water, which would do no-one any good.

Maybe the problem would be clarified by scientists just measuring the different frequencies of the water in a series of simple experiments and testing the length of different vortices and the effect these had on the vibrational pattern of the water. Whole industries could then be developed on the back of such discoveries, from water for agricultural use through to drinking water. This is a vast industry, yet it seems that it is being ignored. If I had the money, I would be investigating it right now, through proper scientific channels, and proving it all very clearly. I would then take this science and show that crops grew better, seeds propagated more reliably and grew faster, and tap water became healthier, and create a billion dollar business within a generation. Anyway, that is my dream, one which I am not going to do for the simple reason I don't have enough money to do it. But if I won the lottery, it is the first thing I would spend my money on!

WATER AND THE MOON

Now this is where two chapters merge and produce powerful evidence that is very scary. I use the word "scary" because once you have an idea that something in your body can pick up on vibrating waves, some very significant ideas will logically follow. One of these is that water is not only a very crucial part of our biology, but is also directly affected by the cycle of the planets. If water itself is affected by the orbiting planets and behaves differently on different days of the week based upon the alignment of the planets, this would have to mean that our bodies are biologically affected via the changing pattern of the water itself.

The next chapter covers many scientific papers proving beyond doubt that the moon does have a biological effect on us. I would argue that this effect is picked up by the water content in our bodies, but this is just my interpretation. The scientists who have proved that the moon has an effect on our biology do not attempt to understand how this works, just the fact that it does. If, on the other hand, you can accept the possibility that water is the conduit for gravitational forces coming from the moon, you really are going to enjoy the leap of faith you are about to make.

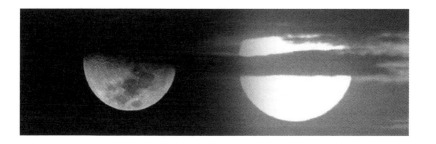

INTRODUCTION TO

THE SUN AND THE MOON

Madness, Menstruation and Manure

" *Whoever desires properly to investigate the art of medicine must first take into consideration the seasons of the year, and how each is capable of operating, for they not only do not resemble each other but differ widely the one from the other in the changes they bring about".*

HIPPOCRATES, GREEK PHYSICIAN 400 B.C.

THE MOON

It wasn't until recently that I became aware of my complete ignorance about the moon. My knowledge was so limited that I actually didn't know how many times the moon goes round the Earth each day. I also didn't know whether there were any nights in the month in which the moon does not appear. In fact,

The full moon

there were lots of things about the moon I really had not bothered to think about. Even though I calculated I had looked at it over ten thousand times in my lifetime, I had never really thought about it. So, when I did take the time to think about it in a very casual sort of way, my thoughts turned to the tides, as this was the only fact I was aware of. I thought that if the moon can move oceans, which are just made of water, and we as humans are made up of, give or take, 70% water, it seemed obvious that the moon must be having an effect on the water in my body. How, or to what extent, I did not know; it just seemed to be logical that it did.

How does the moon affect the tides? Certainly not in the way I had always imagined. I was under the impression the moon somehow pulled the water one way or another, and if it were high tide at one side of the ocean, it would naturally be low tide at the other. But this is not quite accurate. What in fact happens is that the gravitational forces of the moon and the sun actually cause the oceans to bulge, and the tide is caused by this bulge being attracted to the orbiting moon. And this gravitational effect is not the same every day: it varies, due to the unusual characteristics of gravity. When two gravitational forces such as the sun and the moon are aligned, their pull is the equivalent to adding the sun's and the moon's forces together. And if the planet Mercury were also aligned, its gravitational force would then be added to the sun's and the moon's – there would be a cumulative effect. This is why we have very high tides on specific days of the year, commonly when the sun is aligned directly with the moon, such as the spring tide, which is always one of the highest.

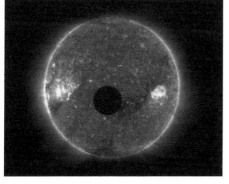

The moon in front of the sun

At the time of thinking about the moon, I did not really care how the moon achieved its effects, just that it did. But it was the idea the moon must also be affecting the water in my body that caused me to question some very basic facts about how my body worked. What effect this internal tide had on me was completely unknown at the time, but my general Western scientific education had instilled in me a belief that the moon does nothing. I imagined that lots of scientific studies had been set up to prove this. But had they? Have studies been done that prove this beyond doubt? Spending time researching this question has in fact caused me to come to quite the opposite conclusion. Indeed, a large number of studies have been conducted which show there is a direct link between the moon's cycle and the behaviour of animals, plants and humans. The same is so with the sun, but even more surprising to me was that it is not just the moon and the sun, but the other planets as well, such as Jupiter and Mars, that affect the biological behaviour of living organisms.

One of the many scientific papers I read was in the journal *New Scientist* from December 1977. It described the following study on a blind man who had been kept in isolation for a month in order to analyse his sleeping behaviour. Drs L.E.M. Miles, D.M. Raynal and M.A. Wilson of Stanford University School of Medicine and the Palo Alto Veterans Administration hospital studied a blind man who displayed sleeping patterns that were more associated with the lunar day of 24.84 hours than the solar day of 24 hours. They discovered that the patient suffered from a complete synchronisation of all of his natural bodily rhythms to a 24.84 hour day that was indistinguishable from that of a lunar cycle:

> Blind man goes lunar
> *The patient is a psychologically normal man who has been blind since birth but has lived and worked in normal society. He is an active postgraduate student at a major university and for several years has suffered severe insomnia and day time sleepiness for two to three week periods followed by one to two weeks of normality. He has made strenuous efforts to adjust to normal living, for example, by using sleep-inducing and stimulating drugs, but these have only marginal effects. A sleep and activities diary kept for a short time by the patient suggested that he had a free-running circadian rhythm with a period slightly longer than the 24 hours. The sleep record showed a distinct drift in his sleep pattern and he entered hospital for a 26 day period of observation and tests. During this period, he was encouraged to work, eat and sleep and interact with others as he wished and he retained all time cues, except of course sight. His sleep cycle settled down to a 24.9 hour cycle with respect to the normal diurnal cycle. He returned home to his normal life style and drug course and his ineffectual attempts to keep a 24 hour cycle are clearly shown. In the final period,*

*he agreed to undergo a form of training during which he was
forced to sleep during the normal night and was kept awake
during the normal day. It soon became clear that his own cycle
continued quite unaffected.*

What is so typical here is that no follow-up study was done by
these or any other researchers. In fact, I have not been able to find
any further research that has been conducted into the lunar effect
and sleep patterns in blind people. There are many studies on the
problems blind people have with sleep dysfunction but none that
looks specifically at the lunar cycle. In an experiment in 2002 into
this "strange" behaviour, twenty-six blind people were assessed over
a fourteen-day period, the conclusions being that blind people suffer
from daytime sleepiness and poor night-time sleep, facts that were
already known. Other studies with titles such as "Day-time naps and
melatonin in blind people", "Sleep/wake disorders in blind people"
and "Disturbance of sleep in blindness" all refer to the same point,
which is that blind people don't sleep very well. But what all of these
studies fail to do is to look for the cause of the problem in order to
find the solution. In fact, I would say that in most of the thousands
of scientific studies I have looked at, this is a recurring problem.
Science is always looking to put a plaster over the problem and fix
it that way, mostly via drugs, rather than looking for the root cause.

In the case of blind people, the problem is caused by their
relationship to the lunar cycle, which means they have daily sleep
patterns that follow the 24.8-hour lunar day and not the 24-hour
sunlight sleep pattern. The blind man's internal clock is regulated
by the moon. Sadly, the only solution scientists are searching
for is a chemical solution to solve why the sleep pattern is out of
order. All of the studies point towards the body's changing levels
of melatonin to explain the issue, but for some unknown reason

no-one is looking at what is causing the melatonin levels to change. Surely scientists can't suggest that the body just changes its natural equilibrium level without reason? So they have come up with new catchphrases to describe the issue, such as "sleep-phase delay" and "free-running rhythms", which could easily translate simply to "lunar sleep pattern" if anyone were brave enough to do this.

IS MY SLEEP PATTERN AFFECTED BY THE LUNAR CYCLE?

Is it just blind people who have a 24.8-hour day rhythm, or do all of us in fact have one? Is there anything else about the moon that we need to know? Have scientists looked at this issue and come up with any other biological issues we should all know about? In some ways, we can find the answers to this question simply by looking through the history books to see if there are any old texts that shed some light on this subject. It did not take me long to discover that the ancient Greeks and Romans all believed in the moon's effect, as did the Egyptians. In fact, every ancient civilised society took it for granted that there was a relationship between the moon and our health. In the quote at the beginning of the chapter, Hippocrates, the famous Greek philosopher, wrote in 400 BC that medicine works most effectively at different times of the year: some medicines will work best in summer, others in winter. This seems to have been common knowledge two and a half thousand years ago, undoubtedly based on observations over a long period of time. I would imagine all Greek medicines were therefore dispensed according to the seasons of the year.

If I am permanently misaligned in my sleep cycle, like the blind person, it would explain why I am not always awake and alert on some days. Maybe my body is trying to catch up or realign itself. My one personal anecdotal evidence that supports this theory is an episode in which I found it very difficult to sleep. I mentioned this to my wife, who, surprisingly, had had similar sleeping problems during those nights. I happened to speak with a few friends over the next few days and mentioned to them that I was having disturbed sleep patterns, and coincidentally four out of the five people I spoke to had had exactly the same sleep problems over those specific days. One of the five people happened to know that there was a lunar eclipse of the sun during that period and suggested that the eclipse might have caused the problem. Now, if she had told me this before I started my research for this book, I would have dismissed her idea as sheer fantasy. But she said this while I was in the very heart of my research, and suddenly I thought, blimey, you might well have a point. I had made a complete one hundred and eighty degree turn because I was now accepting an alternative idea, one that I would have condemned as "quackery science" just a few months previously.

This story was just one experience I have had. I am not recounting it as a scientific theory of any sort; it was just an interesting coincidence for me, as I was already aware of the story of the blind person and his disturbed sleep patterns. What if, though, it were true, and the moon's eclipse of the sun can affect our sleep patterns? Should we not be aware of this? If we were, we could anticipate being tired on specific days, and, instead of being irritable with everyone, we would know that our bad moods were due to some predictable planetary alignment.

I find it very sad that we have dismissed this approach as inferior because it does not happen to be the conclusion of a randomised controlled, double-blind study. Maybe scientists also believe that ancient wisdom was intellectually inferior. We have accepted their political, philosophical and moral innovations, but not, it appears, any of their medical ones. These groups of people achieved feats of engineering that today, even with all our modern technology, we cannot re-create. For example, there are some huge pieces of rock weighing more than two hundred tonnes each that were moved around to build ancient sites, rocks far too big for us to move today despite our modern machinery. Yet we still believe that our medicine, which after all is only about one hundred years old, is better, more sophisticated and more advanced than five thousand years of observation. I personally, would take the observational point of view to be just as important as our present-day double-blind, peer group-reviewed medical studies, which may arise from as much political infighting as that generated in the Roman and Greek political arenas.

A BAD NIGHT'S SLEEP

The moon, the sun, the planets and the Earth all emit electromagnetic vibrations. If it is possible to show that man-made electromagnetic vibrations affect sleep patterns, it would seem logical that natural ones can as well. Could the lights in your house or the electric clock radio by your bed be affecting how you sleep? Apparently they can, as it seems that low-level electromagnetic waves emitted by such devices affect your daily biological rhythms.

In one experiment performed in special underground isolation units constructed to eliminate all environmental noises, patients were tested to see if their body had a rhythm. Each of the two experimental units consisted of a living room, a small kitchen and a bathroom. One difference between the two units, however, was that one was shielded from external electromagnetic fields. It was also equipped with facilities for introducing artificial DC or AC electric or magnetic fields. If there were any different patterns of sleep, daily activity and body temperature rhythms between the two rooms, the difference could therefore only be caused by electromagnetism emitted within the room. This could be further tested by introducing false electromagnetic fields into one room to see if this altered the subjects' behaviour. The findings clearly showed that the patients who spent a month underground in these rooms had a daily pattern that followed an average value of 24.97 ± 0.41 hours, very similar to the lunar pattern.

The scientists concluded that our sleep patterns are affected by changes in the amount of electromagnetic waves within our environment, which can be altered by such objects as a clock radio. Could we extrapolate these results and conclude that the sun's and the moon's electromagnetic waves also affect us? Would it not be true to say that on days when the electromagnetism was particularly strong, such as during the full moon, or days when it was particularly different, such as during lunar eclipses, our sleep patterns would be altered as a consequence of the varying electromagnetism? It now seems to me painfully obvious that it must happen this way. The planets must affect my patterns of sleep.

Why do we dismiss out of hand the idea that the moon affects our biological behaviour? One significant reason is that there appears to be no biochemical association that scientists can turn to. Nothing has been found under the microscope that explains how it is possible for the gravitational forces of the moon to translate into a biochemical effect. If you have read Chapter 1, you can guess what I believe is the answer to this problem – that the properties of water allow our body to transfer the vibrational waves emitted by the moon into chemical reactions. Once you can understand this phenomenon, everything about the moon and the sun and the planets becomes clear.

It is no surprise that anti-moon science is constantly being put forward in studies that are then reported in the media. I will show you, in the following pages, how the science is in fact being distorted and the scientific studies proving a biological effect are being ignored for reasons that I can only assume result from peer pressure and are financially and politically motivated. This is not necessarily a conscious decision, but if you think about it, how much funding are you going to get if you propose a study that is looking to prove that heart attacks are related to the cycle of the planets? You would be right in thinking that not much funding would be coming your way. However, if you were considering a study that looked at the numbers of heart attacks and correlated them with the changes in the seasons, you would more easily get your funding even though the question would really be exactly the same. All you have done is replaced the word "moon" with "seasons", which is, when you think about it, exactly the same phenomenon. The seasons are caused by the cycles of the sun and the moon.

Take the following paper as an example of how we are told about the moon and its relationship to our bodies. An authoritative paper written in 2008, entitled "Human responses to the geophysical daily, annual and lunar cycles", clearly concludes that there is "NO SOLID EVIDENCE THAT HUMAN BIOLOGY IS IN ANY WAY REGULATED BY THE LUNAR CYCLE" (my capitals for emphasis). This report was supported by the EU, the Wellcome Trust, the Oxford NHS/Biomedical Research Centre and the Daimler-Benz-Stiftung network, a hefty group of science-based organisations.

I decided that the two authors, Russell Foster and Till Roenneberg, must presumably have experience in this area as the article was published in the journal *Current Biology*. In fact, after further research, I found that Russell Foster was Professor Russell Foster of the European Biological Rhythms Society, working at the University of Oxford, and Till Roenneberg was Professor Till Roenneberg, Vice-President of the European Biological Rhythms Society, who worked at the Institute for Medical Psychology at the

Ludwig-Maximilians University in Munich. These two men sound like experts in their field. They are clearly knowledgeable in the area of biological rhythms, and I would imagine that they know all there is to know about the subject. Their bibliography cites one hundred and fifteen papers they have chosen work from in order to write this nine-page article outlining why the moon has no effect on our biological systems. Professor Foster has also written a popular science book called *Rhythms of Life*, which attempts to tell the public all there is to know about our bodies' natural daily cycles.

The standard hypothesis for our bodies' natural rhythms, which are technically called circadian rhythms, is, says Professor Foster, genetic. He alleges that "time is embedded in our genes". He gives examples of our daily rhythms that include blood pressure, liver function, body temperature and the production of hormones. His whole book is based on an understanding of the importance of daily rhythms in our life, which makes for fascinating reading. The problem I have with the whole theory is that the solution does not fit the facts. If we were born with a pre-programmed daily pattern of behaviour, including sleep, why would it change? What are the mechanisms by which it could be affected? More importantly, scientists currently do not know any of the biological markers that create the circadian rhythms. It is a theory that does not fit the facts, but as it is such an embedded theory, it is very hard to change.

One scientific example put forward to help prove the concept of genetics affecting body rhythms is the study of a rabbit that is placed in a cage for a year without any access to natural daylight. The rabbit still manages to hibernate at approximately the same time as other rabbits living in the wild. How is this possible? The answer could be twofold. Mainstream scientific interpretation is that the rabbit has a natural genetic body clock that tells it when to sleep. An alternative solution suggests there is a force that lets the rabbit know when to go to sleep. This force is the gravitational pull of the sun, the moon, the Earth, the planets or a combination of all of these. Just because Professor Foster's article has been peer-reviewed and published in a senior medical journal, it cannot be assumed that genetics is the only or correct cause of body rhythms. If I were Professor Foster, I would want to be very clear in my mind that the moon had no effect on human biology. I would also want to be certain that the sun's gravitational forces or solar flares also played no part in our biochemistry. I would take the time to thoroughly research the subject, if for no other purpose than to clear my mind that what I was writing gave the whole picture.

So have the article's two authors thoroughly researched the area in enough detail to categorically state that the moon plays no part whatsoever in our biological make-up? They are aware that "a biological explanation remains elusive" for circadian rhythms, and that "animals are clearly influenced by the moon and possess internal clocks that can predict the lunar cycle". Yet they are categorical that "the moon appears to have no effect upon our physiology". They have no doubt that the moon has an effect on animals of all kinds, even though they believe the effect is too small to affect humans. They acknowledge that the moon produces tides, but they conclude that as it does not produce tides in lakes or smaller bodies of water, "let alone a human body", it cannot affect our biology. They even refer to a paper as summing up the impossibility of the moon playing a part; that paper was written by Roger Culver and colleagues, "who have summarised this point elegantly by pointing out that the moon's gravitational pull was less than that of a wall of a building six inches away". Foster and Roenneberg also agree all ancient civilisations had a relationship with the moon and in fact had lunar calendars that were based on the moon and not the sun. Does this not strike them as odd? Why would you follow the moon when the obvious celestial body is the sun? What relevance would the moon have unless it was thought to play a significant role in either a person's lifestyle or their biology?

The final paragraph of the article comes to the conclusion that the public is "confused", all due to the introduction of street lighting! This is what is causing us to have varied sleep patterns; and even one day's lack of sleep can produce symptoms of mania in adults who are vulnerable to it. Their final sentence clears it all up for us: "as with mania, disruption of sleep in pre-industrialised societies may be the cause of the association between seizures and the full moon". Presumably people in pre-industrialized societies partied so much on nights with a full moon that the sleep loss from such heightened social activity resulted in seizures.

Where did these researchers get this bizarre scientific idea from? On further investigation, it appears to have come lock, stock and barrel from an article entitled "The moon and madness reconsidered" that was written in 1999 by a group of psychiatrists working at the University of California. This paper was the first one to come to the conclusion that any change around the full moon is due to the introduction of street lighting. So it appears that two professors working in the field of biological rhythms are taking their main hypothesis from three psychiatrists!

The summary of Foster and Roenneberg's article concludes with the following paragraph:

We began this review with the observation that there is considerable confusion and ignorance about the influence of the geophysical cycles on human biology. There is a strong belief by many that the moon has marked effects upon our health and well being. Yet, study after study has failed to find any consistent association with the moon and human pathology, physiology or behaviour. Occasional reports have proposed correlations between the phase of the moon and human phenomena, but nothing has been sufficiently replicated to conclude that there is a causal relationship. The reason for this belief is probably linked to the importance of moonlight in allowing human activity at night before artificial light was freely available, coupled with the endless re-telling of stories about behavioural changes associated with the lunar phase. If an individual expects certain behaviours to occur with the full moon then selective recall and/or selective perception will reinforce this view. As Saint Augustine wrote in the 5th century "Faith is to believe what you do not yet see; the reward of this faith is to see what you believe".

Now I don't know about you, but I find that conclusion really patronising: that everyone who believes there is a lunar relationship is suffering from a psychological problem. I like to think of myself as a person who looks at the facts. I have no bias; I have never been interested in the lunar cycles or our biological rhythms; I do not have any conceived or pre-conceived ideas. Are they seriously telling other scientists who have researched this area thoroughly that their science is wrong and it is all in their heads?

The two professors say there is no scientific evidence to support the lunar relationship, only correlations (which are statistical relationships between two variables). The evidence does not show cause and effect. Well, I am sorry to say, neither does their argument for the circadian rhythm as they have yet to discover the cause ("a biological explanation remains elusive"), and without this their conclusion is no better than those of the scientific studies put forward by the proponents of a lunar relationship.

Below is a summary of symptoms that have been shown to have a relationship with the lunar cycle, (see bibliography for full details). All of the studies have come to the conclusion that the sun and the moon play a role in our bodies' daily rhythms. All were conducted under strict criteria, all were peer-reviewed, and all were published in scientific journals. Every one of them is apparently dismissed as mere correlations by the two professors.

List of symptoms:

1. Urological admissions
2. Stroke symptoms
3. Epilepsy
4. Aortic aneurysm ruptures
5. Hospital appointments
6. Gout attacks
7. Mortality rates
8. Levels of stress
9. Blood pressure
10. Lymphocytes (a type of white cell involved in immunity)
11. Aggressive behaviour

Having read these eleven studies, I do not believe that it is possible to state categorically that "there is no convincing evidence that the moon can affect the biology of our own species". For me, I think there is definitely room for doubt, and I would say that the moon does affect our biology in certain – but not all – areas. In order to find a more definitive answer to this problem, I spent a long time looking through papers in many different scientific areas, such as the science of plants and the special properties of water, to provide answers to how our biology might be being affected by the moon.

Are there any lunar relationships in animals that can suggest what the actual biological relationship might be? Does animal behaviour differ at all during the lunar phases? The two big areas of research in humans concern the relationships between the moon and madness and birth rates. So does such a relationship ever occur in animals or plants? Do animals show signs of madness during a full moon? Do animals give birth at a full moon? I have not heard of nor read any scientific papers alleging they do, and I cannot find examples anywhere showing that the moon affects the birthing patterns of animals or their mental stability.

So why are 99% of research studies into the relationship between the moon and human biology looking exclusively at these two issues? What made scientists think that there was a relationship in the first place? Obviously, part of the blame lies with the Romans giving us the word "lunacy", which is derived from the word "luna", the moon, but besides this I cannot find any other examples outside popular fiction and the media. It is therefore not surprising that there has been no proof of a relationship between the dates of children being born and the lunar cycle, nor with criminal acts or mental lunacy. But why would there be?

WHAT THE MOON DOES NOT DO

It is quite clear to me, having read many studies, that children are not born in cycles related to the full moon, nor are there any studies showing that madness is related to the full moon. One study looked at the survival rate of patients who had had breast cancer surgery, but no relationship with lunar cycles was reported. Another study looked at the relationship between lunar cycles and television viewing habits! And there is no tradition in any ancient text that talks about births on a lunar cycle. There are many goddesses who are named after the moon and are associated with fertility yet are not associated with the birth of the children, instead being more related to a child's conception. For some strange reason, scientists have chosen to ignore this important point. It is just an idea that seems to have appeared and cost untold millions of dollars in research grants for papers that serve no purpose. It is as if someone started a rumour and everyone is trying to dispel it, which of course they do every time; it is a big, red herring.

One fact we should be looking for in research, based on the evidence from animals, is that of successful conception during a full moon. This is most evident in fish, who wait for the full moon to produce eggs that the male fish then cover. This has been observed time after time, yet it is not something that we have fully investigated in relation to humans.

In ancient times, the goddess of fertility was also the goddess of the moon. In his authoritative work, Pliny the Elder, writing in AD 23, stated that conception is related to the full moon. Sadly, few contemporary studies have looked at this relationship so there are very few examples to back this up. One area in which there has been research is in IVF treatment, but as the sperm are not completely fresh and have been stored for a period of time, the results cannot, I believe, be considered completely reliable. Even with this problem of freezing the sperm, studies have concluded that "lunar influence may only be one of the contributing factors" to successful IVF treatment.

In the case of spontaneous abortions, a team in Italy found that there was a link between the lunar phases and spontaneous abortions: "In the present paper, the correlation between the perigee extremes and the normalized number of spontaneous abortions is noteworthy. Moreover a periodicity of 205 days was apparent in the frequency of human spontaneous abortions which seems to be somehow correlated with the 206 day periodicity in extreme lunar distances."

But apart from these two studies, I could not find any information on the relationship between copulation based on the lunar cycle and its success rate. I found studies conducted on animals that showed a strong correlation, but none on humans. This is a shame as I believe it is one of the most important relationships that we have with the moon – successful fertilization when the woman's cycle is in harmony with the lunar cycle.

WOMEN'S PERIODS

I am not sure what happened in the 1970s, but there was an explosion of books describing the relationship between a woman's menstrual cycle and the lunar cycle. It seems that, during this period, there was a sudden interest in the topic. The book *Astrological Birth Control* was probably the catalyst in this new area of research. This book was based upon the approach of an unusual Eastern European doctor who announced that he had found a new method of birth control and sex selection. Dr Eugen Jonas from Czechoslovakia (as it was known then) alleged he had discovered astrological methods to produce the child the parents wanted based upon the position of the sun and the moon.

For those who do not know much about a woman's periods, the following description is a basic summary of the process. The ovaries are the woman's sexual organs; they are where the ova – the eggs – are produced. At regular intervals, an egg moves from the ovary and into the oviduct (the fallopian tube), and then down into the uterus (the womb), where it attempts to settle in the mucous membrane that lines the uterus, which has become thickened to receive it. However, if the egg does not become fertilized and conception does not occur, the egg dies and, together with the thickened lining of the uterus, comes away as the menstrual flow. So common knowledge tells us that the woman needs to get pregnant during the period when the egg is in her uterus. Attempting pregnancy in this window is commonly referred to as the rhythm method.

Jonas, on the other hand, made all sorts of different assumptions about the times at which it is possible to get pregnant and their relationship with birth dates and conception. He alleged if the woman was born on a full moon, then when she started to menstruate she would have her ovulation on the half moon and be most likely to conceive on the full moon. And if conception fell on a full moon, the birth would also occur on a full moon. According to Jonas, women have two completely independent rhythms of fertility: the phase of the moon and the women's monthly periods. As a consequence, he built up a programme that contradicted the rhythm method, showing that use of his birth calendar could have four different possible applications: contraception, sex selection, overcoming of sterility and reduction of fetal abnormality. He suggested that his method of creating a timetable based upon the moon and existing menstrual patterns could not only predict the sex of the baby, but also allow infertile women to have children and in addition reduce fetal abnormalities. But only, however, if the calendar was followed exactly.

Jonas set up an institute in which he allegedly helped a lot of women in Czechoslovakia to fulfil one or more of the above objectives, but this institute ran foul of the government and he was banned from practising his theories within his country. His ideas were pretty revolutionary at the time and indeed remain so today. But just because he was banned is no reason to dismiss all of his ideas. Is it possible to determine the sex of your child based upon lunar cycles, or to avoid sterility by having your period at a time that fits in with a lunar cycle?

Dr Jonas thought so, and he provides lots of anecdotal evidence. He cites many different cases and peer endorsements for his ideas. However, science it is not, as he provides virtually no properly laid-out scientific study to support his beliefs. He talks all the time about a 98% success rate but does not give the number of people who succeeded. Later websites that quote from him look scientific but provide as little evidence as Jonas did himself – he was never published in a scientific journal. However, I was still intrigued to know whether anyone else had looked at this possibility to see if they could produce scientific evidence of a relationship between the moon and fertility. In doing so, I came up against much contradictory evidence, mostly showing that the concept that women have a regular period is completely unproven, and this in many ways completely undermines the concept of a lunar relationship.

What I found surprised me enormously as it clearly showed that women do not have regular cycles. Most women consider themselves to be pretty regular, but the fact is that the majority of them aren't regular at all. Which probably explains why there is so much confusion amongst women who are never sure about the timing of their periods. It seems that the facts prove there is no such thing as a regular rhythm. Sorry to be sexist, but maybe it is because most scientists are male that this falsehood has been perpetuated to this day. I would put money on the fact that if this were a male issue, it would have been sorted out a long time ago, and everyone would be perfectly clear there is no such thing as all women having the same regular period, and certainly not one of twenty-eight days, even though some women do have a twenty-eight-day cycle.

To quote from one authoritative study written in 1967 by the World Health Organization (WHO) and published in the *International Journal of Fertility*:

1 There is no substantial justification for the widely held belief that women normally vary in menstrual interval about a value of 28 days common to all. Each woman has her own central trend and variation, both of which change with age. Assemblies of menstrual interval for many persons and covering a wide span of chronologic ages should, however, be expected to average within a few days of the often quoted 28.

2 Complete regularity in menstruation through extended time is a myth ... the only regularity in the menstrual cycle is its irregularity.

3 Women apparently use the reply "regular" meaning "28 days" to indicate belief that they are normal in their menstrual characteristics.

4 The first few years of menstrual life, like the last few, are marked usually by a variation in pattern of mixed short and long intervals with a characteristic transition into and out of the relatively more regular pattern of middle life.

5 From our study of 22,754 calendar years of experience available for this study, the general trend reaches its minimum at 36 years of age.

6 All menstrual histories show individualities that make the norms provided by statistical procedures useful only for comparisons of groups of persons. The characteristics of an individual menstrual history may alter with time and show fluctuating divergences from an average pattern. A woman's personal arrangement that may be influenced by her menstrual cyclicity may be made with greater probability of success the longer the guiding record of her past menstruations.

The authors concluded that the practice of birth control through the use of rhythm methods alone had to introduce elements of such uncertainty as to pose serious problems for all persons affected. If women's periods were not regular, there obviously could not be a relationship between them and the lunar cycle, which is very regular. So the belief that women's periods are all related to the lunar cycle can be put aside as there is no evidence to support it.

There is also no evidence that women's periods synergise when a group of women live together. This is a shame as I like that theory, but countless studies have been done that show there is no statistical relationship between the two.

But, in concluding this subject, why do we assume that there should be a relationship just because they are very similar – 28 days against the 29.4 days of the lunar month? I like to turn to nature for ideas as to why there should be a relationship, and I cannot find any evidence here: there are no animals that show a lunar relationship in terms of their menstrual cycle. Every animal, it seems, is different.

ANIMALS

There are so many research studies showing unequivocally that the behaviour of animals is directly linked to lunar cycles that I will limit this section for fear of repeating myself too much. After a while, I think you will get the idea.

I was not sure whether to put the following study under a human or an animal relationship heading as it could fall under both, but it has been shown there is a strong relationship between admissions to hospitals from animal bites and full moon days. In a study that looked at admissions of patients who attended an accident and emergency department in Bradford, a total of 1,621 patients were analysed. The results showed that there were 56 cat bites, 11 rat bites, 13 horse bites and 1,541 dog bites. The number of bites on each day was compared to the lunar phase in each month. It was shown that the incidence of animal bites rose significantly at the time of a full moon: the graph looked like the map of the Himalayas with a significant mountain peak occurring at the full moon.

In another article that set out to disprove this relationship as complete nonsense, an Australian professor and his senior research officer analysed similar daily admissions to all accident and emergency departments in

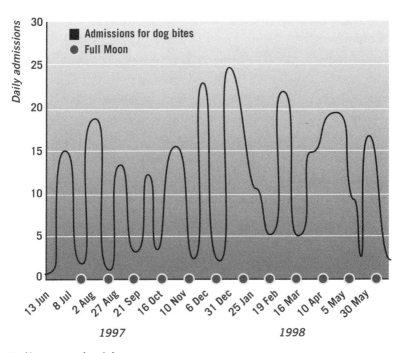

Dog bites over a yearly period

public hospitals in Australia. The title of their article title somewhat gave away their conclusion: "Barking mad? Another lunatic hypothesis bites the dust." They clearly found absolutely no relationship to the full moon and dog bites, as the following chart will show you.

I would, however, just like to draw your attention to the numerous peaks that appear on this chart. Even if you know nothing about what is being shown, it is pretty clear that there is a cycle of peaks at a very similar time within each month. The fact that they do not fall exactly on the full moon seems to be true, but it is pretty blinkered to say that there is no cycle whatsoever, as anyone who looks at this chart can easily see one. Just a quick glance will show that the peaks are regular and they occur at intervals approximating the mid-lunar period.

Another obvious visual relationship that you can observe from the chart is that the lowest number of dog bites occurs each month around the full moon – another fact the authors have chosen to ignore. As this result is completely opposite to that of the previous study, which showed that the dog bites peaked at the full moon, is it just a mere coincidence that the first study was conducted in the northern hemisphere and the second one in the southern hemisphere? Would this situation not be likely to provide two sets of opposing lunar data? I believe the title of the Australian study should have read "Barking mad? Another lunar relationship proven." Yet again, science chooses the conclusion of least resistance, the easy answer, the one that might get more funding, rather than the challenging questions, the less popular ones, the ideas that might cause ripples. In this report, the authors stated that the results should allow "sceptics to rejoice", which is not helpful in a study of this kind.

A research project in 2004 looked at the success rate of horses in stud farms over a fourteen-year period to see if there was a pattern. Stud farm managers keep meticulous records, and horses are indeed the only animal for which complete and reliable records exist in terms of both conception and birth. The study found that there was a significant success rate just after the full moon, although the effect was reduced by lunar latitude, virtually disappearing at the "low node" points, the lunar nodes being the points where the moon's path in the sky crosses the ecliptic, the sun's path in the sky. So the results varied over the fourteen years, depending upon the relationship between the sun and the moon.

A very early study, produced in 1960 by three American researchers – Brown, Barnwell and Brett – looked at the mud snail. Under normal conditions, these mud snails would "travel west in early morning, at noon east and a westerly course in the early evening. At new and full moons the snails' paths veered to the west while at quarters of the moon they tended more eastward than at any other times." When the researchers placed a magnet under the exit to the snails' box, the snails made sharper turns, but their direction stayed the same. Turning the magnet or the enclosure through various angles made the snails' change course by a specific number of degrees. The same occurred in experiments with a worm, which showed exactly the same changes in behaviour when exposed to weak magnetic field disturbances. In all of these experiments, the animals displayed a relationship to that of the 24.8-hour lunar day.

Even the hamster has been studied to see if it follows a lunar clock. In a study in 1985, two hamsters were kept in cages for nine months under low light conditions. They were found to follow a day that was 24 hours and 50 minutes in length – the lunar day. And who would have thought that the sweet old, cuddly cat is affected by the planet Mercury? Certainly not the doctors who conducted an experiment on cats in 1972. It was never their intention to see if there was a planetary relationship when they started their one-year study on changes in the thyroid gland of nineteen cats. They were in fact looking for a relationship based on sunshine, as previous research had shown a tentative relationship. It turned out that the cats' thyroid activity followed a complex rhythm of peaks and troughs occurring at nearly equal intervals that did not match at all with the sunshine data.

Amazingly, the researchers also discovered the same pattern of peaks and troughs in mammals such as squirrels, sheep and humans. All of the peaks occurred in March, July and November, and the troughs in April, June and September. Notwithstanding this, they then went on to discover that the cycles also occur in fish, amphibians and reptiles. In fact, they discovered that in all four different vertebrate classes, there are annual rhythms of the thyroid gland occurring at the same time of year. The only statistical relationship that made any sense was that of a relationship between the Earth, the sun and Mercury, but of course this was a problem as they did not understand any mechanism by which such a relationship could occur. How could the planetary effect of Mercury affect all of these species' thyroid gland? The authors concluded that "the relevance of this correlation is quite uncertain since there is no known causal mechanism by which the extremely subtle effects of Mercury could influence either cloud cover or thyroid activity. Thus it appears unlikely that the synchrony of the Iowa cats is dependent on any known environmental or astronomical event." So science yet again buries the facts when it does not understand them.

This study is rarely quoted, probably because it was published in a biometeorological journal rather than a medical one. But the facts are important because if the thyroid gland, one of the most important glands in our body, is in a cycle of three times a year, surely this should be a factor incorporated into current medical thinking? The thyroid gland controls how the body uses energy and makes proteins and regulates the relationships between a range of hormones. Therefore, if all vertebrates have cycles of peaks and troughs of thyroid gland activity, this must mean that some physiological differences will occur during these peaks and troughs. Maybe our bodies' energy levels will be higher or lower, maybe our emotions will be affected by the change in hormones, who knows? But if this is the case, it would be good to know what to expect. The peaks are in March, July and November, so maybe we should be looking out for changes – whatever they might be – during these three months.

FISH

Salmon are probably one of the most famous fish we know to have a very close relationship with the lunar cycle as they utilise high tides to lay eggs on specific days of the year. For example, on one beach in California, the fish have a spawning time in May. They wait until the tide reaches its peak on the third day after the full moon and allow themselves to be carried up on to the beach by the last, highest wave. There the females lay their eggs in the wet sand and the males fertilise them, and with the next wave they return again to the open sea. As they were brought in on the highest wave in the series, all the rest are smaller, and therefore the eggs are left on the beach and not swept out to sea by any new wave. Not until the fourteenth day later – half a moon cycle – does the tide again attain the height needed to reach the salmon spawn. The eggs hatch a few minutes before being washed out to sea, not to return to the shore until years later, fully grown, for one moment on this third day after full moon in May. For only one moment in the year are the sun, moon and Earth in the correct relative positions.

The relationship between high tides and spawning is true for a majority of fish species. It seems that it is very common for fish to spawn on the high tides that follow each new or full moon. The relationship is always lunar and not tidal, which is shown by those fish that spawn even when there is no tide, and by fish that live in such deep waters that they have not only no access to tides, but also no access to the light from the moon, so it cannot be the moon's light that is making them behave this way. The advantages of synchronising spawning with the high tides is obvious as it means that the hatched young can be kept away from predators, enabling a greater survival rate, although which came first – the high tide or the lunar factor – is impossible to determine. It is a "fish and egg" problem!

The Palolo worm

Although not a fish, the palolo worm, which lives in the seas off the Pacific islands of Fiji and Samoa, is one of the most famous examples of creatures that use the moon as a signal for when they choose to reproduce. Data recording exactly when this reproduction occurs go back as far as 1843. But why would there be records for this worm as far back as that? It is because, during this reproductive period, the worms create the equivalent of free caviar for the local communities who fish for it. The islands become awash with this caviar, and the locals celebrate the event with public feasts. The missionaries made notes of these feast days in their diaries, providing excellent data for later scientists to analyse.

The palolo have very strict behaviour patterns for when they swarm, which are directly related to the moon. Analysing the data starting from 1843, it can be shown that the worms follow an 18.6-year lunar cycle, and that on specific days of the monthly cycle swarming takes place, but only in October and November. This worm is the most studied of all animals that have an observable relationship with the lunar cycle, and it is undisputed that its behaviour has anything other than a lunar influence.

METALS

I am sure you were not expecting metals in this chapter – the fact that there could be relationships caused by electromagnetism between metals and the moon, the sun and in fact all of the planets.

Well, neither did I, but I have read some very interesting science experiments that show, through photography, the different effects that a total eclipse of the sun has on various different metals.

In 1947, a scientist named Lilly Kolisko analysed the effect that a total eclipse of the sun had on solutions of gold, silver, copper, iron, lead and tin by using diluted amounts of these metals (as gold chloride, silver nitrate, copper sulphate, iron sulphate, tin chloride and lead nitrate). She placed drops of these on filter paper and watched as the patterns changed with the hours of the eclipse. There was a significant difference in the metal's behaviour, as visually shown on the filter paper, every hour during which the moon was blocking out the sun's rays. The best way to describe the image is by imagining a piece of paper onto which you have spilt some tea or coffee – the wet area spreads out, leaving behind a gradually fading amount of the coffee or tea, with a final line left at the point at which the coffee or tea reaches its maximum size.

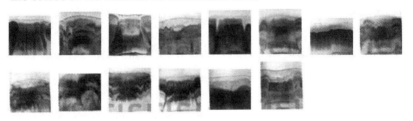

The different effects of the total eclipse of the sun in 1947 on silver over a 10 hour period L. Kolisko

If you were to reproduce this experiment with tea or coffee over and over again, you would be left with a similar pattern each time. But when you use metals, the pattern is somewhat different as the different metals leave behind an image that is like creating a cake – there are lots of different layers of different colours and widths. If you repeat the experiment on a non-eclipse day, the pattern that the metal creates from, say, a drop placed in the middle of the filter paper is pretty similar every time. However, on the day of an eclipse, there is a very noticeable visual change in the pattern during each hour over which the experiment is conducted. When you look at the images shown in the table above, produced during a total eclipse of the sun in 1947, the patterns left by all of the silver metal solutions are completely different throughout the solar eclipse, only returning to a regular pattern at the end.

If I were to guess which metal would react most to the effects of the planets, I am pretty sure I would not think the answer was silver. I know almost nothing about the uses of silver, but on further investigation I was reminded that it has regular functions when it is used in conjunction with light. Obviously, mirrors are a common usage of silver, as it has the amazing property of reflecting light in a way that no other metal seems to be able to do, which is probably why it was used in photography to capture images before the advent of digital cameras. What is interesting though, for this chapter, is that tests conducted by Lilly Kolisko over fourteen years, using her filter paper experiments, show that the images involving silver changed in a daily pattern in relation to the moon. The full moon and the new moon have specific characteristics, and when she extended the studies over many years, she found that no two years were the same.

In some ways, we can conclude that the images that Kolisko produced on the filter paper are photographic reproductions of the moon's effect, if we consider that photography uses silver and its relationship with light in a similar way. So if you are looking for a visual representation of the effect of the different lunar cycles, using silver appears to be the best method. I would be fascinated if someone were to publish daily images on the internet of the changes in silver so that it could confirm any sleeping pattern changes that I might or might not have had. It would also provide physical evidence that there is a direct relationship between the chemicals and electromagnetic forces emanating from the moon, sun and planets. But, as far as I was concerned when I saw them, these images clearly showed that, even in the 1940s, science was aware of a relationship between metals, the moon, the sun and the planets.

PLANTS

It is probably less surprising to learn that plants react to the moon's electromagnetic forces. In a study conducted in 1973 by Brown and Chow, it was shown that "the rate of water uptake by bean seeds during the initial four hours displays a significant quarterly lunar variation". Also, "under what appear to be minimally disturbed environmental conditions relative to environmental electromagnetic fields, maximum rates of water uptake tend to occur close to new and full moon and the moon's quarters".

This information is not, however, new: it has been known for thousands of years. One of the first people to write down the information for later historians to "discover" was Pliny the Elder, writing in AD 23 in his book *Natural History*. He refers to the relationship between the moon and plants in a matter-of-fact way, showing that it was common knowledge two thousand years ago. He cites many instructions for gathering plants and pruning or cutting trees according to the phases of the moon:

Pliny's book talks at length about the very strong relationship between the moon and the constellations, and much of his book on agriculture – four hundred pages out of a mere total of approximately four thousand pages – mentions this relationship. I could quote in detail all of the different names and dates it was necessary to know in order to maximise the yields from the crops, but that would become very boring.

It took until 1926 before there was contemporary proof that a lunar relationship with plants existed. It was again Kolisko who conducted these experiments, which involved planting 11,520 wheat seeds over a year. Her purpose was to see whether seeds planted at specific times of the month showed any noticeable growth differences, and if there were any, whether there was a direct relationship between the seeds and the moon's cycles.

Kolisko's experiments involved sowing thirty seeds in eight glass vessels at the same time and planting them at the full moon. The seeds were taken out of the glass vessels after fourteen days and measured. This experiment was repeated so that the seeds were placed in glass containers at three other periods for fourteen days – at the new moon, the waning quarter and the waxing quarter – so 960 seeds in all were planted every month. In the first month of the experiments, Kolisko achieved considerable results: the largest plants were achieved in the planting phase of the new moon to full moon (waxing), and the smallest in that from the full moon to new moon (waning).

The second month, however, brought a corresponding disappointment: the growth had steadily decreased, something that at first Kolisko and her team could not understand. Had the moon's influence somehow changed? Was it just chance in the first month? But it occurred to them, following subsequent experiments, that the seasons also played a significant role in the plants' development. The initial experiment had taken place in October, and in the subsequent months of November and December the seeds' development had been stunted; this must have been due to the seasonal changes. In January, the positive growth re-emerged and the seeds began to show a growth cycle peaking with a maximum growth at the height of summer, all the time showing maximum and minimum relationships to the waxing and waning periods of the moon.

What was of most interest, however, was the fact that the relationship to the moon changed during the year. At the beginning of the year, the plants' growth showed a favourable relationship to the waxing phase, the middle of the year tended towards the waning phase, and by the end of the year it was also a waning phase that gave better results. So the plants were following not a simple pattern but a variable one. It would have been very useful to see if there was a relationship every year – maybe if the experiment had been conducted over, say, a ten-year period, more valuable information could have been uncovered.

When the experiments were taken out of the laboratory and conducted in the fields outside, there were similar results. The maize seeds that were used were planted two days before the full moon or two days later, on the full moon itself. Despite just two days' difference in the planting, the results were significantly different. The seeds planted two days before the full moon reached a height of 1.2 m, whereas those that were two days younger grew to only 80 cm. The yield also proved to be different, with a significant reduction for seeds sown on full moon. One other important result from planting in field soil was that the timing in relation to specific months was also very important. In this case, seeds sown too early grew less than seeds grown later, even though the latter were younger. Sewing the maize seeds in April was too early, and plants from seeds sown in May were the same size six weeks later as the ones sown in April.

Exactly the same experiments were conducted with tomatoes, cabbage, peas, gherkins, radishes, beetroot, carrots, kohlrabi, celeriac, tarragon, pimpernel, asters, lovage, larkspur, cardoon, peppermint, sage, chamomile and thyme, and in all these examples there was a significant difference in the growth of plants from seeds planted two days before a full moon compared to two days before the new moon.

The only factor that influenced the growth of the plants in these experiments was the amount of rainwater that was available. If no rainwater was available when the seeds were planted, this had an effect on the plants' relationship with the moon: if the ground was dry, Kolisko found that the moon's influence was reduced. The reason for this, she alleges, is because "the conducting medium which leads the moon's forces into the plants is lacking". Although this is not a scientific conclusion, it does tie up with my chapter on water and everything that I have been saying so far in this book. If everything vibrates and the moon's vibrations affect plants and other living organisms, it is the water within the plants that actually picks up the vibrations and retains them, and it is this retention of the vibrations that is the vehicle moving the vibrational change around the plant. In the case of humans, it would be the blood, which is mostly water, that moved the vibrations around the body. This is a really important point that changes many preconceptions related to the way living organisms behave.

THE MOON AND TREES – THE KEY PIECE OF THE JIGSAW

If you were looking to test a theory on living systems from which you could obtain records for many years providing a constant unchanging barometer on the effects of temperature, humidity, air pressure, sunlight, weather conditions, atmospheric potential gradient, cosmic rays and sunspot activity, what better subject would there be to choose than a tree? A tree's growth patterns over its lifetime can easily be measured by its tree rings, that is to say, the size by which the tree has grown each year, as shown by a clearly defined ring in the tree's trunk.

LAWRENCE EDWARDS

Lawrence Edwards analysed the growth pattern of trees over a sixteen-year period and made a huge discovery. He showed that all trees have a specific growth relationship to the planets and the cycle of their movements past the Earth, and that trees grow in approximately fourteen-day cycles. Edwards' book *The Vortex of Life* was the first one I read when I was conducting my original research, and it was his scientific conclusions that opened my eyes to the possibility the science we have been taught can be very economical with the truth.

Edwards conducted a series of very rigorous but simple experiments between 1982 and 1998 to assess whether or not trees grew in any particular cycle. In order to obtain his results, he set himself exacting standards. In order to measure the growth of the tree, he measured the leaf and flower buds of each species of tree but made sure each bud was from a specific number of branches, based on the fact that whether the branch faced north or south affected its growth pattern. So each tree had buds taken from south-facing branches on specific hours of the day over a sixteen-year period. These buds were individually photographed in the first few years, but Edwards subsequently used an electronic scanner to achieve his measurements quickly and more accurately – the buds were measured from these resulting images for both their length and diameter, the results then being analysed by computer.

One of Edwards' major findings was a phase shift of the trees. This is a phenomenon that few people apparently acknowledge, yet it would seem to be of incredible significance. The basic premise is that trees grow out of sync with the planets on a yearly basis. For example, a beech tree will grow in a seven-day cycle in relation to the planet Saturn on a Monday to Monday cycle in the first year, but in the second year the cycle will follow a Tuesday to Tuesday pattern. This will continue for seven years forward and another seven years in reverse until, after fourteen years, the tree starts off again at the beginning with a Monday cycle. This phase shift can clearly be seen in the diagram. These results did not depend on the type of tree or its relationship with the planets; it affected all trees at all times irrespective of what was happening in the solar system in terms of specific planets.

One major question that arises from this phenomenon is that if the trees grow following this seven-year cycle, yet there is no planetary cycle matching it, it could be easily concluded that the effect is likely to be coming from the Earth's magnetic influence on the trees. If this is the case, there is likely to be a strong relationship to other living organisms that are affected on a seven-year cycle, including ourselves. How this manifests itself has never been considered, but if it were included into data collection in long-term scientific experiments, I am sure there would be a strong correlation.

PUTTING YOUR MONEY WHERE YOUR MOUTH IS

Some people are so confident in the lunar and solar cycles that they are prepared to put massive amounts of money into gambling that specific crops will fail in certain years. As long ago as Roman times, people were making money from this "certainty". One story describes the Roman philosopher Democritus, who was allegedly the first person to recognise and point out the alliance that unites the heavens with the Earth, when he got into an argument with a wealthy town member who despised his beliefs. Democritus decided to prove his point by betting on the price of olive oil, knowing that the following crop was going to fail and therefore the price of the oil would rise. He bought up all the spare oil in the country and when he had made vast amounts of profit, he gave the money back to the olive oil owners because he was more interested in proving his point than in making money.

Fast-forward to today, and you will discover that there are Wall Street investors who bet on the crop failure cycle and make huge sums of money from it. This is based on the fact there is an 18.6-year lunar cycle. Evidence provided by Louis Thompson, using data from 1891 to 1983, showed there was a period of low US crop yields every 18–19 years and also a peak in yields every 18–19 years. This is a direct consequence of the moon's lunar cycles. Other research, conducted in 1997, looked at both lunar cycles and solar cycles and showed there is a definite 22-year drought cycle associated with the sun that can be shown as far back as 1700, with a lunar 18.6-year cycle also being a definitively reported phenomenon.

Several books have in fact been written on the relationship between financial investment and the lunar cycle. One such book suggests that there is a strong lunar cycle that affects stock returns. The authors discovered that returns in the fifteen days around the new moon were about double the returns in the fifteen days around the full moon. This pattern was found everywhere, in all major US stock indexes over the last one hundred years, and in nearly all major stock indexes from twenty-four other countries over the last thirty years. The authors conclude by saying that this is evidence that lunar cycles affect human behaviour.

Another financial research paper in 2005 stated that, having investigated the relationship between lunar phases and the stock market returns of forty-eight countries, a direct relationship could be seen. Stock returns were found to be lower around the full moon than on days around the new moon. The difference, which amounted to between 3% and 5%, appeared to be solely down to the lunar effect and could not be explained away by macroeconomic indicators or by any global shocks that might have taken place. The authors allege that the lunar effect was also independent of any calendar-related anomalies such as holidays or days of the week.

Let's start investing then – it seems pretty easy if you just follow the lunar calendar. But hold on to your money for one moment because one Chinese financial analyst in 2008 investigated the relationship between lunar phases and stock market returns in China. He found that returns were lower on the days around a new moon than on the days around a full moon, and that this had happened for Chinese stocks over the previous sixteen years. He had no other conclusion than to state that lunar phases do affect stock returns in China. A paper in 2008 confirms this view but suggests that the US stock market has since 1990 performed better on average around new moons than full moons, and during waxing moons than waning moons.

So you have been warned (although the data don't say how many people bet on the crop failures and made a mint!). I will leave it to budding investors to check for the next 18.6-year cycle and to determine when the failing or bumper harvest is to be expected and invest accordingly. Now that will be an interesting experiment.

THE BUSINESS OF WINE

If you can make money, then who cares whether the science is right or wrong, crazy or sane? This is the approach that large organisations may take if they see a financial opportunity. Imagine you are a manager of a large organisation and someone comes to you with the idea that you can make money by producing your product on certain days of the week. In addition, you can only sell it on very specific days of the yearly calendar. And the reason for this commercial insanity is because the moon affects your product. I do not believe that, in the first instance, anyone in their right mind would consider this to be a basis for altering any marketing or production ideas. Yet it is. There is a multibillion-dollar industry that chooses to produce goods based around a moon calendar and sell them only on specific days of the month. And what crazy industry is this? It's the wine industry. I am sure you did not know that the taste of wine apparently changes by the day and even the hour, and two of the largest wine retailers in the UK, which between them sell a third of all the country's wine, only invite critics to taste their ranges on dates that are determined by a biodynamic farming calendar that maps the lunar cycle.

A little book has been published for the past forty-eight years by a German woman called Maria Thun which provides the data for biodynamic farmers; it contains a yearly calendar telling them when certain fruits, including red grapes, are at their best. It suggests that as red wine is made up of a lot of living bacteria, the consumer should drink the wine only on specific days and hours as it will taste much better. In fact, the wine might even taste downright horrible if you happen to drink in on the wrong lunar day. As an example, during June 2009, the only days to drink wine were from 9 pm on June 3rd to 2 am on June 6th, 10 am on the 8th to 3 am on the 11th, 2 pm on the 13th to 1 pm on the 15th, 2 pm on the 18th to 5 am on the 20th, 7 pm on the 21st to 7 pm on the 22nd, and 10 pm on the 25th to 9 am on the 28th, a total of approximately 13 days. For the rest of the time, you should remain abstinent if you want to get the most from your wine appreciation.

In an article in the *Guardian* newspaper from 18th April 2009, Jo Ahearne, wine buyer for Marks and Spencer, became convinced of the theory when she sampled more than one hundred and forty wines over two days – all one hundred and forty on the first day, and then exactly the same wines on the following day: "Before the tasting I was really unconvinced, but the difference between the days was so obvious I was completely blown away. They were like chalk and cheese. The difference was staggering, on the second day the wines were all wrong, deadened and hard and bitter, almost corked."

Wine journalist, Victoria Moore, a wine critic and author of *How to Drink*, heard about Marks and Spencer's idea and at first thought it was lunacy. But after she went back through her diary and marked off the days when she thought the tastings had been generally poor and compared them with the calendar, she was amazed to find that they indeed matched up.

THE SUN'S EFFECT ON OUR BIOLOGY – MAN IS A LIVING SUNDIAL

Russian scientists have never had a problem with the relationship between the sun, the moon and our biological make-up as they have been analysing it for more than fifty years. Sochi on the Black Sea is a Russian resort famous for its health sanatoriums. In 1957–1958, around the peak of a sunspot cycle, Russian doctors noticed that something odd was happening to their patients' blood. There

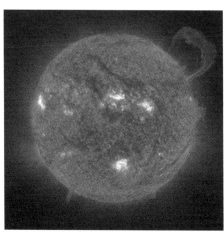

appeared to be an abnormal increase in lymphocytes. They found an almost perfect parallel between the percentage of blood lymphocytes as measured by haematologists and the sunspot frequency recorded by astronomers. The sun was influencing people's blood!

In Japan, a famous haematologist, Maki

Sunspots and solar flares

Takata, had also recognised this effect. As early as 1939, when measuring the coagulation rate of blood albumin, he was suddenly aware of a problem when all of the hospital's reported coagulations (clotting) occurred more quickly than normal. What Takata discovered was that speed of the reaction rose as the frequency of sunspots increased. He also found that the only thing that could prevent the sun affecting the blood was the moon, when it stood right in front of the sun blocking out the sun's rays during a total eclipse. This fact has been further confirmed by Russian scientists in 2004 who looked at the years 1993, 1994, 2001 and 2002 and found that the level of lymphocytes in animals during these periods varied with the solar activity.

Other studies have confirmed that the sun affects the rate at which human blood coagulates. One scientist actually tested her own blood coagulation levels in Venice in three different locations and found that they varied depending upon the building she was in when she conducted the test. One place was the catacombs, where coagulation took nine minutes, and another was her laboratory building, where it took only three. Not only was the location a factor, but so too was the time of day when she ran the tests. In her laboratory, the blood took three minutes to coagulate in the 9 am test, but only two minutes in the 2 pm one.

TRAFFIC ACCIDENTS

Don't drive on high sunspot activity days as you are more likely to be involved in an automobile accident. In a study conducted in 2009, six scientists in Israel and Russia analysed the most severe traffic accidents, which had caused 7,588 deaths and 1,647 severe injuries between the years 2000 and 2005 in the Grand Baku area of Azerbaijan. This period was chosen as it fell during the maximum and declining phases of the twenty-two-year solar cycle. What the researchers discovered was that the number of traffic accidents that occurred in a given month was related to the solar and cosmic ray activity. Increases in traffic accidents were also significantly affected by geomagnetic disturbances. The only conclusion these scientists could draw was that changes in the "space weather" might have had a negative impact on human health and, through the influence of geomagnetic disturbances, on the "human brain's functional state and behaviour".

This statistical research does not exist in isolation as other studies have also come to the same conclusion. As long ago as 1955, a German researcher reported that traffic accidents were more frequent when there were changes in the geomagnetic field. He also went on to analyse why this might be so and found, in studies on human reaction times, that reaction times were much slower during periods of disturbed geomagnetic activity. This fact was also confirmed by two other researchers five years later.

If a correlation was found fifty years ago, why are we still conducting research five decades later? Was it not proved then? There are, in fact, investigations heralding from Russia, Germany, Hungary, Japan, Poland, Israel and Lithuania that have all shown correlations between different levels of solar activity, geomagnetic activity and an increased number of traffic accidents for both developed and developing countries.

Other large studies have looked at the effects of geomagnetic storms on human biological systems and have come up with similar results. In fact, it appears to be the severity of the electrical storm that is of importance as mild storms seem to have limited effects on the brain's bioelectrical activity. However, severe storms:

create negative influences, seriously disintegrate the brain's functionality, activate braking processes and amplify the negative emotional background of an individual.

The conclusion in this particular study was that these disturbances affected humans' physical and emotional states but did not affect individuals' personalities.

PROFESSOR PICCARDI

Professor Georgio Piccardi, Director of the Institute of Physical Chemistry, Florence, whom we met in Chapter 2, set about looking at whether or not there was a chemical relationship between the sun and human biology. He called this form of study "medical climatology". Writing as long ago as 1962, he sought to prove that changes in the climate altered chemical reactions and therefore had a direct effect on our biology. In order to do this, he set up a number of experiments over a ten-year period that proved beyond any doubt the existence of a direct correlation between changes in solar activity and chemical reactions.

During the period between 1951 and 1960, Piccardi's team conducted four tests repeatedly three times a day, totalling a staggering 257,442 different tests – a nine and a half year period of experiments. Tests were conducted every day, including holidays, in Brussels, Vienna and Florence. This man really was a dedicated scientist. The chemical experiments involved such things as the "precipitation and sedimentation of oxychloride of bismuth" and the "polymerisation of acrylonitrile", and the results showed an almost exact relationship with solar activity. Not only did Piccardi find a regular annual rhythm in which the minimum chemical reactions took place during March and August, but his conclusions were also unquestionable: there was a direct relationship between chemical changes and the movement of the Earth.

This study was one of the most thorough ever undertaken looking at such phenomena caused by the sun, and Piccardi ascertained that the sun is, by chemical means, affecting our "colloidal systems in evolution" and consequently our biological systems. He found that, in every year, the reaction varied even though it was a standard chemical procedure that should have produced very similar results, just as tossing a coin one million times should produce a very clear 50/50 result. If, however, in one year there is a 60/40 result and in another year a 47/53 result, something else outside the normal arena must be going on to interfere with this. In the case of the coin toss, there is no logical explanation for why it should not average out at 50/50 as long as it is exactly the same coin being tossed in exactly the same way. Piccardi's is probably the most convincing research project ever undertaken proving that there is a chemical and thus a biological effect on our bodies. But still this research seems to have been completely forgotten. How could scientists ignore the weight of 257,442 experiments?

THE TIME OF DAY

In an authoritative paper, two Canadian scientists analysed patterns of bacteria and the way in which the time of day affected the number of bacteria within the human body. They did not, of course, look at any lunar relationship, as that would have been scientific suicide, but they did acknowledge that there was a definite pattern. For instance, are any of us aware that when we get a cold, this actually peaks at 4.00 pm? If we have a fever as a result of a bacterial infection, the fever is worse in the evening, compared with a viral infection, in which the fever is worse in the morning. We are never told to take our medication at a specific time of the day depending upon our illness, but don't you think it would be best to take our medication when our fever is at its lowest so that our body has enough energy to fight off the bacteria? – so if we have a bacterial infection, we should take our medication in the afternoon or at night.

Scary as it might seem, an experiment infecting mice with *E. coli* bacteria showed that 20% of them died when they were given the bacteria in the middle of the day, but 80% of them died when they received the bacteria at night. In order to see if this was the same in humans, tests were conducted giving *Salmonella* to volunteers (I hope they got paid a lot of money). The results showed that the volunteers who were given *Salmonella* in the evening showed twice the increase in body temperature and plasma levels of the hormones ACTH and cortisol (which are produced in greater quantities when the body is stressed) than those who were given it twelve hours earlier.

For obvious reasons, many more studies have been conducted on animals than humans. All of the animal studies show that the time of day is very important for the body's behaviour, particularly in relation to the number of bacteria within the body. In one of the few studies on humans, it has been shown that an injection of hepatitis B vaccine that was given in the afternoon produced a significantly higher number of antibodies than a similar vaccine given in the morning. So the next time I need a vaccination to travel abroad, I will definitely make an appointment to have the injection in the afternoon so that I'll get double my money's worth compared with having it in the morning.

While I am writing this, I am wondering which part of our body contains the most bacteria, and where in my body am I most likely to be affected on a daily basis by such changes in bacterial levels. To me, it is obviously the gastrointestinal tract, which contains billions of different bacteria, part of whose purpose is to break down our food. Now if the number of bacteria varies throughout the day, surely we should eat more when our bacteria are active than when they are less active? This sounds like excellent advice; it's just a shame that I can't find any research investigating it. And I haven't been able to find such advice in any food literature – "eat me only in the afternoon because I will be digested more efficiently" is not a recommendation that advertisers seem to have used. Maybe they should, but if the science showed that it was better to eat breakfast cereal in the afternoon rather than the morning, this would be a big problem for the breakfast cereal industry!

One study into stomach ulcers, which are associated with the bacterium *Helicobacter pylori*, backs up this timing issue. Three doctors analysed the incidence of ulcer perforation in 1,480 patients in Norway between 1935 and 1990 to identify any daily, weekly and yearly time effects of ulcers. However, the researchers found even more detailed information whereby they showed a relationship with not only the time of the day, week and year, but also the age and sex of the patient. We are all very different, it appears: men's, women's and children's stomachs all behave differently. But duodenal perforations showed the highest incidence in the afternoon, while gastric perforations showed a major peak around noon and a secondary peak near midnight. The duodenal ulcer perforation showed a six-month rhythm with a significantly higher incidence in May, June and July, and in November and December.

It would be even more complicated to discover that bacterial levels are based not on a solar relationship but a lunar one, so that our body's bacterial levels would change with the moon on a 24.84-hour day – our bacterial levels would be different in the morning in any one week compared with the next. You would need to have a tidal calendar to eat efficiently. But no studies have been done in this area to see if there are 24-hour relationships – solar ones – or 24.84-hour relationships – lunar ones – let alone to see whether such relationships exist at all. And not only do we have to look at the daily level of changes, but experiments on mice have suggested that there are significant seasonal as well as daily changes. This would mean that if you were taking medication over a long period, you would have to consider not only the time of day, but also the month – winter drugs would need to be different from summer drugs.

An authoritative study into the area of daily changes in bacteria written in 2007 concluded sadly with the words "the delivery of antibiotics and its low level effectiveness at night for targeted tissues and organs seems worthy of exploration". Why is it taking so long to look at this area of research? In this case, possibly because it will cost drug companies a lot of money to learn that some of their drugs are only half as useful when delivered at specific hours of the day, and it might not be in their best interests to develop this area of research further. But we should know about it, our health authorities should know about it, and all governments should save themselves billions of pounds by utilising this simple piece of advice. Giving certain drugs in the afternoon could be more than twice as efficient as giving them in the morning, and therefore you could take them half as often, which could dramatically cut the cost of some medications. Hallelujah, I have just saved the NHS a fortune. Maybe I should send them a bill.

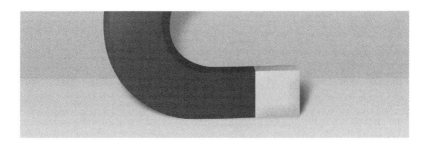

INTRODUCTION TO

MAGNETISM

– What's the attraction all about?

What do you know about magnets and electromagnetics? For most people, the answer is likely to be, not a lot. You probably know two facts about magnets: that they attract and repel each other, and that they have a north and a south pole. But besides these two small observations, most people don't know anything else – how they are made and what specific uses they have, for example.

Magnets are everywhere. They are used in audio products, video and computer technology, telecommunications, automotive sensors, electric motors, medical imaging, energy supply and transportation

A typical horse shoe magnet

as well as stealth airplanes. If magnets have been utilised so well in every field of science, could there be a case for their also being involved with living organisms? If you were to believe a lot of scientists, there isn't any use for magnets in health-related issues; this is often referred to as "quackery science". But this view is a real shame – it did not take me very long in my research to uncover a good deal of evidence showing that, far from being passive players, magnets and electromagnets can play both a beneficial and a damaging role in living organisms.

The difference between an electromagnetic field and a magnetic field lies in the fact that an electromagnetic field emits an additional electrical field as well as a magnetic field. Electromagnetic fields are all around us, whereas magnets are either found in naturally occurring iron outcrops or are made artificially by wrapping a coil of iron with metal and passing an electric current through it. An electromagnetic field is the same as an electromagnetic vibration; they are two ways of saying the same thing. We are all surrounded by natural and artificial electromagnetic fields. The electromagnetic properties of the atmosphere are derived from waves emanating from radioactivity at the Earth's surface, cosmic radiation, ultraviolet solar radiation, power lines, radio stations, nuclear facilities and wi-fi masts, to name but a few. Many studies have equated electromagnetics to changes in our behaviour such as anxiety, irritability, restlessness, depression, insomnia, fatigue and faintness.

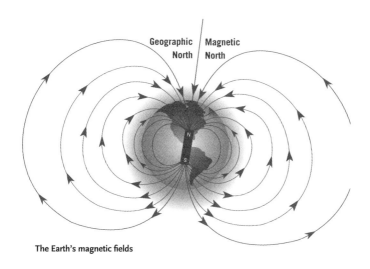

Geographic North | Magnetic North

The Earth's magnetic fields

Are there any magnetic fields to which our bodies react that are so fundamental to our organism's ability to survive that we take them for granted? Do we have our own north and south pole; are we ourselves magnets? Is the planet we live on a magnet? If you think about those two questions in isolation, we know that the Earth must be a big magnet because of the properties of a compass. We also know it has a North and a South Pole. Everyone knows this, but we seem to forget we know it. We are standing on a big magnetic lump called Earth. Surely we are being affected by its electromagnetic field, and, if so, it follows that we must have a north and south pole within our biological make-up.

This idea, however, raises many questions for which I do not have any answers. If I were to stand on a long metal magnetised bar with one end being south and the other being north, would my internal north and south pole be affected? If so, how would I know? Would it mean that my feet became south, and my head north? I have not had any scientific education that allows me to work out the answer to this issue. Maybe the answer is simply that the magnetic bar has no influence on my biochemistry.

But can I, with my hand on my heart, say conversely that magnetic forces are not likely to have any effect on my body at all? In order to find the answer to this question, I had to work out a logical theory. Was there an issue that could answer this simply once and for all? A question that occurred to me was this: what would happen if I swallowed several magnets? How would this affect me? If the magnets directly affected my body, this would prove that magnets have a direct biological effect. My instinct was to assume that this would be true, for no other reason than it just seemed to be obvious. How and why, I did not know, but I felt pretty sure there was a strong possibility that swallowing magnets would not be a healthy idea. And, not surprisingly, I found medical studies that provided me with an answer showing I was right.

So who in their right mind do you think would swallow magnets so that a study could be created? Children, of course. They love swallowing bits of everything. Several studies published in the *Journal of Paediatric Surgery* have shown that children can suffer terrible effects on their gastrointestinal tract from swallowing magnets; these magnets caused "perforations, adhesions and fistula formation". Ingestion for as little as five hours seems to cause severe internal problems, even though the magnets showed no signs of corrosion when they were extracted surgically..

These swallowed magnets seem to produce an incredibly fast toxic reaction, but I could not discover from my research how this works biologically. So yet again we have to go with the observational facts that magnets can cause a direct effect on our biological make-up if swallowed. However, the magnets do not affect everyone who swallows them: many children can swallow a magnet and have no side effects. So it must be something within those particular children that is different.

The research into internal damage caused by swallowing magnets proves that there is something about the properties of magnetism that causes a direct biological change. I would go so far as to argue that every living organism is affected by magnetism. If the world in which we live has, since the day of evolution, been bombarded with magnetic forces, all life forms will have developed in harmony with these. But if, for any strange reason, the electromagnetic forces changed, this natural harmony would be altered, causing a biological change. Exactly what this might be was what I hoped to discover in the scientific journals. Sadly, there was very little scientific research in this field, and what there was contradictory.

In an editorial in the *British Medical Journal* in 2005, written by Professors Finegold and Flamm, the title "Magnet therapy: extraordinary claims, but no proven benefit" sums up the way in which the medical profession views this area of science. This editorial was on page four of one of the most influential scientific journals in Britain. The problem I have in this instance with the

British Medical Journal and the authors of the article is that they seem to rejoice in a collective attack against the possibility that there could be any scientific principle behind the use of magnets. They conclude by saying "theoretically magnet therapy seems unrealistic". Why do they have such a problem with it theoretically? Where is the science for this? How can they state that "patients should be advised that magnet therapy has no proven benefits"? I find it very depressing that this type of preaching with the full support of the medical media does not take the time to assess all of the evidence before it starts attacking some fundamental principles of science. Do these two professors not know that magnets are used daily in hospitals to treat the non-union of bones? If magnets do not work and have no proven benefits, why are they helping hundreds of thousands of patients every year in hospitals throughout the world in bone-healing treatments?

What is even more dispiriting is the fact that, only a few months previously, the very same magazine had published an article by six scientists, including Edzard Ernst, Professor of Complementary Medicine, who had found "evidence of a beneficial effect of magnetic bracelets on the pain of osteoarthritis of the hip and knee". Their findings, they say, were consistent with previous studies on magnetic therapies and pain: "the benefit from magnetic bracelets seems clinically useful". What was interesting in their conclusion was the fact that they found no positive results in the studies that used weak magnets, but there were positive effects in those studies that used strong magnets – therefore, the strength of the magnets was important. This study, along with all of the others in a similar vein, should have shown that magnetic treatment works and opened the forum for further research. Yet only a few months later, in the same publication, two other professors dismissed this study as mere nonsense. What hope is there for any proven science to be accepted as fact in the medical establishments if it is up against old-fashioned dogma?

So how can we prove whether magnetism has an effect on our biological make-up other than by swallowing a magnet? Incredibly, the subject was dealt with over fifty years ago, to the extent that I find it ridiculous that it is even necessary to write this chapter. But it appears that scientists do not believe the findings even though, every day of the week, they can just look up into the sky and know that the astronauts sitting in the space station are living proof that we are affected by magnetism.

If you are old enough to remember the early launches of the Apollo spacecraft back in the 1960s, you will recall that, as soon as the astronaut landed in the water, he was helped out of the space module and almost lifted into transport that whisked him away to an isolation ward for several weeks in order for his body to recover.

Astronauts space suits have magnets built into them

Today the reusable spacecraft lands on a runway like an aeroplane and the astronauts walk out of the craft as if they had been the pilots of a standard aeroplane, and proceed immediately to a press conference, showing no side effects from their space travel.

What has happened over the past fifty years to allow this difference? Initially, the first few astronauts had to be assessed medically after returning home from space. It was found, on inspection, that they were losing bone density and calcium, and that their immune system was functioning poorly, hence the need for immediate short-term isolation from bacteria and viruses. And what did NASA do to solve this problem? It stole ideas from the Russians. The Russians had already successfully put astronauts into space for long periods of time. The Salyut 6 space laboratory had housed astronauts in space for two hundred and eleven consecutive days, and they had shown no signs of health issues on returning back to earth. NASA had to find a way to compete with the Russians, who were at this time its arch rivals. How could NASA maintain the astronauts' bones and immune systems while in space?

The reason the Russians discovered the solution long before the Americans can simply be found in the way the Russians investigate medical change and how they write up their research papers. The Russians have been more open to new ideas. They had been investigating the use of electromagnetic forces in nature for the previous thirty years and had developed an established science related to these phenomena. It was only in the 1960s, when America was concerned by the scientific discoveries that were being made within Russia, that its scientists began to translate Russian scientific papers to see if they could learn anything from them.

The Russians realised that the only difference the astronauts were experiencing was related to the gravitational field in space, which was very small compared with that of the Earth. In order to provide an environment that was stable for the astronauts, they had to artificially create the same magnetic fields in space as the astronauts were used to on Earth. The solution was simple: they put magnets in the spacecraft. Initially, these were very heavy, so they developed lightweight but very strong magnets within both the spaceship and the astronauts' spacesuits. These completely counteracted the previous absence of a magnetic field. How NASA eventually came to the same conclusions nobody knows.

So NASA has agreed that there is a direct effect of the Earth's magnetic waves on our biology. But if this is so, why don't doctors acknowledge it too? It seems to be obvious. If NASA is fully aware that the Earth's magnetic field is important when you do not have enough of it, surely the same would be true if you had too much of it. Our bodies have a natural equilibrium, and any change in the balance will have a biological effect. It appears, based upon the findings from the astronauts, that if you want to reduce the amount of calcium (found largely in the bones) or the bone density in the body, stick a patient in a sealed room that blocks out any magnetic input. On the other hand, if you want to increase bone density, apply extra magnets to the patient. It must also follow that subjecting the body to additional magnetic forces will increase the amount of calcium that is taken up in the bones, and if the magnets are placed locally over a specific bone, it is logical that more calcium will be produced and that bone will heal more quickly. This is, however, my own interpretation of the science that I have researched; I have not read this statement as such anywhere, but it seems to be the logical conclusion from what NASA has proven.

Would it also follow, therefore, that increased magnetic forces would also improve the body's immune system? This may not be as straightforward as the calcium concept as the immune system is a very delicate balance of many different cells, organs and hormones. It is not the same as saying that fewer or weaker magnetic forces reduce the immune system and stronger magnetic forces increase it. We know that a reduction or an increase in hormone levels to beyond the normal range has an immediate effect, usually negative. I would argue, therefore, that any level outside the normal level of magnetic forces would similarly undermine the balance of the immune system and push our bodies out of equilibrium, destabilising them.

This brings us back to the idea that all the electromagnetic waves we are generating through technology, such as electrical currents, wi-fi signals, mobile phones, satellite television and so on must be affecting our immune systems, just as the astronauts suffered. We are all reacting to being blasted by too many electromagnetic waves, but in a slower and more drawn-out process. This correlates with the rapid increases in immune-related illnesses worldwide, such as hay fever, chronic fatigue and diabetes. Most scientists dismiss this as impossible, yet they do nothing about it, maybe because there are no pills available that are a cure for these immune-related problems. You can read pages of scientific evidence that develop this line of enquiry in Chapter 6, on how technology is killing us.

Maybe someone in authority will one day write about NASA and its use of magnets and show the scientific community that, far from there being no scientific basis for the effects of magnets, there is an overwhelming scientific case to support this. But as this hasn't yet been done in the fifty years since the launch of the Apollo spaceship programme, I am not exactly holding my breath.

And the Russian and NASA discoveries are not even new. Ancient Greek, Egyptian and Roman civilisations were all aware of the concept and powers of magnetism. In fact, the Chinese were the first to develop any benefits from it when they discovered the magnetic compass. The Chinese writings of Gui Guzi and Han Fei (280–233 BC) showed that the orientation of natural lodestone towards the earth's geographical poles had been known for a very long time. What is a lodestone? A lodestone is a naturally occurring magnetic rock made from iron ore, commonly referred to as magnetite. It can be mined for or picked up in surface outcrops. This substance was revered in ancient Crete, in the palace of Knossos (2000–1300 BC), where the throne room of Minos is paved in the centre with a rectangular flagstone made of iron oxide, consisting mainly of magnetite.

So magnetism is not a new phenomenon to the world – just to Western civilisation. Do you know when we in the West first discovered magnetism? As recently as 1269, from the knowledge of Pierre Pèlerin de Maricourt, as revealed in a letter in which he introduced the concept of magnetic poles. But it took another 400 years until an English physician and physicist, William Gilbert, wrote a book – *De Magnete* in 1600 – in which this concept was brought to a wider public. It was said that Galileo was so impressed by it that he took up Gilbert's thoughts on magnetism.

It took around 2,000 years from the Chinese discovery of the compass for it to be used in navigation in the West, allegedly by Marco Polo in 1295 after he had visited China. This meant the Chinese had had a long time during which they could make discoveries on the possible healing properties of magnets. Surely then, some of our scientists should investigate the idea that the Chinese might have discovered evidence for magnetic treatment. Is it not likely that an ancient civilisation that made most of the world's major discoveries also spent a long time analysing human biological functioning? Maybe this ancient science should not be dismissed as being alternative or complementary science – maybe it is our Western science that should be called alternative!

I discovered that there was a good deal of ancient knowledge on the healing properties of magnets. Gilbert, writing in 1600, refers to the medical benefits of magnets and takes advice from ancient traditions, particularly those of the "Arabic writers" who used magnets for treating the liver and spleen. Even in that early period, Gilbert was writing "for it is beneficial in many diseases of the human system and by its virtues, both natural and acquired through fit and skilful preparation, it brings about wonderful changes in the human body". In one quote from his book, Gilbert refers to someone from Greece by the name of Platea, who discovered that magnets are "principally of use to the wounded". Maybe the science of treating bone healing and magnetism was discovered thousands of years before we rediscovered it in the West – as recently as the 1980s.

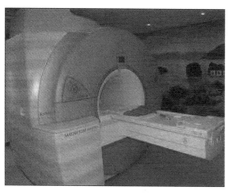

An MRI scanner – a giant magnet

Science has certainly not forgotten about magnets. I stated at the start of the chapter that they are used in virtually every part of our modern life. In fact, all hospitals contain machines that utilise magnets, such as the MRI scanners that create three-dimensional read-outs of your body – they are in essence one huge magnet, maybe big enough to affect other things in the surrounding rooms or even buildings. I wonder if anyone has gone around hospitals with a compass to see how magnetised the hospitals have become by their use of these machines. They could in fact be having a negative effect on the health of all of the hospital's patients. This highlights the need for science to complete research into the effect of magnets. What a sad irony that would be – that a machine that is supposed to help patients might in fact be doing the complete opposite.

Hundreds of scientific papers have investigated the effect of magnets of varying strengths on different ailments ranging from arthritis and ankle sprains through to urinary problems and wound healing. In almost all of the studies, the effect of magnets has been positive. I could write pages and pages on the successful studies that have been done, but it would be very repetitive; after the first few pages, you would get the idea – magnets have a strong effect on our bodies. So yet again I am going to ask the question, if they are so effective, why do we not use them in our everyday life? I believe there are three reasons for this: first, of course, is the scepticism of Western medicine to take on board anything that is not drug-based;

second is that you cannot patent a magnet, so there is very little profit incentive for companies to develop this area of research; and third is the fact that so many sellers of magnets of different shapes, sizes and strengths make false medical claims. It seems that anyone selling a magnet can now state that it will cure almost anything. This is not, however, true and has helped to provide ammunition for those people who want to dismiss this area of science as quackery.

One paper, published in 2009, assessed the work of all the scientists who had previously conducted experiments into the effect of magnetic fields. It was highly dismissive of those who had conducted the experiments and found that only two out of fifty studies were actually fully compliant with scientific criteria. This study showed that many scientists really do not understand the ideas behind the experiments and use one strength of magnets to justify that "all magnets" work or don't work. It is not scientific to compare a magnet with a strength of 100 Gs with one of 10,000 Gs. So only around 4% of the recently published clinical studies properly reported the protocol of the study – no wonder the scientists call the results controversial. Maybe it is time that we called the scientists themselves controversial, as well as the science.

Bone healing is another example of confusion within medical ideology. It was shown a long time ago that the use of magnets can help to heal bones. This technique is used in some hospitals as a matter of course, but in others only a last resort, when other treatments have failed. Now this strikes me as peculiar as it typifies the fear and ignorance that doctors have of different forms of science that might not necessarily be in their textbooks. How is it, when so many studies have shown this approach to work, that some doctors embrace this science whereas others still don't?

A broken bone is pretty simple; you know when it is broken, and you know when it has healed. There are standard lengths of time that it takes for most bones to heal, and if you apply magnets to bone that has been broken, it will heal more quickly. Scientific studies in the 1980s had remarkable results with the use of electromagnetic fields on bone fractures, with a success rate of 90% in adult patients. In fractures that had failed to heal four months after bone grafting, the success rate was 99%. The surgically non-invasive outpatient method that was approved by the American Food and Drug Administration in the 1980s produced confirmed end results for 1,007 non-united fractures; it had an international success rate of 79%, with a success rate in the USA of 76%.

In a study in 2008 on the effect that magnets have on healing wounds in rats, it was found that the magnet group healed in an average of 15.3 days, whereas the sham (fake treatment) and control (standard treatment) groups took 20.9 and 20.3 days respectively. This report stated that there was a paucity of scientific research into this field in humans. Other research in China in 2009 into deep wound healing in rats confirmed the results. Is it possible that the use of magnets could have the same effect on humans as on rats? Maybe, but as magnets have not been approved in the use of treatment by the American Food and Drug Administration, we will have to wait for an answer. Until doctors try using and understanding the power of magnets instead of large complicated pieces of machinery, we will never know the answer. Instead, most people will have to rely on a lot of bogus science that is being peddled by marketing companies making wild claims about the curative powers of magnets.

As an example of poor research that exacerbates confusion, a group of scientists headed by Cepeda in 2007 declared that the goal of their paper was to evaluate the effect of magnetic therapy on pain intensity, but failed to mention either the strength of the magnet employed or its strength at its target. The study aimed to measure the effectiveness of a magnet for postoperative surgery, but the magnet was placed on a wound for the limited time of two hours. Why was this random period chosen? And why did the authors also not provide any information on the strength of the magnet they had used? Surely they must have known that this is very important information. What did they think the magnet was going to do? Did they think that magnets are miracle cures that will cure anything in a matter of hours? If so, I think we would all have known about this phenomenon a long time ago.

Their conclusion was that "magnetic therapy lacks efficacy". How could they come up with such a conclusion based on this one experiment? Are they saying that all of the science in this area is wrong and they are right? Are they arrogant enough to dismiss this whole area of science based on one experiment? Especially as, conversely, Eccles, two years earlier, had conducted a critical review of randomised controlled trials of static magnets for pain relief and found that "73% of the analysed studies demonstrated a positive effect of static magnets in achieving analgesia across a broad range of different types of pain". Or to put it more simply, three out of four studies proved that magnets had a positive effect on pain relief.

Hundreds of papers published in scientific and medical journals have clearly demonstrated that selected magnetic fields have a beneficial effect on the healing process of damaged tissues and speed up the process of regeneration of these damaged tissues. One periodical, *Electromagnetic Biology and Medicine*, exclusively publishes scientific studies specialising in this field. Sadly, this magazine does not have a huge readership, otherwise the negativity surrounding this area might be minimal.

So what is the process that allows magnets to affect our biology? I would argue that it is simply a vibration emanating from the magnets that causes their curative properties. How can I prove this idea? – very easily. Magnets emit magnetic waves, which is the same thing as saying a magnet emits specific vibrations depending upon its strength. If it were possible to pinpoint the correct strength of a magnet and then measure its vibrational frequency, it would be possible to reproduce this using a frequency-generating machine. Such a machine is used daily throughout the world – it is called an ultrasound machine. If this machine produced successful results when used on bone healing, it would logically follow that it is the vibrations of the magnets that is curative.

I am delighted to say that the first reported use of ultrasound in enhancing fracture healing was demonstrated over fifty years ago by Hippe and Uhlman. In their experiments, they discovered that ultrasound reduced the healing time of bones from one hundred and fifty-four days to ninety-six days. The use of ultrasound is now highly established, yet electromagnetic treatment that has been used for thirty years in bone healing is still not completely accepted. Magnetic treatment, on the other hand, is mostly ridiculed and characterised as being a sham science. It is just another battle against medical doctrine that will eventually win, but how long do we all have to wait for the sceptics to accept change? Why are the good scientific papers not getting through, yet the bad ones are receiving more media attention?

It is no surprise that people are buying magnets for themselves, ignoring the advice of the medical establishment as they prefer to try out so-called alternative and complementary ideas rather than take drugs to reduce inflammation. If only doctors revised their opinion from believing that "theoretically magnet therapy seems unrealistic", progress could finally be made. If you ever find yourself discussing this with a doctor, just remind them about the Apollo space missions that have been taking place for the last fifty years and see how they attempt to wriggle out of that proof!

MAGNETS CAN CURE THE WORLD'S FOOD SHORTAGES

If magnets have a potentially hugely significant role to play within our biological make-up, is there another area of science in which they could play an important role? It was not hard to find the answer to this – it is plants. I find it very sad, however, that this knowledge is not more widely known. It is I think a crime that you are reading about this in a book on science. A crime that you are not at all aware of what I am about to tell you. A crime that it took me only a few weeks of research to discover that it is possible to eradicate a large amount of the world's food shortages by simply using sound or electromagnetic vibrations on plant seeds and growing plants. A crime that the seed companies have not spent large amounts of research money to develop seeds that have been exposed to these vibrations. A crime that the scientists who conduct experiments on seeds do not have a basic understanding of the behaviour of plants. And I believe it is a crime that we have not compiled a table of sound waves that are appropriate for each plant type.

I think you will gather that I am a little bit angry on this subject, and I hope you will be too after reading this section. But can you imagine what could happen if plants could grow by up to 50% simply by giving the seeds a little magnetic tickle? No fertilisers would be needed in the fields. There would be no genetically modified crops and no technical trickery. No adverse effects on consumption. No adverse effects on our digestive system or our biology. In fact there would be literally no downside, except a financial one for large corporations who rely on producing fertilisers, or seed companies who rely on farmers buying genetically modified seeds. All of this could be a thing of the past if only scientists would conduct the research. Although judging by most of the research papers in this field, much of the blame can also be passed onto the scientists whose poor research methods have not helped the science progress further.

I am giving away a billion dollar idea here as I believe it is more important that the world should know about it than one company should be able to make vast sums of money for its shareholders. I will admit, however, that as a businessman it did cross my mind that I could become seriously rich by creating a seed company that retained the specific vibrational frequencies required in order to facilitate extra growth. I could patent the idea and then either manufacture the seeds or sell out to a large multinational organisation. But my major concern would be how I could get this idea out to as many people as possible so that the idea would take off. I feel that, even though I could probably make a good attempt at it, the idea would work best if researchers around the world took it upon themselves to find the specific frequencies of each individual plant of most interest to them. Then the table of frequencies could be compiled significantly more quickly than one person or company could achieve. I also do not want a patent to be put out on the unique vibration of each plant as I feel that this should be an open access piece of information.

ELECTROMAGNETIC EFFECT ON PLANTS

The first person to carry out large-scale experiments into the effects of electrical vibrations on plants via an electrical current was Karl Lemstrom – this was back in 1904, before Bose (see Chapter 7) produced his results on the behaviour of plants. Lemstrom surmised, after a trip to the Arctic, that the green and healthy vegetation he found there might be a result of the weak electric currents carried through the atmosphere by ions from the aurora borealis. His ideas were confirmed when he compared the annual growth rings of fir trees in the region with sunspot cycles when the aurora would have been at its most active. Lemstrom tested his theory by exposing a range of different crops in several European countries to high-voltage gradients from wires suspended above them. He found that the treated plants were greener, sturdier and often showed dramatic increases in yield compared with the untreated samples. On average, there was a yield stimulation of around 45%.

What was the reaction of the scientific community? Well, there was a flurry of activity by agricultural scientists in the 1920s (yes, they took their time), who showed similar results but also discovered that the amount of electrical flow was an important factor in the success of any experiment. They also found that not every field trial with wheat, barley or oats was successful: out of eighteen field trials, only fourteen gave significant results. Most of this research died out in the 1930s, probably because the results were inconsistent.

Interpretations of why the experiments did not always work have been very mixed. One scientist suggested that it was related to the way plants behave in an electrical storm and how they adapt to the best use of water in such conditions. My suggestion is more contentious than this and is based upon reading up on hundreds of different experiments and on the knowledge of the behaviour of plants that I have gleaned from reading the books of J.C. Bose. I would argue that maybe the reason for the misunderstanding about the effect of electromagnetic forces on plants is because scientists do not understand plants very well. Would scientists conduct a drug trial on a giraffe, a pig and a rhinoceros and expect to get similar results just because they are all animals? If not, why do they think that oat, barley and wheat will behave the same just because they are all plants? Each plant must be treated individually. You cannot expect one strength of electromagnetic wave to affect an oak tree in the same way as a geranium.

Each plant has its own unique behaviour. It is important, when conducting any study on plants, for the experimenter to be aware that the length of time each plant is exposed to an electromagnetic field is imperative. Why is this? If I wire myself up to an electrical stimulation (TENS) machine that is constantly on, all day every day, for a matter of weeks, my body will react badly. However, if I were to use the TENS machine for only thirty minutes a day, my body would be less likely to react badly. Experiments by Bose have shown that electrical stimulation causes fatigue, just as if you over stimulate a muscle, it will behave negatively. If you provide only a small electrical stimulation, the muscle behaves positively up to a certain point, after which it behaves negatively, so finding the perfect length of stimulation is essential when conducting any experiment. As Chapter 7 describes, muscle fatigue is exactly the same as plant fatigue, so when conducting experiments on plants, it is essential not to over stimulate them, otherwise they will slow their rate of growth. Most experiments do not take these basic fundamental facts into consideration.

Research on stimulating seeds with electrical currents has also met with mixed results. Initial favourable reports were the trigger for some very poorly administered scientific experiments in the 1960s and 1970s, which led to a dismissal of the concept and most of the research. Recent research, however, has shown that an electrical current can have a positive effect, although this research has not met with a wider audience as it was conducted only very recently and by a group of Chinese authors. But the fact is that you can increase crop growth in all plants by the use of either an electrical vibration brought about by an electrical current, or a sound vibration created by a sound wave.

This has been proved, but it has been a question of finding the right scientific papers whose researchers have conducted experiments based on sensible scientific principles, not ones that over stimulate the plants with sound or electromagnetic currents that are on for twenty-four hours a day. These will produce results that are obviously going to be poor. Not surprisingly, those studies that stimulated the plants for only a matter of minutes or seconds produced positive results. Fortunately, in an experiment conducted on tomato seeds in 2006 in Cuba, it was shown that the seeds treated with a magnetic field for only three minutes or ten minutes had a significant growth increase over untreated seeds. Maybe other scientists should look at these results and take note that you only need a quick zap to generate significant results. This experiment showed there is a remarkable increase in the plant's production of tomatoes – but not the number of tomatoes, just their size. It seems to have the same effect as fertiliser. And a follow-up study conducted four years later found similar results.

In an experiment in India in 2008, chickpea seeds were exposed to magnetic fields of varying strengths for between one and four hours, which is up to eighty times more exposure than the tomato experiment. But why did the researchers choose this timescale? It is a constant conundrum to me why scientists choose random lengths of time and random frequencies. But even with these longer exposure times, the researchers achieved significant results. They found that the less the seeds were exposed, the greater the effect, so one hour's exposure was more productive than a four-hour exposure. It is a shame that they did not continue the experiment downwards from one hour to one minute to see the difference.

Not only is the length of time important, but so is choosing the correct vibrational frequency. At about the same time, in Taiwan, a group of scientists was looking into the effect that different magnetic frequencies had on the seed germination of mung beans. As an aside, it's interesting to note that the seeds experimented on in different countries are of particular interest to that country:

mung beans are as popular in Taiwan as chickpeas are in India. In this particular experiment on mung bean seeds, different magnetic fields induced by a differing current of 10, 20, 30, 40, 50 or 60 Hz had dramatically different results on the mung beans. The 20 and 60 Hz magnetic fields were best at producing increased growth of the seeds, water uptake and root diameter. The 10 Hz magnetic field showed no noticeable change over the control group, and the 30, 40 and 50 Hz fields produced poorer results – 50 Hz in fact had an inhibiting effect on the early growth of the mung beans.

These few studies show very clearly that there is an underlying certainty that plants can react both positively and negatively to electrical stimulation. This stimulation has an effect on the plant's ability to grow and therefore produce more fruit, which for the 21st century is obviously a fundamental objective.

INTRODUCTION TO

THE BEES AND THE BIRDS

" Today, unprecedented exposure levels and intensities of magnetic, electric, and electromagnetic fields from numerous wireless technologies interfere with the natural information system and functioning of humans, animals, and plants. The consequences of this development, which have already been predicted by critics for many decades, cannot be ignored anymore. Bees and other insects vanish; birds avoid certain places and become disorientated at others. Humans suffer from functional impairments and diseases. And insofar as the latter are hereditary, they will be passed on to next generations as pre-existing defects".

PROF. K. HECHT, DR. M. KERN, PROF. K. RICHTER, DR. H. SCHEINER, "EFFECTS OF WIRELESS COMMUNICATION TECHNOLOGIES" 2009

The decline in the bee population is a catastrophe! It seems to have slipped under the radar for most people, but if the decline continues, our food supply is in grave danger. Bees allow plants to pollinate, and without pollination new plants are not created. If that happens, the food chain will break down, and animals, birds and humans who rely on plants for their food source could starve. If the bees collapse and die out, so will a large proportion of the world's food supplies.

What a terrifying thought! Thankfully, governments have finally acknowledged this problem and are financing investigations. The US government is investing $10 million into looking at how our food chain is going to be affected, but doesn't that sound like a paltry sum to investigate such a potentially major crisis? If the problem is so significant and the outcome is so damaging, isn't this a tiny amount to invest?

I have to admit to having no previous knowledge of bees. The only fact I can remember from my childhood is the one I think we all know, about them not being able to fly as their body is too big and heavy for their wing size – aerodynamically, they defy science (which does not say much for the experts on aerodynamics). I profess to not taking much interest in bees until recently, but I was forced to when I read a few years ago about the declining numbers of bees and the effect this would have on nature. But like most people, I have just relied on the scientists to come up with an answer that would solve this predicament. Sadly, however, comparatively little is being done. The most depressing part is that I managed to find a solution to the problem without having received any funding, a solution that would cost virtually nothing to put in place and could possibly entirely eradicate the disappearance of bees.

This solution is based on simple logic. I am lucky in that I am able to look at the problem from a neutral position, by considering both the scientific evidence and the anecdotal evidence (even if only because it is so interesting). I am going to walk you through my idea and hopefully you will be able to draw the same conclusions as I did. Then you can ask yourself these questions – how is it that more people don't know about this area, and why is the science community still funding parochial research projects that cannot possibly solve the problem?

So why are bees so important? It is because nature has devised a system that requires the insects to play a major role in pollination, which is the equivalent of sexual reproduction in flowering plants. Pollination is an essential part of the process in the reproduction of plants that then go on to produce fruit, nuts and vegetables – indeed, 90% of flowering plants require insect assistance to help them pollinate. Bees collect nectar from flowers in order to make honey, and while they are collecting it, they rub up against the pollen, on what is the equivalent of the male sexual organ, and

Bee pollinating a plant

some of this pollen attaches itself to the bee's body. The bee then flies around to other flowers to collect nectar and in the process transfers the pollen from flower to flower and takes the pollen to the carpel within each flower, which is the equivalent of the female organ. Thus, the bees act as a sexual conduit. Without the bees, the flowers could not pollinate, and without fertilized flowers, there would be a severe worldwide shortage of fruit, nuts and vegetables.

I think it will come as a bit of a surprise to many people that bees are also used as a commodity, a sort of "sexual guns for hire". Tens of thousands of bee hives are transported around the US in order to help pollinate specific crops at certain times of the year if there are not enough local bees in order to do the job. Bee hives are not stationary; they are a mobile business. In fact, during the growing season, bees are moved around the country two or three times. One of the harvests the bees are needed for is that of almond crops, as there are not enough local bees to be able to pollinate the vast numbers of almond trees. In the US alone, the total contribution of pollination in terms of added value to fruit crops exceeds $15 billion per annum. In the US alone, the bees pollinate one hundred and thirty different crops.

In the US between 2008 and 2009, the number of honey bees fell 29% according to a survey by the US Department of Agriculture. This followed on from losses in the previous years of 36% between 2007 and 2008, and 32% between 2006 and 2007. Understandably, the US honey industry has been severely affected by this catastrophe. The consequences are so large that the US government has set up a committee to investigate the phenomenon and present a paper outlining the ongoing research. The US Department of Agriculture estimates that every third bite that Americans consume in their diet is dependent upon honey bee pollination.

I find it very alarming that mainstream research ignores the only obvious solution to the problem, the only answer that fits the facts. Bee experts and bird experts are all looking at the same issues. The conclusions in all of the research documents I have read are almost identical. If a group of students who were not experts in the study of bees but who were being taught science at college were asked for the likely causes of the bee collapse, I believe their answers would be very similar to those in the Congress report. They are textbook answers. The point I am making is that the researchers have not taken the time to look at alternative ideas, ones that are related to the observed behaviour of the bees, rather than continuing the scientists'

Relying on Bees

Some of the most valuable fruits, vegetables, nuts and field crops depend on insect pollinators, particularly honeybees.

	Crop Value *in billions 2006*	Percentage pollinated by honeybees	Percentage of crop pollinated by...		
			Honeybees	Other Insects	Other
Soybeans	$19.7	5%			
Cotton	5.2	16			
Grapes	3.2	1			
Almonds	2.2	100			
Apples	2.1	90			
Oranges	1.8	27			
Strawberries	1.5	2			
Peanuts	0.6	2			
Peaches	0.5	48			
Blueberries *cultivated*	0.5	90			

Besides insects, other means of pollination include birds, wind and rainwater.

Sources: United States Department of Agriculture;
Roger A. Morse and Nicholas W, Calderone, Cornell University

current research into issues that are not specifically related to the disappearance of the bees.

COLONY COLLAPSE DISORDER

The problem facing the bee industry has been called colony collapse disorder, or CCD. What exactly is this? Well, put very simply, it means that the bees take off one morning and disappear, never to return to the hive. No-one knows where they go or what happens to them after they leave, or how they end up dying. If you owned a few hives and the bees slowly started disappearing, so that in the end all of your hives were completely empty with no indication of any sort as to the cause of the problem, alarm bells would be ringing! You would panic as you would see your business disappearing in front of your eyes. This is the position the Apiary Inspectors of America find themselves in. And they are not alone. This is a phenomenon that is happening throughout the world. All honey bee production is being affected – it is not just in America.

A report for Congress in 2008 entitled *Recent Honey Bee Colony Declines* found that the authors believe the potential causes of CCD to include but not necessarily be limited to the following:

1. Parasites, mites and disease loads in the bees and brood;
2. The emergence of new or more virulent pathogens;
3. Poor nutrition amongst adult bees;
4. A lack of genetic diversity and lineage of bees;
5. The level of stress in adult bees (for example, the transportation and confinement of bees, overcrowding or other environmental or biological stressors);
6. Chemical residues or contamination in the wax, food stores and/or bees;
7. A combination of these and/or other factors.

The document has been thoroughly researched and discusses with great alarm this new phenomenon of CCD. It underlines the fact that this is a new phenomenon, and although there have been losses in the number of bees before, there has never been a situation in which bees have failed to return to their hive, particularly in such large numbers:

Among the key symptoms of CCD in collapsed colonies is that the adult population is suddenly gone without any accumulation of dead bees. The bees are not returning to the hive but are leaving behind their brood (young bees), their queen, and maybe a small cluster of adults. What is uncharacteristic about this situation is that the honey bee is a very social insect and colony-oriented, with a complex and organized nesting colony. Failing to return to the hive is considered highly unusual. An absence of a large number of dead bees makes an analysis of the causes of CCD difficult.

The report did not produce a final conclusion as to the specific determinants of CCD; it has been left to other research organisations to discover a possible cause. One such research paper has discovered what the authors believe to be the answer to this problem – a parasite. In a study published in the new journal from the Society for Applied Microbiology, *Environmental Microbiology Reports*, scientists from Spain analysed two apiaries and found evidence of CCD. They found no evidence of any other cause of the disease other than infection with the parasite *Nosema ceranae*. When the researchers then treated the infected surviving underpopulated colonies with the antibiotic drug fumagillin, they demonstrated the complete recovery of all infected colonies:

Now that we know one strain of parasite that could be responsible, we can look for signs of infection and treat any infected colonies before the infection spreads.

Really? Is it that simple? A parasite can affect all bees, but will destroying this parasite cure a problem that appears in many countries across the world? Maybe it is that simple, and again maybe it isn't. Maybe scientists are going down the same road as they always do while looking for a problem, focusing in on smaller and smaller specialist ideas rather than stepping back and looking at this problem as a whole. For example, are bees the only insects that are having this problem? Are there any other areas of nature that are suffering from the same issues? Of course there are, and this is going to be the way we can work out the real reason why bees are disappearing.

Maybe parasites are the answer, or at least part of it, but what about agriculture and the use of pesticides? What research has been conducted there? US scientists have found one hundred and twenty-one different pesticides in samples of bees, wax and pollen, which has added weight to the belief that the pesticides are the cause of the problem. In fact, this is probably one of the largest areas of research into the causes of CCD in the US as it seems to be the most logical and easiest explanation for the bees' disappearance. If the bees, while out pollinating, also pick up the pesticides that have been used on the crops, there is no doubt that the bees will be affected by them. But this is not a new issue: pesticides have been used in agriculture for a long time. Some experts, however, conclude that it must be due to some "subtle interactions between nutrition, pesticide exposure and other stressors that are converging to kill colonies".

But there is no actual evidence anywhere to support the fact that the pesticides are the cause, only statistics that say the bees have a lot of pesticides within them, which they have probably always had. None of the numerous research papers that has looked at pesticides has in fact shown that this is the cause of any demise whatsoever. It is like saying that if you were to analyse the human body and discovered that we had pesticides within our bodies, which we of course do, these are the cause of cancer. It is not a conclusion that you can make with any authority. Yes, there is a statistical relationship, but this proves nothing whatsoever.

The question that must always be asked in the first instance in order to solve this problem is why are the bees disappearing; why are they not found dead in the bee hives? Does a bee that is contaminated with a pesticide answer this riddle? To me, the answer is no, because if the answer were a pesticide, I believe you would find dead bees in and around the hive. But you don't, so this seems to be an area of research that is not going to find a solution.

One other point to mention is that bees kept on organic farms that do not use pesticides are also suffering from CCD, causing a scientific dilemma for those who think that pesticides are the sole cause of the problem. How is it possible that bees on organic farms are suffering the same fate? The only way for this to happen would be for the bees to stray from the organic farm and then pick up pesticides in adjacent non-organic fields. This might well be true. But then there would have to be a mechanism by which it spread to all of the other bees that had not strayed away from the organic area (for which a transmission process has not yet been recognised).

So that leaves us with the bee management, viruses and environmental factors. Has anything changed in the way bees have been managed over the past few years? I can find no research anywhere suggesting that this can be the cause; in fact, bee management has hardly changed since Roman times – the principles are still pretty much the same.

So let's move on to another idea that was put forward by the US Congress report I mentioned above: viruses. Can this explain the problem of CCD? If it did, it would mean that a virus somehow affected the bee's ability to fly or caused it to lose its sense of direction, and this virus would have to affect all of the bees in exactly the same way. As none of the bees is dying within the hive, it is unlikely that the cause of the problem is a virus that has affected the bees' ability to fly because then you would find many bees dead or dying either in the hive or very near to it. A virus that somehow affects their ability to navigate, however, is a distinct possibility as it would explain very simply why the bees die away from the hive. Imagine a virus that attacked the bee's navigational homing system. The bee, while out collecting nectar, would fly around in all directions gathering nectar from plants, but when it had found enough it would not be able to return home – it would simply be lost. The bee would not be able to find its hive and would eventually die in a field somewhere.

From a logical point of view, this seems to be the most plausible. However, it presupposes one thing that maybe not every scientist agrees with, and this is the fact that bees are homing creatures and use a homing system that allows then to navigate back to their hive. Many scientists believe the bees also tune into visual and chemical signals in order to find their way around. However, one story will clearly dismiss the idea that bees use anything other than their homing abilities, employing gravitational magnetic signals, to navigate to find their hive.

What is this story? It is one I read in a bee-keeping journal written by a bee-keeper writing in 1902. When I first read it, it seemed quite astonishing as I had not at that time concluded that bees were in fact homing creatures. Mr F.W. Hilgendorf was looking into the proposition put forward by fellow bee-keepers that ants and bees find their way home not by any special sense of direction, but by a knowledge of the district in which they are working. In his address to the Philosophical Institute of Canterbury, New Zealand, Mr Hilgendorf went on to describe what had happened to him in the week after hearing this proposition:

During the same week I was working with my bees and in the busy time of the day when many of the bees were out foraging, I had occasion to move a hive 3ft to one side. In a few minutes a number of bees had alighted on the former site of the hive and crawled about there, or rose and circled around the spot, without making any attempt to enter the hive standing only a foot or two away. All those that were out at work when the hive was moved came back to the old site and stayed there until night fell, when they perished of cold: and this experience is not exceptional, but is familiar to all bee-keepers.

This evidence disproves what Mr Hilgendorf had originally tried to explain, and it was of interest to him because it actually discredited his theory. The experiment he conducted was a very simple one. When the bees left the hive, he moved the hive one metre away from its original position. The bees had no idea the hive was just a metre away; there were no clues from any visual shapes or patterns, and no chemical smells they could pick up on. The only clue to the location of their hive was an electromagnetic one coming from their homing abilities. It seems to me that this is a fundamental point we all need to be very aware of because once we understand it, it follows that bees use unknown sensors to find a path back to their hive, using the earth's electromagnetic signals to calculate where the hive is located. They do not use their sense of smell or sight in order to find their way home.

The most troubling issue for me about this piece of research is that I have not found it replicated anywhere. I have mentioned it to a few bee-keepers, but they have had no idea that the bees did this. Maybe scientists and bee-keepers are not aware of this fundamental behavioural pattern of the bee. If so, this is pretty alarming because it would mean that much research has been wasted over the past hundred years. This information also provides a very simple answer to the problem of CCD: the bees are getting lost and are looking for a hive somewhere else due to an external electromagnetic signal affecting their homing abilities.

It could of course be a virus that is affecting their homing abilities, and not an external electromagnetic source. But does this solution provide the answer to the problem of bees dying out all around the world at the same time? The virus would have to spread faster and wider than bubonic plague and affect only bees. This is theoretically possible, but somehow it seems just too much of an easy option – plus the fact that obviously no-one has found such a virus, although that is no reason to rule out the possibility of its existence.

Could there be another much simpler solution, one that answers all of the issues, one that fits very neatly with all of the facts, one that is pertinent to not only bees, but also every other insect or bird that relies upon its homing abilities? If only scientists would look at the bigger picture and investigate similar occurrences in other areas of research, they might find answers to their problems very quickly. It did not take me long to discover that the same thing happening to bees is also happening to the bird population within cities around the world.

One clue to the bee's problems was discovered by Siegfried Vogel, who was a small honey-producer in Germany for fifteen years until the year 2004, when all of his bee colonies died out. At the time, he had four colonies that he kept housed in an old wooden truck trailer in his garden. What led Vogel to conclude that there was only one cause of the problem was the fact that his son, Reinhold Vogel, also kept three bee colonies in the same truck, but none of his bee colonies disappeared. What was the difference between the two styles of bee-keeping to cause this anomaly? – the only variation was that Reinhold kept his bee colonies in an old aluminium-lined container within the trailer, and this aluminium seemed to be protecting them.

This is not scientific evidence in any way – it is purely anecdotal – but when you start putting together all of the pieces of the jigsaw, a simple solution becomes so obvious that it is hard to conclude that there is any other. In this case, there must be something that the aluminium is doing to protect the bees from a very damaging effect. Siegfried Vogel concluded that there was only one cause: the three new mobile phone masts that had been built in his area. This, he concluded, was the only logical cause of the problem. The aluminium shield was somehow protecting his son's bees from the electromagnetic waves that were being emitted from the masts.

By an extraordinary coincidence, I happened to be watching a cooking programme on television presented by Jamie Oliver, the British celebrity chef, who was in Greece filming an episode for his series. The recipe that he was working on involved honey, and as he was showing the audience how to cook the dish, he started talking about bees and their disappearance. Of course, I suddenly sat up – in hope rather than expectation as I was curious as to what he was about to say. Incredibly, he started talking about the experiences of the local bee farmer who had noticed that in areas in which his mobile telephone worked, he had lost most of his bees from CCD, but in isolated areas in which his mobile phone had no reception, he had lost none of his bees. At this news, I began whooping with satisfaction all alone in front of my television as here was anecdotal confirmation of everything that I believed to be true! Sadly, when I trawled the newspapers the following day, no-one seemed to have picked up on it. At least, I thought, the four million people who might be watching the programme had been offered a new insight into an alternative idea that might help solve the problem, so that when this book was finally published, the public might not be so surprised to find that mobile phone masts are the most likely cause.

In 1985, two scientists, Walker and Bitterman, proved that bees are affected by magnetic fields, and their experiments were subsequently replicated to confirm the results in 1991. So there is clear scientific evidence that bees possess a sensitivity to magnetic fields, and that changes in the direction of the magnetic field affects their behaviour. These experiments led to much research into how this occurred and, just as with birds (see below), to much debate that has proved inconclusive. However, from my point of view, I am interested not in how it works, but in the fact it does work. If bees are affected by magnetic fields, it follows that any disturbance in this magnetic field can have an effect on their behaviour. What that effect is, however, is very speculative due to the lack of research in this field. I am always prepared to speculate, and I would suggest that changes in the magnetic fields caused by human interference are a major contributor to CCD.

One scientist who has investigated this area more than anyone over the past forty years appears to be the lone voice trying to get his message across to the authorities. He is Ulrich Warnke, presently chairman of the Institute Physiology Forum at the University of Saarland, Germany. Sadly for him – and a tragedy for everyone else – it seems that he has not yet been heard despite conducting experiment after experiment clearly showing that bees are affected by electromagnetic signals:

> *Insects such as bees receive these oscillations (from electrical storms) and recognise them as storm warnings. We were able to show that bees return in great numbers when these oscillations are simulated and transmitted, using a highly amplified signal generator. If the amplitudes of the artificial oscillations overlap with the natural signals, however, the return rate rapidly decreases. The bees fail to find their way home.*

In his early research in the 1970s and 1980s, Warnke investigated the effect of artificially created electrical fields on the bees' behaviour. He found that a stimulation of 50 Hz:

> *caused significant restlessness of the bees in their enclosure. The colony temperature increases greatly. The defence of the social territory is uncontrollably increased to the point where individuals in a colony stab one other to death. They no longer*

recognise one other. After a few days in the field, the bees tear their brood from the cells; no new brood is reared. Honey and pollen are also depleted and then no longer collected. Bees that were newly established in their hives shortly before the start of the experiment always abandon the hive again and disappear when the electrical field is switched on. Bees that have lived in their hive for a long time, plug all the cracks and holes with propolis, including the entrance. This otherwise only happens in winter in a cold draught.

Since an acute lack of oxygen develops when the cracks and the entrance are plugged, the bees attempt to introduce air by intensive fanning. In this process, the wing muscles generate temperatures high enough to melt the wax. The animals attempt to fight the temperature increase by more fanning. In the end, the colony burns itself out. This implies the death of all members of the colony – which we could obviously prevent in future.

With experiments using 30–40 Hz:

When the field is switched on, the animals suddenly move their wings and buzz at frequencies of 100–150 Hz.

But the most relevant effect for CCD (which I've emphasised in the quote below) happened at the lowest frequency Warnke and his team tested, 10–20 Hz:

With signals in the frequency range of 10 to 20 Hz, the aggressiveness was increased and the homing ability much reduced even though the natural meteorological and electromagnetic environment was intact in the flight space.

This last paragraph makes a very important point. The earth's natural magnetic waves are in the 10 Hz range, so it is obvious that bees will have ways of using this specific frequency in line with their homing abilities. This is true of every animal – they all use this frequency. Therefore, if you interfere with it, the bees' capacity to use their homing skills will be affected, which is why it comes as no surprise to discover that emitting an interfering frequency in the 10–20 Hz range "reduced the homing ability of the bees". Mobile phone technology uses a range of different frequencies: 2 Hz, 8.34 Hz, 30–40 Hz and 217 Hz. Any one of these could be the cause of the problem, but the fact that there are four types makes it easier to believe that the combination of all four is very likely to be a major factor in the bees' inability to navigate home.

One would expect, following Warnke's results in the 1970s, that there would have been a lot of follow-up research into the effects of telecommunication on bees' behaviour. However, I can find only one significant scientific paper since that first research was completed in 1975 that analyses the relationship between electromagnetic waves from telecommunications technology and bees' behaviour. This study has been picked up by newspapers, sadly for the unsuspecting scientists, and used to prove that mobile phone technology has been the cause of the bees' disappearance. It would be good to use this study as evidence to support the theory; however, all it does is show how the media distorts the truth. The study tested the concept that cordless phones might affect the bees' behaviour, but it did not look at mobile phone technology, which is a completely different area of science. It would be negligent to say this one study proved any relationship – all it really did was just to give an insight into what might be the truth.

The study was conducted in Germany at the University of Koblenz-Landau by Jochen Kuhn and colleagues in 2007 and was entitled "Electromagnetic radiation: influences on honeybees". It investigated the use of cordless phones – but not, as I have said, mobile phones – and the behavioural effect these had on bees. This experiment only lasted forty-five minutes. I am not sure why as it might have been more interesting for the experiment to last a lot longer, and it would be very simple to have put a camera on each hive so that the number of bees leaving and returning over a longer period could easily be counted. Maybe that was going to be the follow-up study, who knows, but as far as the scientists were concerned, this study was a very simple experiment and not one that set out to prove one thing or another.

The results, however, of just this forty-five minute experiment were intriguing, to say the least, and definitely worthy of a follow-up: 63% of the bees in the control group returned within forty-five minutes, compared with 49% of the exposed groups. In their conclusion, the scientists came up with a contradiction, stating on the one hand that "a significant difference between exposed and non-exposed bee colonies could be observed" and then a few sentences later that:

> *A possible influence of the radiation intensity could not be proven by this study, because no significant differences between the group-pairs could be detected. Also, a clear distinction between the low-frequency pulse of the DECT base station and its high-frequency sending radiation could not be drawn, despite the fact that a significant difference between the non-exposed bees and the fully irradiated ones can be counted as a result of the influence of high-frequency electromagnetic radiation.*

What they are basically saying is that this simple experiment is of interest but does not prove anything. That is all very well, but journalists are renowned for "not letting the facts get in the way of a good story". What the media did is just quote the first part of the scientists' results and conclusion, that is the sentence in which they say "a significant difference between exposed and non-exposed bee colonies could be observed", and run with that story. An internet search will reveal hundreds of related stories all saying that a link had been found proving that mobile phone technology was the cause of CCD. This is not true, but it does point to the possibility that it might be, although it is just a forty-five minute experiment: we cannot say that mobile phone technology and low-level electromagnetic waves are not the cause of CCD, only that this experiment is not the smoking gun that proves it one way or another.

My problem with science within this field is why, after this initial experiment, hundreds of others have not been conducted to try to prove the initial results of this German study in greater detail. If you look at the US Congress report that was written a year after the experiment, it does not refer to this type of research at all; it is as if it has been completely ignored. But this is a major issue because it brings out all the fears that people have about big business or governments interfering and massaging the truth for political or financial reasons. Let's look at two facts here:

1. The bee colonies started dying out only very recently – it was only in 2000 that bee-keepers started to notice there was a problem.
2. The growth of mobile and wi-fi technology has grown exponentially over the past 10 years.

This is not scientific proof of anything, but it would make me want to study the relationship in greater detail if I were a scientist, particularly if I knew that bees were homing creatures.

It would be a very simple theory to prove. All it would require would be research into the geographical areas where the bees have been affected, and the areas in which they have not been affected. I would guess that any developing country that does not possess any mobile communication system or internet technology would not be affected. If this simple piece of data were available, it could be used to prove that something we were doing was the cause of the problem, rather than it being a virus or a hive-management issue, as scientists keep trying to identify.

Take India as an example. It too is now suffering from CCD, as predicted. A plunge in the bee population has been found in Kerala, a part of India that has only recently introduced mobile phone towers. Is this a coincidence? Not at all, says Dr Pattazhy, a reader in Zoology in at the Sree Narayana College in Kollam, who has allegedly conducted a study in this field. I say "allegedly" because his study has been reported in a number of newspapers in India but I have been unable to view the original source so I cannot confirm his exact discoveries. However, the newspapers report that his study has shown the collapse of a bee colony in five to ten days when a mobile telephone was left next to the hive, the worker bees failing to return home, and leaving the hives with just queens, eggs and hive-bound immature bees.

So what am I trying to say about the bees? It is simply that scientists must now, as a priority, investigate the relationship between technology and the loss of the bee industry, and test a very simple solution to curing the problem. I believe that a very cheap and simple method of wrapping the hives in a protective cover that prevented the bees from picking up electromagnetic waves would provide a solution.

If the bees were an isolated incidence, it would be much easier to dismiss this idea as New Age nonsense but, as you will read in the following section, this is not a one-off problem but one that is affecting birds as well.

PIGEONS

What can we learn from birds that might help us in our understanding of the effects of electromagnetic waves on the homing capabilities of bees? It seems pretty logical that if there is any effect on bees, this same effect would manifest itself with all homing creatures.

Now, there is nothing more "homing" than a homing pigeon; it is one bird we can all agree that does have navigational abilities. In fact, these abilities have been known for thousands of years and were said to have been used by the Romans as a form of communication

A homing pigeon

between different armies. The possibility that birds have this homing capability is therefore not in dispute, but what might cause it and how it can be affected has been open to debate. Research clearly shows that the birds' homing abilities are affected by electromagnetic vibrations, but what is important in the research is that only very specific vibrations of a particular type are relevant – namely square-shaped vibrations in a small frequency range.

In 1985, Paolo Ioale and Dante Guidarini conducted a series of experiments using magnetic fields placed around the heads of homing pigeons and surrounding the areas of their cages. Their experiment used a variety of types of magnetic wave – sine-shaped, triangular and square-shaped waves – but they found the pigeons' orientation was only strongly affected by square-shaped waves. Studies on the growth of plants have shown that it is the square-shaped waves that have the most significant effect, and not the sine-shaped waves that most scientists seem to utilise in their experiments.

So how does this help us to investigate whether or not electromagnetic waves affect bees? Clearly, what is important is not that all electromagnetic waves cause bees to lose their homing abilities, but that it is likely that only specific frequencies using specific wave shapes cause the problem.

Do birds use forms of magnetism in order to find their way around? It seems obvious that birds use something, otherwise how would they find their way around the world with such efficiency? But exactly what piece of their body they use has yet to be identified. There have been hundreds of scientific papers postulating the idea that magnetic fields affect animals, yet the phenomenon has remained elusive and is still to this day sometimes treated with scepticism.

Why is this? The nature of any scientific experiment is that it can only look at the behavioural pattern of the animals in question, sometimes producing unambiguous results. Birds are, however, completely different. We have known that migratory birds can find their way over great distances for a very long time, and the use of an internal compass was first suggested back in the 19th century when sailors were using similar instruments to find their way across oceans. But additionally for science, birds show that, at certain times of the year when they are due to migrate, they exhibit distinct physical and behavioural changes. This is often manifested even when a bird is kept in a cage. Very often, this migratory restlessness is accompanied by attempts to move in the direction corresponding to the seasonal migration route.

Science has steered itself into a bit of a corner when looking at how birds migrate, and it is typical of this area of science, as it is with plants, that scientists are still looking for a chemical or physical solution to the problem. Current research into birds looks principally at two theories: the "magnetic mineral" and the "radical pair model" theories. The magnetic mineral theory is based on the universal presence of iron-containing compounds in living organisms. This supposes that the iron somehow acts as a compass within the bird's beak (where it is mainly found) and that this facility is the basis of the bird's ability to direct itself while migrating. However, in experiments in which birds have been blindfolded in one eye, research has shown that covering the right eye caused the birds to lose their sense of direction, whereas covering the left one had no effect on their migratory skills. This would suggest that some structures in the eye are involved in navigation.

The radical pair model, on the other hand, is based on the assumption that the geomagnetic field changes the rate of radical pair chemical reactions in a certain light-responsive protein in the bird's eye, affecting certain receptors that detect magnetic fields. A lot of time has been spent trying to work out the biochemical mechanisms underlying how birds and bees actually transfer information within their bodies rather than on the damage that is caused by erroneous external magnetic forces. It was an attempt to prove the radical pair model that threw a giant spanner into the scientific research. Experiments on the effect of weak oscillating magnetic fields and how they influenced the birds' magnetic compass discovered that birds' orientation was disrupted by emitting a magnetic field in a variety of different field lengths (vibrations). These results appear to disprove the radical pair model as it cannot explain these effects.

So if these experiments show clearly that one theory does not work, you would imagine that all of the research would then go into looking at how and why magnetic waves of specific frequencies affect birds' behaviour. Sadly, this is again not the case. To quote

K.V. Kavokin, a Russian scientist who investigated this area in 2009:

> *One of these requirements is that if an experimental result contradicts the general theory, the experiment should be repeated with special attention to all imaginable effects that could give the same result – until all of them are, one by one excluded. Only then the new phenomenon can be believed to exist.*

So let's look at other scientific papers that do not make any attempt to understand the biology or chemistry of the problem but just look at the observational side of science. If it is seen to happen in several experiments, surely it does not matter if we do not have a scientific explanation for its occurrence. If the observational disagrees with the science, could it not be the science that is at fault rather than the observations? If the science does not explain the visual results, maybe more time and money should be made available to look at alternative ideas on what is causing migrational problems within the bird community. It might come as a surprise to the scientific community that a very familiar pattern is being observed, a pattern of behaviour that is occurring not only in birds, but in insects, plants and humans as well. In fact, it might even show that the effect is similar for all types of living organism because, as I have previously stated, we all come from the same genetic pool, and if something affects one type of living organism, it is likely that it will affect all types of living organism.

OBSERVATIONAL BIRD SCIENCE

I am going to attempt to describe different scientific research projects that have looked at measuring different patterns of behaviour amongst birds with particular reference to mobile phone masts and stations, as this area provides the most compelling evidence that there is a direct effect between birds' behaviour and magnetic fields. It is my belief that if I recount numerous scientific documents, you will start to think that perhaps the observational part of science should outweigh the chemical and biological science, and that society as a whole should start to open its eyes and base more of its behaviour on things that we can see existing rather than on scientific experiments that are looking for biological and chemical answers.

THE HOUSE SPARROW

There has been a massive decrease in the house sparrow population in the UK and in several western European countries in the last few years. In London, there was a 71% decline in the population between 1994 and 2002. Studies have shown that the population is more affected in urban areas than in the countryside. In 2002, the house sparrow was added to the Red List of UK endangered species. The same picture can be seen in Brussels, West Berlin and The Netherlands. But in rural Scotland and Wales, house sparrows have actually been on the increase.

A number of hypotheses have been put forward to explain the population decline of the house sparrow in urban areas, and these have all been investigated by scientific studies. Guess what these suggestions are? I am sure that if I refer you back to the US Congress report on bees, you might be able to hazard a guess. They are almost exactly the same suggestions as the ones put forward for the decline of the bee population. In this case, the areas of investigation include:

1. Lack of food;
2. Pollution from vehicles;
3. An increased number of predators;
4. A loss of nesting sites due to building changes;
5. Pesticides;
6. Disease transmission.

What about low-level electromagnetic waves, I hear myself screaming? Why are they not on the list? In fact, very few investigators have looked at this area, but those who have all reported a relationship between house sparrow numbers and the electromagnetic waves emitted from mobile telephone transmitters.

Let's start off with one recent paper that investigated the possible effect of radiation from mobile phone base stations on the number of breeding house sparrows in Belgium. This study was conducted by Joris Everaert and Dirk Bauwens in 2007 and looked at 150 locations distributed over six residential areas in East Flanders, Belgium. The conclusion they came to was that fewer house sparrow males were seen at locations with relatively high electric field strength values of mobile phone base stations, and they concluded that this therefore supports the notion that long-term exposure to higher levels of radiation negatively affects abundance or behaviour in the wild.

Everaert and Bauwens do, however, make the point that their study should only be a preliminary one, for a number of reasons. Firstly, they visited locations only once so counts were not always accurate. Secondly, the study period was short, and thirdly, only the radiation from mobile phone base station antennae was measured. But most importantly, the authors say they cannot prove a relationship as this is only what they technically call a "descriptive field study" and not scientific proof. All they can say is that it "strengthens the possibility that the relationship is not a spurious one".

So let's look at some other reports to see if we can qualify this … Oops, there don't seem to be many. In fact, there appear to be only three other studies, carried out in 2005, 2007 and 2009, and all by the same author, Alphonso Balmori. His first study found that there were significant numbers of white stork nests exposed to relatively high electromagnetic radiation. Balmori concluded that electromagnetic radiation could interfere with reproduction in wild stork populations.

His second study looked at the population of house sparrows in Spain, and his third and largest study, published in 2009 and entitled "Electromagnetic pollution from phone masts. Effects on wildlife", was a peer review of all of the evidence he could find in this area. This study looked at the evidence for an effect of phone masts not only on birds, but on all wildlife. It was a very thorough investigation that came to the following conclusions: "pulsed telephony microwave radiation can produce effects especially on nervous, cardiovascular, immune and reproductive systems". The effect caused:

1. Damage to the nervous system;
2. Disruption of circadian rhythms;
3. Changes in heart rate and blood pressure;
4. Impairment of health and immunity;
5. Problems in building the nest, impaired fertility and problems with the number of eggs, embryonic development, hatching percentage and survival of chicks;
6. Genetic and developmental problems.

What was it that Balmori discovered in his research that caused him to come to these conclusions? He drew on his own research into storks back in 2005 to support his view that there was an effect, and he also quoted from the research on house sparrows in Belgium to which I referred earlier. One other report he quotes from was his Spanish study that looked at the relationship between the number of sparrows and the mean electric field strength in the area of Valladolid during the period 2002 to 2006. He also drew on observational data such as those available in the UK related to sparrows and their decline. The sparrow population in England decreased from 24 million to less than 14 million over the last thirty years, with 75% of the decline taking place between 1994 and 2002. This, Balmori concludes, coincides with the roll-out of mobile telephony. But does he have enough evidence to say that mobile telephone masts are exclusively the cause of the sparrow or stork problem? I would say that the world needs more evidence than this before the phone masts are torn down, but it does point the finger in their direction.

PHYSIOLOGICAL EFFECTS ON BIRDS

This is an area in which there is a good volume of scientific evidence as it seems that experiments are easier to conduct in the laboratory than they are in the field. Balmori draws on a number of these research studies, but in every case he uses expression such as, "current scientific evidence *indicates* that prolonged exposure to electromagnetic frequencies at levels that can be encountered in the environment *may* affect the immune system function by affecting biological processes". I have chosen to emphasise "indicates" and "may" as Balmori is not saying that there is proof, only that the tests are indications they might be true. He consistently uses words such as "looked in general", "might be involved", "studies indicate", "may have negative effects", "could become" etc. It is as if a lawyer had been through the paper very thoroughly and taken out any areas that might cause publication difficulties. When I compare Balmori's remarks with those of the scientific papers on which they are based, the same vocabulary seems to come up. No-one it seems wants to put their head on the block and say one way or another that their research confirms a fact – instead, all of the research papers use terms like "seems to indicate" and "further research is required".

One paper investigating 2,500 chick embryos showed that exposure to weak magnetic fields increased the abnormality rate in the early development of white leghorn chick embryos, but it still used the expression "can increase the abnormality" even though their studies proved that it does affect them.

EFFECT ON INSECTS

One study conducted by three Greek scientists in 2004 on the fruit fly *Drosophila melanogaster* found that a pulsed radio frequency from mobile telephones at 900 MHz modulated by the human voice decreased the reproductive capacity of the insect by 50–60%, whereas a non-modulated (non-speaking) field decreased it by 15–20%. In this experiment, the insects were exposed to the mobile phone antenna for six minutes a day during the first two or five days of their adult lives. The authors concluded that mobile phone technology has a direct effect on the gonadal development of the insects and thus its reproductive capabilities.

Why is this scary? It's because the cellular processes are largely identical in insect and mammalian cells. Can I refer you to Chapter 7 on J.C. Bose, which states that, behaviourally, plants and animals are the same? Well, you may be surprised to know that insects and animals are behaviourally the same as well. In fact, insects are shown to be more resistant to electromagnetic fields than mammals, so if something is happening in insects, it is more likely that the effect is greater in mammals, particularly with ionising electromagnetic radiation.

In the concluding paragraphs of the Greek report, the authors write that a mobile phone signal with a frequency of 217 Hz can possibly disrupt cell function, which will consequently *"affect the reproductive capacity of a living organism"* (my emphasis). Ouch! No more kids for me then. The researchers then go on to say:

> Although we cannot simply draw a parallel from our results to possible corresponding effects on humans, we think that our results imply the need for prudent avoidance of exposure to GSM [mobile communications] radiation and the cautious use of mobile phones. Because the exposure levels in our experiments are within the current IRPA–ICNIRP [International Radiation Protection Association–International Commission on Non-Ionizing Radiation Protection] exposure limits, these results possibly suggest a reconsideration of the existing exposure criteria toward a direction to include also nonthermal biological effects.

Double ouch! This article was written in 2004, and the world has obviously not paid any attention to it.

FLYING FORMATION OF BIRDS

I have always wondered how birds fly and fish swim in such tight formation. On many wildlife television programmes, I often see schools of fish in their tens of thousands swimming in amazing synchronised patterns within millimeters of other fish, yet they never seem to swim into each other. Large flocks of starlings can perform complex flying manoeuvers within five milliseconds. How can the birds, each at a different location in the flock, receive and react to signals in such a short time?

The answer was again provided by Ulrich Warnke, from his

A flock of starlings

research into the electromagnetic properties of birds and insects. He first looked at whether communication between birds was transferred by sound but found that this was not possible as "it would require more time and visual observation of a lead animal if it is blocked by other animals". He therefore conducted research based on the hypothesis that the flying manoeuvers were coordinated by electromagnetic signals:

> *Such a signal, propagating at approximately the speed of light, could reach all individuals at the same time and independent of their position. This hypothesis appears more plausible when taking into consideration that the flying animals are highly electro-statically charged.*

In his recent publication, *Birds, Bees and Mankind*, published in 2009, Warnke goes into detail as to how birds and fish manage to communicate with each other so quickly in order to coordinate their group activities – I've added emphasis to highlight what is important to my argument here:

> *We were able to record by oscilloscope that the electrical field caused by the aggregation of animals resulted in a predominantly positive overall electrostatic field ... These data allow us to conclude that flocks of small birds flying at a height of about 40 meters*

are electrically charged to more than 6 000 Volts. We can only speculate about the type of coded signals given for direction changing manoeuvers. It appears that each individual bird has a set beat frequency and amplitude that is corrected immediately it weakens, by changing the direction of flight.

Electromagnetic fields therefore have a role to play in formation flying of birds as well. They serve as orientation and navigation aids and determine the position of a single animal in the flock. Depending especially on wing width, wing span and body length, our observations and calculations show that the biophysical relationships influence the species-typical V-formation flying of flocks. Computer calculations of the flight order allow us to predict natural formation flights. And photographic records, vice-versa, also agree well with computer simulations. The observations demonstrate a unique information and orientation system of the animal kingdom. *But they also explain why this is destroyed by the interference of technically generated electrical and magnetic fields.*

So, again, nature chooses to use the electromagnetic fields emitted naturally by the earth, this time to coordinate movements between living organisms. No doubt all animals communicate using this technique in various ways – probably humans as well – but maybe we have lost touch with this ability, or we have it and don't recognise it!

My objective in this book is purely to get people to try and change the way they look at life and interpret science in ways that seem to be logical, rather than being persuaded by science that there is only one answer. In this particular chapter, I have attempted to show that the decline in bee populations is one common problem that is caused by factors affecting all wildlife, and that scientists should stop being so parochial in their solutions to these problems. If any scientists investigating the cause of bees dying out happened to read Balmori's article, maybe they would change their stance and develop hives that would protect bees from any outside effect of electromagnetic waves, thus saving the farming community and creating a new business at the same time. All that is required is to cover the bee hives with a protective metal film that stops the hive being contaminated by the external waves being transmitted to it. This would be a very simple answer to the bee problem, and one that I seriously hope will be put into practice.

INTRODUCTION TO

TECHNOLOGY

– The Invisible Invader

ARE THE BENEFITS OF OUR TECHNOLOGY REALLY WORTH THE DAMAGE THEY ARE DOING TO OUR HEALTH?

Animals, plants, humans and insects have one thing in common: they are all living organisms, and as such they will all be affected to various degrees by electromagnetic waves. This statement is sadly not universally accepted by scientists, for reasons only they can explain. However, I am pleased to say that the great juggernaut of science is finally turning towards a few research papers that are incrementally pushing the evidence towards its obvious conclusion. Electromagnetic waves affect our biological make-up, thereby proving that they are, in part, a significant factor in the exponential growth of illnesses such as diabetes, chronic fatigue, autism and multiple sclerosis.

Electromagnetic waves are the waves that you can't see but are now everywhere around us, transmitting radio signals, television signals, mobile telephone signals and wi-fi. How do we know they are there? Simply because you can now pick up a mobile telephone almost anywhere in the world and make a telephone call. Somewhere out there in the invisible landscape, a vibration is being emitted so that your mobile phone can pick up that vibration and connect with a satellite in space that will relay your message via a chain of satellites to another mobile phone half way across the world.

If each of these vibrations of electromagnetic waves were coloured so that you could see them, I would reckon that you would not be able to see very much else as they would completely cloud your vision. You would not see clear lines of trees if you were in the park, just wave after wave of coloured light coming from everyone who was carrying a mobile phone, plus all of the waves of light coming from nearby houses and offices, and not forgetting the waves being sent through the air from TV transmitters and radio transmitters. We are therefore very lucky that we cannot see these vibrational waves.

So here is the BIG dilemma, one that pains me to explain it. Unless we decide to take technology back to where we were fifty years ago, there is no possibility that anything is going to change. I, for one, am not advocating that as I am a realist. I do not see how anyone would vote for a change in technology that would ban the mobile phone and internet service or reduce the amount of satellite television being used. So of course this is not going to happen, but the price we will have to pay is also pretty terrible. I think that there is good reason to recognise and evaluate the effects, however negative, of the technology which is now part of our lives.

DIABETES

According to the World Health Organization (WHO), 30 million people across the globe in 1985 had diabetes – 0.6% of the world's population. This had increased to 171 million (2.8% of the global population) by 2000, and it is expected to more than double to 366 million (4.5% of the world's population) by 2030. Doctors attribute this rise in diabetes to poor diet and limited exercise resulting in obesity, and seldom look for causes other than lifestyle and genetics. But is this explanation good to enough to provide the answers to the following newspaper headline in 2010: "One in ten Chinese adults are diabetics, study finds"? The article went on to say, "with 92 million diabetics, China is now home to the most cases worldwide, overtaking India. The change is happening very rapidly."

There appears to be only one major cause – diet. But have the Chinese and Indian diets changed that much? Is it not possible that this diabetic catastrophe has as much to do with access to new technology as it does to the food they eat? Indeed, in the Far East, the diet has barely changed over the last century, most of the population still eating a traditional diet. Very few of them eat Western-style food with its added salt and sugar content. This is particularly true for members of the rural community in China, who survive on an income as little as $2 a day and have no access to Western-style foods. These people are suffering from diabetes at a greater rate than their urban counterparts. Unless there is evidence that their diet has changed significantly, this cannot be the exclusive reason why there is such an epidemic in new cases of the disease. There has to be another factor.

One scientific paper suggests another cause for diabetes, one which has been brought upon us all inadvertently – so-called "dirty electricity", or what I would call man-made electromagnetic fields. In a study published in the journal *Electromagnetic Biology and Medicine*, 2008, Magda Havas cites overwhelming evidence that there should be a shift in the way we look at diabetes. In addition to the current type 1 and type 2 diabetes, she suggests that there should be a third type, which is exacerbated or induced by exposure to electromagnetic frequencies. The following case studies were taken from her report, and if you are reading this and have been told you have diabetes, it should make you think very carefully about how you might be able to reduce your blood sugar level without needing to be dependent on drugs.

In a study following a 51-year-old man with type 2 diabetes over a one-week period, it was found that changes in his blood glucose levels were not related to his food intake but were directly related to his working environment. The more he worked on his computer, the more his levels rose, and the levels quickly receded as soon as he walked away from the computer. An astonishing fact, however, was that the doctor's surgery where he had his tests directly affected his diabetes levels. On entering the doctor's clinic, his blood sugar levels were tested and found to be prediabetic. Then, after sitting in the doctor's waiting area for only twenty minutes, his blood sugar level had risen to that of a type 2 diabetic. He then left the building and waited in the car park, an environment with no obvious electromagnetic fields, for a further twenty minutes. Upon measuring his levels immediately after the rest period, it was found that the glucose levels had gone back to normal. So what was in the doctor's clinic that could have made the difference? Dr Havas alleges that is was the five computers kicking out electromagnetic fields that had caused the changes. The conclusion one can draw from this is that if you are going to test a patient for diabetes, do it in an electromagnetically clean environment to prevent misdiagnosis and to accurately determine the severity of the disease.

A second experiment involved a 57-year-old woman with type 2 diabetes who was taking no medication for her diabetes yet managed to control her plasma glucose levels simply by exercise and a strict diet. In this study, she was tested throughout the day. The results showed that exercising by walking caused her blood sugar levels to drop from a mean of 11.8 to 7.2 mmol/L. However, if she practised the same amount of walking on an exercise machine, her blood sugar levels actually rose from 10 to 11.7 mmol/L. What could have caused this? It is suggested the large electrical motor used to generate the moving tread kicked out such a large electromagnetic field that it caused the blood sugar level to rise. How ironic that doctors recommend exercise for patients thinking that it will always help them – if this exercise is carried out indoors, on a running machine, it seems it will in fact have completely the opposite effect. So if you have diabetes, do not go to a gym with a high number of electrically powered exercise machines as the gym environment could be doing you enough damage to outweigh the positive effects of the exercise.

Another study was conducted on a 28-year-old man with type 2 diabetes who found it very difficult to reduce his blood sugar levels despite the fact that he was taking medication three times a day. In an attempt to reduce his levels, he introduced four GS filters into his home. GS filters are an invention that supposedly reduces the amount of electromagnetism in a localised area, such as your living room or bedroom; they simply plug into the socket. Within three days of introducing these filters into his home, the man's blood sugar levels dropped significantly to an amount that he not been able to achieve using just medication.

What I believe these case studies show, quite clearly, is that environmental factors play a significant role in the likely causes of illnesses, particularly diabetes. If one thing is to be learned from the studies described here, it is that we should all immediately go out and buy a pack of GS filters and stick them in our homes. After reading Havas's article, it was the first thing I did, and I now have them in every room at home. In one of my offices, the reading went down from 240 to 40 GS units as soon as I put the filter in. The office has five computers – I had never thought about them before, but as soon as I observed the change in the filter reading, it awakened my thoughts on how large and prevalent these types of waves are.

Anecdotal success of GS filters has been shown in one school in Wisconsin that was supposedly diagnosed with "sick building syndrome", whatever that encompassed. According to the district nurse, once the GS filters were installed, only three of the thirty-seven students in the school who used inhalers on a daily basis subsequently required their inhalers, and then they only needed them for exercise-induced asthmas. GS filters were also placed in a school in Toronto, and approximately 50% of the teachers documented an improvement in their own energy, performance, mood and/or health in a single-blind study. Student behaviour, especially at the elementary level, also improved. The symptoms that changed were the ones we associate with attention deficit disorder (ADD) and attention deficit hyperactivity disorder (ADHD).

Following on from her studies on diabetes, Havas then investigated whether electromagnetic fields had an effect on other illnesses. It was not much of a surprise that the few case studies that she completed showed similar results to those for diabetes. In one study on multiple sclerosis, a teacher in Wisconsin suffered from double vision, cognitive difficulties and memory issues. She managed to persuade her school to introduce GS filters, and within days her symptoms disappeared. Havas attempted to analyse other people with multiple sclerosis, with similar positive results. One man aged twenty-seven noticed improvements within twenty-four hours and steadily improved over the following weeks. He suffered from common symptoms of multiple sclerosis: he could not walk without the use of an aid, he had tremors, and he suffered from exceptional tiredness. Three days after he installed GS filters in his home, the study discovered that his symptoms had begun to disappear, only returning when he went shopping in the local centre. The symptoms then disappeared three hours after he had rested at home within the confines of the GS filters.

If these case studies are to be believed, what other illnesses is electromagnetic radiation causing? What are the most recent increases in illnesses that are occurring in the West besides those in multiple sclerosis and diabetes? Two illnesses that I personally am aware of are chronic fatigue/fibromyalgia and hay fever. The prevalence of these two illnesses is growing at a rate similar to that suggested for diabetes by the WHO. Could they be all related to the same problem – dirty electricity? If this is the case, surely the governing bodies know about it and have the situation under control. Well, yes and no. The WHO is aware that appliances emit low-level electromagnetic pollution but believes this to be at such a low level as to be insignificant. However, I believe the WHO needs to change its attitude very soon, as more and more scientific studies are reporting biological and health effects associated with electromagnetic pollution well below WHO guidelines.

Studies so far that show a direct link between electromagnetic pollution and heath include the following:

Author	Biological effects
Ahlborn (2000)	Greater risk of childhood leukaemia
Havas (2000)	Greater risk of various cancers after occupational exposure to low-frequency electrical and magnetic fields
Li et al. (2002)	Miscarriage
Neutra (2002)	Lou Gehrig's disease
Kundi et al. (2004)	Brain tumours associated with mobile phone use
Alpeter et al. (1995), Michelozzi et al. (2002)	Cancers and symptoms of electrical hypersensitivity (for people living near mobile phone and broadcast antennae)
Liburdy et al. (1993)	Laboratory studies reporting an increased proliferation of human breast cancer cells
Lai and Singh (2005)	Single- and double-strand DNA breaks
Blackman et al. (1985)	Changes in calcium flux
Havas (2008)	Changes in plasma glucose level leading to diabetes

I am not the only person to suggest that there has not been enough research in this field – many scientists believe this too. In a paper that reviewed all of the recent research in this area, the conclusion was that the "literature is scant ... The health effects of this type of exposure on epidemiological research on biological and health effects are lacking even though human exposure is actually increasing." Quite! So why is more not being done? In a paper written in 2001 that looked at the effects of electric and magnetic fields at the frequency of 50 and 60 Hz – that of electricity – the conclusion was that "the current data available do not show that these fields can be dangerous for health. More particularly, no consistent and conclusive proof shows that residential exposure to electric and magnetic fields can be responsible for cancer, undesirable neurobehavioral effects, or effects on reproduction or development. Five years later, no new data has been published to change this position."

In a study in 2008 that reviewed all of the papers written on the subject and used a meta-analytic technique to assess the statistical likelihood of cherry-picked papers, the authors concluded that "this review showed that the large majority of individuals who claim to be able to detect low level EMF [electromagnetic fields] are not able to do so under double-blind conditions. If such individuals exist, they represent a small minority and have not been identified yet." I was not sure whether to laugh or cry at this study.

Another paper, written in 2010 by psychiatrists in London, concludes after having reviewed all the scientific papers that "despite the conviction of EMF sufferers that their symptoms are triggered by exposure to EMF fields, repeated experiments have been unable to replicate this phenomenon under controlled conditions ... there is no robust evidence to support the theory that exposure to EMF is responsible for triggering symptoms". I find this surprising. To me, it is saying that no matter what scientific papers you read, even if they have been conducted in the most professional way using perfectly executed double-blind studies, you can simply ignore as wrong any reported fact that there is a relationship.

So, of course, I had to search out this particular paper to see how many studies the authors had included in their bibliography and then analyse all of these studies to try to see how they came to their conclusion. On reading the paper, the reason soon became apparent. Remember that the paper was written by psychiatrists, so it was of no surprise that, hidden away in the document, they admitted that, in all the studies, "we did not extract data concerning EEG measurements, blood chemistry results or objectively measured cognitive function". Of course they didn't as they were psychiatrists; what was the point of them looking for results showing actual physical changes in the body? No, they only looked at changes that were psychological in nature.

This is all very strange because, after I had read this article, I went looking for papers that researched the 50 and 60 Hz frequency levels. These are the levels that are used in electricity in both the US and the UK. The first paper I found was from 1982, and this looked at the effects of a 60 Hz frequency on bone growth in rats. Its conclusion was clearly that the rats exposed to a field of 60 Hz showed throughout their life "enhanced bone growth in the long bones causing increased length and mass". Did the government not put two and two together? – they know that you can repair human bones using electrical currents as the process is used commonly in hospitals around the world, so it should be no surprise that exposure to certain Hz levels can cause bone growth in different animals at different frequencies. Wouldn't it be beneficial if they treated all individual animals differently and tried to find out which animals were affected at this exposure as not all animals are the same? Then, when they conducted their experiments, they should not be working solely on rats but on a cluster of different animals to prove that different animals behave differently in response to the same frequency.

I then found a study showing that people were highly allergic to a wide range of electromagnetic fields. This study, conducted in 1991, reported that a group of patients who were exposed to a variety of different frequencies reacted to them in the following numbers: 75% reacted to 1 Hz, 69% to 2.5 Hz, 69% to 5 Hz, 69% to 10 Hz, 69% to 20 Hz and 69% to 10 KHz, and many reacted to the 50 and 60 Hz levels that the US government had analysed. The conclusion was that, for any given individual, susceptibility to electrical frequencies may develop at any frequency, and produce reactions.

The symptoms of the exposure were neurological (tingling, sleepiness, headache, dizziness, unconsciousness), musculoskeletal (pain, tightness, spasm, fibrillation), cardiovascular (palpitations, flushing, tachycardia, oedema), oral/respiratory (pressure in the ears, dental pains, tightness in the chest, shortness of breath), gastrointestinal (nausea, belching) and dermal (itching, burning, prickling pain). Two of the patients had such a severe reaction (unconsciousness and severe itching) to the weak fields and short exposure time that they were given intravenous vitamin C, magnesium and oxygen to remedy the prolonged and delayed reactions. To me, this underlines the fact that the body reacts in a myriad of different ways to the same thing.

There were approximately twenty-five completely different reactions to electromagnetic waves from a variety of different wavelengths, producing a complete variety of reactions. As most experiments do not list all of these reactions and just look for one specific outcome, it is probably no surprise that they do not find what they are looking for and do not show what is actually happening. If these patients could not tell us what was wrong, how many reactions would it be possible to see from cutting them up and testing their blood changes or bone sizes – I would suggest none. So it is vital that more experiments are done on humans rather than animals to ascertain the effects of low-level waves.

One point raised was that the same person can react to different frequencies at different times depending upon the medications they are taking. One patient with asthma was sensitive to high-power voltage lines as well as low-voltage house wiring, experiencing muscle spasms in the head, neck, arms and legs. This patient was also sensitive to dust, weeds, dust mites and some foods. He reacted in tests to 2.5 and 60 Hz and 5 and 50 KHz with tightness in the chest. He then received an antigen shot to neutralise his hypersensitivity reactions. Five months later, he was completely unreactive to any electromagnetic frequency.

SCIENTIFIC CONFUSION

Maybe the problem in researching the negative effects of electromagnetism is that scientists are confused. This whole area is controversial because there is a fundamental misunderstanding of the underlying science. It is not true that if you plug a cable in and wrap it around your body, this will give you cancer or cure your cancer. Why would it; what has it got to do with cancer? It would be just as likely to cause tooth decay or be the cause of the common cold. Perhaps wrapping yourself in these cables might affect the body in some way but not in the ways that the scientists are investigating. The cables, I believe, are more likely to affect the body at the level of diabetes rather than cancer, but research grants are focused on cancer rather than on diabetes.

Why would you conclude that if an experiment failed to create cancer, all forms of electrical stimulation were safe? As one science paper in 2007 said, "discrepancies in this field reflect the variability in the magnetic field strengths and frequencies that have been applied to these models, thus results between studies are hard to compare". Of most importance to me personally was their discovery that "our findings indicate that matrix dynamics and cell metabolism/energy balance are processes which are affected by the electromagnetic field application". If you recall from the book's Introduction, I became interested in all of these things because my son had chronic fatigue syndrome, and this fatigue can be referred to as an energy imbalance. If these scientists are to be believed, it could be that the low-level electromagnetic fields being kicked out by all sorts of electrical apparatus are causing the elevated levels of chronic fatigue that we are seeing throughout the world. If such machines affected the cells' ability to produce mitochondria, which create the energy that the body can use, it would mean that the body was not creating enough energy. What an alarming possibility, that my son's illness, and all his and our family's suffering, could have been caused by technology!

MOBILE PHONE TECHNOLOGY

So do mobile telephones cause ill health? The International Commission on Non-Ionizing Radiation Protection, the International Committee on Electromagnetic Safety (ICES) and the WHO are assuring us that there is no proven health risk and that the present safety limits protect all mobile phone users. However, a study in 2010 reviewed the underlying science and concluded that it was not much use for drawing such conclusions. It suggested that the majority of the evidence had come from in vitro laboratory studies, which are of very limited use for determining real-life health risk. It also alleged that there was a lack of human volunteer studies that would demonstrate whether the human body responded at all to mobile phone radiation. The authors believe that the available scientific evidence is insufficient to prove the reliability of the current safety standards. Therefore, they recommend "to use precaution when dealing with mobile phones and whenever possible and feasible, to limit body exposure to this radiation".

An earlier study, by Stopczyk in 2005, had already shown that 900 MHz electromagnetic fields produced by mobile phone masts affected the activity of elements within the human blood platelets, which are involved in blood clotting. This report concluded that the "oxidative stress associated with exposure to microwaves may be the reason for many adverse changes in the cell and may cause a number of systemic disturbances in the human body".

A conference in Italy arranged by the International Commission for Electromagnetic Safety (ICEMS) in 2006 suggested the following solutions to help solve the problems caused by our electronic pollution. (For a list of the scientists who signed their name to this paper, take a minute to look at the bibliography in the ICEMS paper and in this book). I have quoted the first five points here as they make alarming reading.

1. More evidence has accumulated suggesting that there are adverse health effects from occupational and public exposures to electric, magnetic, and electromagnetic fields, or EMF1, at current exposure levels. What is needed, but not yet realized, is a comprehensive, independent, and transparent examination of the evidence pointing to this emerging, potential public health issue.

2. Resources for such an assessment are grossly inadequate despite the explosive growth of technologies for wireless communications as well as the huge ongoing investment in power transmission.

3. There is evidence that present sources of funding bias the analysis and interpretation of research findings towards rejection of evidence of possible public health risks.

4. Arguments that weak (low intensity) EMF cannot affect biological systems do not represent the current spectrum of scientific opinion.

5. Based on our review of the science, biological effects can occur from exposures to both extremely low frequency fields (ELF EMF) and radiation frequency fields (RF EMF). Epidemiological and in vivo as well as in vitro experimental evidence demonstrates that exposure to some ELF EMF can increase cancer risk in children and induce other health problems in both children and adults. Further, there is accumulating epidemiological evidence indicating an increased brain tumor risk from long-term use of mobile phones, the first RF EMF that has started to be comprehensively studied. Epidemiological and laboratory studies that show increased risks for cancers and other diseases from occupational exposures to EMF cannot be ignored.

This conference took place in 2006 and several years have now passed. Their advice has apparently fallen on deaf ears.

HUMAN INFERTILITY

There have been a few studies on the relationship between cell phone use and semen quality in recent years. One investigation measured the level of semen of three hundred and fifty men who were attending an infertility clinic and divided them up into four different groups depending upon their hourly usage of mobile telephones per day. The results showed that a greater use of mobiles diminished semen quality by decreasing the sperm count. The authors concluded that mobile phones play a role in male infertility, the mechanisms behind which are completely unknown.

This conclusion was backed up by an earlier study on three hundred and seventy-one men showing that the prolonged use of cell phones may have negative effects on sperm motility characteristics. Again, the men involved in the study were attending an infertility clinic. The research concluded there were significant decreases in the proportion of rapidly progressive motile sperm with increases in the daily transmission time of the phones.

Are these two tests not of major significance for us all? As soon as I started this line of enquiry, I told my teenage children to reduce their mobile phone usage if they planned on having children. Although the research did not go on to claim that the sperm level goes back to normal after reducing the amount of usage on the mobile phones, I hope for my sons' sake it is not a permanent affect as they are on the phone all the time.

These findings suggest that a high number of men will have great problems in fathering a child due to the widespread use of mobile phones. *In the UK alone, the sperm count has fallen by 29% over the last decade.* Mobile phone usage is not the only suggested cause of a low sperm count – other reasons such as weight, stress, smoking and pollution have also been put forward as a cause of this condition. What worries me most, though, is that unless you happened to read a newspaper on the days following the release of the studies mentioned here, you would not be aware of this danger. Could there have been a more urgent call for action than this in any scientific paper? The clear implication is that unless we get rid of mobile phones, they will have a damaging affect on our biological make-up.

Strangely, for such an important document, this research paper was very hard to find. I only came across it by accident while searching for other documents relating to birds. There are very few references to it, and I could not find even one newspaper that had picked up on the story. This is probably due to the fact that the article in question was printed in the magazine *Pathophysiology*, which I doubt is on many journalists' reading lists.

THE EFFECT ON PLANTS AND ANIMALS OF ELECTROMAGNETIC WAVES

In the following few pages, I am going to run briefly through the many scientific experiments that have investigated the effect of electromagnetic fields on plants and animals, look at what is happening and try to work out why we have not been told by our governments that this is a problem for our health. If plants and animals are affected, we as living organisms are also going to be affected.

Much of what I am going to be talk about is based upon the size of the frequency, or, to put it another way, the size of the vibration and how fast it is vibrating – low-pitched sounds vibrate slowly, and high-pitched sounds vibrate quickly. To put it into perspective, a frequency of 1 Hz (cycles per second) is very, very slow, and a 1 kilohertz (KHz) is a frequency 1,000 times faster than a 1 Hz one. Signals that come in from space emitted by distant planets are often in the very low-frequency band, such as 60 Hz. The light that we pick up via our eyes is in the range of 400–790 terahertz (THz, with 1 THz being a million million Hz), that is, many millions of times faster than the slow waves from space. Microwaves range in frequency between 300 million Hz (300 megahertz, written as 300 MHz) and 300 billion Hz (300 gigahertz, or 300 GHz).

But what effect, if any, are these waves having on our bodies? The problem for science has been the lack of information on the mechanism by which microwaves influence our biological systems. The standard view is that microwaves only have one effect on living organisms and that is via heat. So if you can measure the change in heat in the living organism and discover that this is small to negligible, you will be perfectly happy in the knowledge that the microwave will have no effect on the biological living organism. If, however, you were to show that there is another effect on the living organism apart from heating, a detrimental effect, this could open up another huge area of research, one that could show how potentially damaging the microwave could be.

Prior to the 21st century, there had been very few investigations into the effects of radio and microwave frequencies on plants. Most of these had been carried out in the 1960s and were based on the science of increasing crop growth via improved germination, but the results were not significant enough for scientists to pursue the matter further. This area of science I have covered in the section on how to increase plant growth via vibrations (see Chapter 4). To summarise that section quickly, the reason why all of the early experiments failed was because the scientists did not understand the basic principles of botany, in that every plant is different and if you attempt to put one frequency out to multiple plants and expect them all to react the same, your results will be completely inaccurate. It is like playing rock music to a hundred people all aged one, two, three, four, up to one hundred years old and asking them for their reaction– they will obviously be different. It's a similar situation with plants.

In 2005, researchers set out to investigate the effect of electromagnetic waves of 400, 900 and 1900 MHz on the growth pattern of the plant duckweed. In this experiment at least, they attempted to utilise three different wavelengths to see what the reaction would be. It is not surprising that the three different wavelengths had a different effect – certain frequencies will affect the plant more than others simply because it has its own natural vibrational level. If, for instance, the plant naturally vibrates at a level of 300 Hz, the electromagnetic wave that is closest to this value will cause the plant to react more than the one furthest from it.

In this duckweed experiment, the scientists played around with three variables: the strength of the signals, the time that the plants were exposed to them and the actual frequency themselves. The outcome was that some combinations of these parameters caused the plants to slow their growth levels significantly, whereas others caused no significant decrease. Most of the changes in the plants were very small –around only the 10% mark – and in scientific terms this is not significant. My problem here is that I would like to know how long the experiments lasted and what long-term effects this original small 10% had on the plant. In this experiment, the test ran for a whopping twenty-four hours, yes that's all, just a day. The experiment was looking at short-term changes that could be measured, and even with such a short-term exposure, the plants were affected. So why did the researchers not look for long-term changes in the plants, say over a few years. Is this of no interest to us?

A review of the bio-effects of microwaves in 2002 looked at scientific evidence for the effects of microwaves and found that, in plants, the microwaves "athermally induced different biological effects by changing the structures by differentially partitioning the ions, altering the rate and or direction of biochemical reactions". Since 2002, there have been many different scientific papers reporting on microwave irradiation. Why? – because it is big business. Many people have discovered that if you zap fruit and vegetables with specific frequencies and wave shapes of microwaves, it is possible to increase the products' shelf life so that the fruit or veg will stay fresh longer on supermarket shelves. This process of decreasing the growth rate of yeast through microwave radiation was known as far back as 1994 when Dardanoni reduced the growth rate of the yeast *Candida albicans* by 15% and increased its growth by 25% by using different continuous radiation levels.

HUMANS

More worryingly, Pakhomov in 2001 found that the human body absorbs significantly more electromagnetic radiation when the frequency exceeds about 15 MHz. The absorption rate varies for different parts of the body, as it should, as each organ vibrates at a unique frequency, and the microwave will only affect those which are stimulated by that specific microwave signal. The heart, for instance, might vibrate at a level that is affected at 10 MHz, whereas the liver could be affected by a frequency of, say, 24 MHz. In the frequency range of 70–100 MHz, the range over which television and FM radio is broadcast, the human body acts as an efficient radiation antenna absorbing these wavelengths. So we are all human TV and radio receptors. Pretty worrying if you suspect that being bombarded by TV signals all day every day can't be doing our bodies any good at all.

In 1993, Belyaev found that microwave radiation can in fact have a genetic effect by affecting the chromosomal DNA in living cells. And already in 1959, Heller and Teixeira-Pinto had reported results showing that low-power microwave radiation could produce mutations in mammalian cells in insects. In the 1960s and 70s, researchers showed that DNA and the protein RNA, which is involved in, among other things, making new DNA and proteins, absorbed 65–75 GHz radiation, and that microwaves were able to interfere with repair mechanisms or even to induce gene mutations in bacteria.

These studies looked at fast frequencies at the microwave level, but what about the low-level frequencies? Do they affect us as well? If they do, it seems most sensible to assume that all wavelengths have an effect on our bodies – some neutral, some positive and some negative. Back in 1910, Bose showed that plants are responsive to all wavelengths, and if plants are 100% behaviourally identical to animals (see Chapter 7), it follows that animals will be responsive to all wavelengths as well.

In 2009, pioneering work by scientists in Canada showed that humans are affected by very weak electromagnetic waves with a frequency as low as 500 Hz. They studied the effect that low-level waves had on brain activity and discovered that after only five minutes of exposure, the brain's activity changed. The difference between this study and previous ones was that it was attempting to show that low-level microwaves had an effect while the subjects in the experiment were at rest. The researchers found that the pulsed magnetic waves altered the human electroencephalogram (EEG) at rest specifically within the 8–13 Hz range.

RATS

Most laboratory work is conducted using rats, and that on microwave radiation is no exception. There have been several studies on the behaviour of rats exposed to different levels of irradiation. A very early paper in 1997 looked at the effect that microwave radiation had on rats' body temperature. Now, this is a very important experiment as one of the major fears of microwave technology is that it will raise the body temperature as if we were all being cooked in a microwave oven. This is the measure that those in power have studied in order to assess the safe levels to which humans can be exposed. So the first experiments conducted were a means to establish levels of microwave radiation that were safe for human use. Of course, in order to change those levels, major new scientific studies would have to be carried out to prove that the levels were set too high. As you have probably read, not many studies are being conducted, so it is very unlikely that the levels first established will be changed without significant political will to do so.

So do rats heat up under exposure to microwave irradiation? The 1997 study showed that earlier tests at 700 MHz, a faster signal, resulted in little heat increase, but when the rats were exposed to radiation of about half that amount, 300 MHz, the heart rate, body temperature and blood pressure were significantly elevated. These levels are referred to as sub-resonance exposures. Most studies on microwave radiation have investigated the thermal effect of microwave radiation, and almost all of the studies are looking at the effect that this has on cancer. As I said, very little work is being done on the non-thermal effects on the immune system. The National Research Council examined these non-thermal effects and stated that:

> *the connections among the various experimental findings and the theoretical constructs do not yet lead to a comprehensive conceptual structure for the reported phenomena sufficient to enable an evaluation of the significance of the theories.*

So it is going to be hard to change their opinion, much more research will be needed.

One early study that the National Research Council looked at and is frequently referred to was conducted in 1996 and considered the reproductive effect of chronic microwave radiation. This study gave the rats a huge blast of microwave radiation for one hour every day up to fifty-two days. The level was as high as 9,450 MHz. Compare that with the previous experiment of 300 MHz and you will appreciate how high that is. It was not surprising to learn that these massive exposures to microwave radiation significantly reduced the rats' ability to reproduce. It was these and similar studies that guided the authorities to make sure that workers were not exposed to high levels of radiation, and it was primarily this fear, rather than the fear of low-level radiation, that affected the authorities' decision to create their safe levels of exposure.

One study that was published in 2009 by researchers in India showed that chronic exposure to 2,450 MHz radiation altered the thyroid hormone levels and behaviour of male rats. It demonstrated that, following chronic exposure, the rats were hyperactive and aggressive, and a change was shown in the blood levels of the thyroid hormones T3 and T4, which had been shown in previous experiments to have a relationship to aggression. The result is much more significant when you consider that these lower levels of radiation affect the levels of thyroid hormones as well as the emotional reactivity of the rats. The question is, how low can the microwave levels go before they stop affecting the thyroid gland? If they affect the gland at 2,450 MHz, maybe they also affect them at 24.5 Hz but more gradually. Another study in 2009 did in fact look at lower levels and found that long-term exposure to frequencies as low as 915 MHz caused "increased damage in blood leukocytes of the exposed rats".

POSSIBLE TREATMENTS TO ALLEVIATE THE EFFECTS OF ELECTROMAGNETIC FORCES

The then-editor of the influential magazine *Electromagnetic Biology and Medicine*, A. Liboff, wrote an introduction to a conference held in 2007 into new ideas in this field. In the April conference held at the University of Bologna, a set of scientific papers investigated the effects, if any, of a new device called the SEQEX. Interestingly, the reason for the scientific community trying this product was that the manufacturer had sent them a free sample – it was this simple piece of marketing that encouraged the scientific community to look at its potential. This machine utilises one key piece of technology, ion cyclotron resonance, which is used to accelerate charged particles, or ions.

Eleven papers were presented at the conference. One looked at the side effects of chemotherapy and found that applying extremely low-frequency electromagnetic fields using the SEQEX machine reduced the body's oxidative stress and thus alleviated the side effect of chemotherapy. When combined with a diet rich in antioxidant agents, further improvements occurred. Other papers showed that a treatment using the SEQEX reduced levels of cholesterol; it also improved keratoconus, a non-inflammatory degenerative disorder of the cornea that mainly affects young people; it stabilised cholesterol level and blood pressure; it caused improvements in autism; it improved the treatment of non-cystoid macular oedema diabetic disease; it reduced pain in rheumatoid arthritis, arthritis and osteoporosis; and it stabilised muscular sclerosis and chronic pulmonary disease.

I want to quote from one of the papers as, having been aware of the pain that parents suffer from having autistic children, I was completely overwhelmed by the results of one of the studies that showed amazing results for eight children suffering from autism:

Within the first five treatments, the children had accentuated the stereotypes and showed internal hyper stimulation with elimination of great amounts of parasites. Parents reported finding in the faeces something like "colourful leaves". All the children produced smelly faeces, urines of darker colour, also very smelly. But nearly all seemed to demonstrate more attention and interest in their surroundings. Within ten therapies, and re-programming the therapeutic cards, the children substantially changed the relationship with their relatives. At school, the teachers said that the children were unrecognizable. The physical therapist, the speech pathologist and the doctors who aided with psycho-linguistic rehabilitation found many changes. Three of the eight began to relate with their school friends and to go to the toilet by themselves. The stereotypes had diminished and the children demonstrated interest for games differently from the obsessive way they had done before.

All of the children showed less opposition to their parents and followed orders with little or no difficulty. One key indicator

*was the comments by mothers. They told of the improvements
obtained with phrases such as: "now my son is a child, I did not
know what he was before" or "my son has re-awakened, now
he begins to have contacts with the world", etc.*

*The greatest surprise was tied to a series of contemporary
events: Three children had therapy scheduled in the same day.
All had had a complete stop of language from the time they
were three or four years old. All had begun the ion cyclotron
resonance therapy at the same time as they were being treated
at a speech rehabilitation center. All three children began to
speak at the same time, expressing some words in the same
day after an identical number of therapies (five). Two of them
constructed some phrases following the fifteenth treatment.
This observation concerning an apparent synchronous response
in these three patients suggests that the dose dependence and/
or timing of the treatments is quite critical.*

Another group of scientists at the Institute of Biological Medicine
in Milan reported their experience using the SEQEX machine over
a five-year period by publishing three case studies. Two of the cases
involved multiple sclerosis, and one heart disease. They found that
using the SEQEX device improved the symptoms of the patients
with multiple sclerosis and reduced the inflammation of the patient
with heart obstructions. The studies only lasted six weeks, with two
treatments every week for six weeks. Imagine if the researchers had
treated the patients over a longer period – maybe the machine could
have significantly helped them even further.

The bad news is that the SEQEX machine is available only in
Italy. Why is this so? Why do some Western medical authorities feel
that they have superior knowledge compared with others and ban
the use of proven successful products? Over one hundred Italian
medical institutions are using the SEQEX machine to treat patients.
Are we saying that these trained doctors are wrong, that the scientific

studies are inaccurate? Or are we hiding behind the fact that the trials are too small or some other such nonsense to withhold this machine from a wider audience?

The Havas study on diabetes, and other similar reports, highlights many issues. One sad fact that seems to come out of these is the idea that there is only one solution to any medical problem, and that is the one described in all the medical textbooks that doctors read at university. If an idea is not listed there, the chances of doctors being able to change their attitudes seem to be very slim. But those textbooks patently do not provide all the answers.

I will always remember watching the TV film *Super Size Me*. This was a documentary film based on an experiment in which, for a month, the reporter ate a diet of food bought exclusively from McDonalds. At the beginning of the film, he went to his local doctor to have various biological parameters measured, while the doctor merrily chatted to him about his upcoming project. At no point, does the doctor seem aware of the damage to the body that eating a diet of sugary, salty and fatty foods can have. During the early days of the film, the reporter has regular check-ups, and after only a very short period of time, about three weeks, the doctor tells him that he has to cancel the experiment immediately as his body has responded so quickly to the new diet that his organs face malfunctioning. This was a very dramatic part of the film, but it highlighted to me how limited the medical establishment is in terms of the effect food has on us. Now, if they are unaware of this fundamental understanding related to food, there is absolutely no chance that they will be aware of the damage that electromagnetic forces cause in our bodies. It clearly reinforces my belief that doctors lack a significant understanding of how the body works and are very slow to change to any new ideas.

Depressingly, there is very little difference between the previous chapter on bees and this chapter. Most research is going down similar safe paths to find cures for illnesses, apparently looking for a single smoking gun. In studies on autism and chronic fatigue, scientists seem to be searching for a faulty gene or a specific virus. As I have frequently mentioned, I believe this is a complete waste of time because the scientists are not looking at the bigger picture. How can the exponential growth in illnesses such as autism and diabetes be due to a gene issue that has seemingly just appeared in our biological make-up? It is more likely that something in our environment is causing these dormant genes to re-ignite themselves and play an active role in our health rather than being the passive players they previously were.

My dream would be to set up a charity that investigated these illnesses in a completely new way, one that was based on the evidence and not on the rigged structures of peer-reviewed papers that require fellow scientists to decide whether one's research is worthy of funding. I believe that a new set of charities should be developed to spend money on investigating alternative methods of treatment so that machines like the SEQEX can be made available to everyone rather than just those who live in Italy. If these charities obtained funding, patients suffering from illnesses such as autism, chronic fatigue, diabetes and muscular sclerosis might have a chance of finding some relief or cure for their illness. I wait in hope.

INTRODUCTION TO

SIR J.C. BOSE

– A forgotten genius

" *Bose's whole book abounds in interesting
matter skilfully woven together, and would be
recommended as of great value, if it did not
continually arouse our incredulity*"

COMPARATIVE-ELECTRO-PHYSIOLOGY –
NATURE, MARCH 8, 1908

How is it possible that the man who spent thirty years working on revolutionary science had his books published worldwide and is publicly recognised eighty years later as the real inventor of radio technology, before Marconi, yet he is still relatively unknown? There are probably very few people in science today who recognise the name of Sir Jagadis Chandra Bose.

So why am I dedicating a whole chapter to a man few have ever heard of, who died over seventy years ago and whose books are hardly read or studied? Or more to the point, why have we forgotten about a man who was famous in his day, whose science was recognised around Europe and whose lecture tours were sold out? Why did the machines that he invented, which could magnify the growth of plants by a factor of ten million, disappear along with his existence? (His machines literally made it possible to watch a plant grow in front of your eyes.) Well, the reason I have written about him in such great detail is simply because I have read his books and been astounded by his discoveries. I have waded through thousands of pages of scientific experiments and become dazzled by the new ideas I found there. These proven scientific ideas are so important to our basic understanding of how living organisms behave that it really beggars belief that Bose has not been given the fame and recognition he deserves. So if you want to know how plants and animals behave at the most fundamental level, you have to read this chapter.

BRIEF HISTORY

In order to show how remarkable Bose's ideas were, I have decided that it is relevant to describe his upbringing and the social and economic barriers he came up against. It is important to remember that he was born and educated in India at a time when it was part of the British Empire. I have a good general knowledge of the history of India because one of my hobbies involves collecting certain antique objects that were made there at the beginning of the 18th century. India was a country in which the English dominated and all of the key jobs were created for and by the English. However, as India was so big, local Indians were needed to run parts of the civil service, the bureaucratic element needed to run the country. I have read examination papers that the Indians had to pass in order to become eligible for one of these civil service jobs, and I can promise you that these tests are more rigorous than any examination questions I have ever seen at degree level. In order to pass, a candidate had to be incredibly well educated and obviously be fluent in English. Therefore, while you might think that India was a very poor and backward country in the 19th century, which was probably true for a large proportion of its citizens, the select few who managed to achieve a good education were as sophisticated as anyone educated in the developed nations.

Bose was born into a middle-class family of five sisters and two brothers. His father, Bhagwan Chandra Bose, was headmaster of a local school and later became a deputy magistrate. His mother came from an aristocratic family. When Jagadis Bose was ten years old, he was sent to St Xavier's College in Calcutta, a school for Europeans and Anglo-Indians, and it was there that he developed his knowledge of English and science. He was a first-class student, and when he finished school, he applied to Calcutta University, passing the exams with distinction, and for his reward he was given a scholarship on the science course. Having completed his degree, he applied for a degree in science at Cambridge University, UK, where again he won a scholarship in natural science at Christ's College, Cambridge.

In a country where all things were run and dominated by the

English, science was no exception. The one institution that was of sufficient merit for Bose to return to was the Imperial Educational Service, a scientific institution aimed at scientific teaching and research, but it was only possible to work there if you were British. Luckily for Bose, on his return to India following his degrees, he was furnished with a letter of recommendation that was passed onto Lord Ripon, Viceroy of India, who forced the education authorities to accept Bose. He was subsequently employed by the Imperial Educational Service, albeit at one-third of the salary of British employees. In defiance of these terms, Bose refused to accept the payment and for a number of years was paid nothing. It was not until three years later that he was put on an equal footing to the British employees and received full pay for his work. He was by then a full professor.

It was the discovery of electromagnetic waves by the German scientist Heinrich Hertz in 1887 that really started the remarkable chain of events that led Bose to make his initial major discoveries. This discovery eventually led us to discover most of the ideas that we take for granted now, such as the radio, X-rays and microwaves. At the time, however, Hertz himself did not realise the significance of his discoveries:

> It's of no use whatsoever ... this is just an experiment that proves Maestro Maxwell was right – we just have these mysterious electromagnetic waves that we cannot see with the naked eye. But they are there.

Asked about the ramifications of his discoveries, Hertz replied:

> Nothing, I guess.

Other scientists, however, could see the implications of his discoveries, including Popov in Russia, Marconi in Italy as well as J.C. Bose in India.

Bose must have been a very frustrated man when he read about Hertz's discoveries. There he was, teaching in the finest institution in India, but an institution with no means to reproduce Hertz's experiments. There was simply no apparatus available for Bose to conduct his own similar experiments. But this did not deter him; in fact, it drove him to develop his own unique apparatus, equipment that would be far more advanced than any other in his field of research.

Initially, in order to conduct experiments into electromagnetic waves, he had to find a room in which to carry out experiments within the college. Bose knew that he had spare space in a room that adjoined a bathroom at the Presidency College where he was teaching. He ascertained that this was an empty room so he surreptitiously converted it into his own small laboratory for the sole use of his team in order to investigate electromagnetic waves. A local tinsmith was employed to manufacture apparatus designed by Bose that would allow him to make electrical waves. These new invisible rays could then be measured and detected at a distance by a receiver.

The significance of what Bose discovered the following year was monumental. He showed that waves could be sent from one area and could travel through the air to be collected at some considerable distance from their source. It was as if someone had discovered a magical invisible force. It did not take long for him to go public with his discoveries, and a year after creating the laboratory he gave the first public demonstration of his invisible rays in 1895, two years before Marconi was granted his patent for radio waves.

Bose's experiment showed that electromagnetic waves could pass through walls. He set up the wave emitter in one room and the wave detector in another room twenty-five metres further down the corridor; the waves could be picked up clearly in the second room. Bose demonstrated that the waves could dramatically travel not only through walls, but also through the body of the Lieutenant Governor. The dramatic success of this display to his fellow professionals led to a public demonstration at the town hall in Calcutta in the presence of Sir Alexander McKenzie, the Lieutenant Governor of Bengal. He was so impressed with Bose's experiment that he agreed to give him extra funding to continue further research in this new science.

These two demonstrations remain important in the history of radio because they were the earliest demonstrations of radio waves travelling over a long distance. The experiments must have seemed amazing to the public watching them as Bose was able to turn on the electromagnetic waves in one area of the demonstration, and then, as if by magic, a bell would ring at a completely separate location from where he was standing. It was the first remote control device that was demonstrated publicly. He also set up a demonstration purely for dramatic effect that he knew would cause a public sensation. Using remote control and new apparatus, he caused an explosion by detonating a miniature mine and then also showed that a pistol could be discharged remotely.

One of the more remarkable facts about Bose was that he was not interested in making money from his experiments. His significant inventions could have made him a fortune, but he chose to ignore any chances of profiting from it through patents. It was perfectly apparent after his first experiment that there were substantial commercial possibilities. The *Electrician Journal*, writing on Bose's paper of 1895, drew attention to these commercial possibilities in terms of an invention to communicate from land to sea:

A practical system of electromagnetic 'light'-houses, the receiver on board ship being some electric equivalent of the human eye.

As mentioned previously, and to his credit, Bose had from the outset always stipulated that he did not intend to make any profit from his inventions. In a book written by Patrick Geddes in 1920, which recorded much of Bose's life's work, the author claims that:

his child memory had been impressed by the pure white flowers offered in Indian worship; and it came early to him that whatever offerings his life could make should be untainted by any considerations of personal advantage. Moreover, he was painfully impressed by what seemed to him symptoms of deterioration, even in scientific men, by the temptation of gain; and so he made the resolve to seek for no personal advantage from his inventions.

The best scientific explanation of what Bose was trying to achieve in his experiments comes from some of his writings in which he was attempting to explain to the reader the concept of different wavelengths (vibrations) and what possibilities there were still waiting to be discovered. The following paragraph is important, and I would suggest that you read it carefully as it explains in a simple way the very nature of vibrations, which contribute fundamentally to life itself:

Imagine a large electric organ, provided with an infinite number of stops, each giving rise to a particular ether note. Imagine the lowest stop producing one vibration in a second. We should then get a gigantic ether wave 186,000 miles long (this is because it travels at the speed of light). Let the next stop give rise to two vibrations in a second and let each succeeding stop produce higher and higher notes. What an infinite number

*of stops there would be! Imagine an unseen hand pressing
the different stops in rapid succession, producing higher and
higher notes. The ether note will thus rise in frequency from
one vibration in a second to tens, to hundreds, to thousands, to
millions, to millions of millions. While the ethereal sea in which
we are immersed is being thus agitated by these multitudinous
waves, we shall remain entirely unaffected, for we possess no
organs of perception to respond to these waves. As the ether
note rises still higher in pitch we shall for a brief moment
perceive a sensation of warmth. This will be the case when the
ether vibration reaches a frequency of several billions of times
a second. As the note rises still higher our eyes will begin to
be affected, a red glimmer of light would be the first to make
its appearance. From this point the few colours we see are
comprised within a single octave of vibration – from 400 to 800
billions in one second. As the frequency of vibration rises still
higher, our organs of perception fail us completely; a great gap
in our consciousness obliterates the rest. The brief flash of light is
succeeded by unbroken darkness.*

What Bose was so elegantly describing was that our eyes pick up
only a tiny range of vibrations, and that the rest of the vibrations are
not picked up by any bodily organs he was aware of at the time.

He also stumbled upon another invention that was later to be
recognised as the predecessor of the transistor. In transistors, small
crystals of metal instead of valves are used for receiving radio waves.
Bose developed the use of galena crystals – crystals of a lead salt –
for making receivers for his electrical waves. Using these crystals,
he invented a special device, which he named the Tejometer, that
could receive and measure short radio waves as well as white and
ultraviolet light.

When Lord Rayleigh, one of Bose's Cambridge tutors, visited

Calcutta, he was impressed by the Presidency College Laboratory set up by Bose. He felt it was high time that the aspiring scientist should visit Europe and come into contact with the latest trends in scientific research. However, in those days, things were not easy for an Indian. An American scientist could go to Europe on a government deputation, but would the authorities extend this opportunity to an Indian? Fortunately, Bose had the Lieutenant Governor, Sir Alexander McKenzie, on his side. McKenzie attached the greatest importance to Professor Bose visiting Europe and conferring with the scientific community there. Thus, he was finally granted a dispensation to leave. This was the first in a series of visits to Europe that Bose used to call his "scientific missions".

Bose was invited to present a paper on electrical waves at a meeting of the British Association for the Advancement of Science, which was in session at Liverpool, and this was very well received. The English scientific community was used to the huge apparatus used by European scientists to generate electrical waves. Bose's small and handy gadgets were entirely novel to them – they were held to be marvels of inventiveness. Lord Kelvin, "who already had occasion to express his admiration for Professor Bose's work, not only spoke in the warmest language after his address, but limped upstairs to the Ladies Gallery and shook Mrs Bose by both hands". Lord Kelvin was quoted as saying:

I believe it will be conducive to the credit of India and to scientific education in Calcutta, if a well-equipped physical laboratory is added to the resources of the University of Calcutta in connection with the professorship held by Dr Bose.

During his time in England, Bose started work on research that was so revolutionary in its day that parts of it were dismissed as nonsense by his peer groups in London when he addressed them later in public lectures. Without funding, Bose had to set about creating his own equipment that would allow him to conduct his revolutionary research. One of the items he invented was the "Crescograph", a unique piece of equipment that allowed him to measure the minutest reactions of plants to external stimulation such as electromagnetic waves.

BOSE'S EXPERIMENTS

Reading one of Bose's books, and there are about ten of them, is an interesting experience. They read like a series of scientific experiments, each building upon the previous one, with literally hundreds of separate investigations being conducted within each book. None of them has a summary or an introduction; they just go from experiment to experiment with very little effort to place them within a wider context. As soon as Bose has proved a piece of science, he does not need to conduct any further experiments – he assumes that it has then been proven and moves on to another topic. He felt that it was not his responsibility to put the results into context; that was for other people to do. The first book Bose wrote, in 1902, is very similar to the following six books in terms of chapter titles. The only difference is that, with each printing of the book, he made more significant discoveries because he had built bigger and more technically advanced machines with which to conduct his experiments.

Bose's early experiments in 1901 began with ideas that went against current thinking. He set out to show that living and non-living organisms behaved in a similar fashion. Who at the beginning of the last century would have guessed that a metal would react in the same way as living tissue? Even today, it is hard to imagine anyone saying that a sheet of iron is going to behave in the same way as living tissue, but that was exactly what Bose did, and he proved it was the case. He showed not only that they both reacted similarly to fatigue with overuse, but also that they both reacted in the same way to poisons (yes, you can seemingly poison a metal) and that they could be revived using antidotes.

In experiment after experiment, he showed that plants, animals and metals all reacted in the same way to being poisoned. With living organisms, both plants and animals, chloroform was used as the poison. Bose's strangest idea was then to adopt the concept of poisoning metal to see how a metal would behave. Surprisingly, the shape of the electrical response was the same as that exhibited by plants and animals. A whole series of

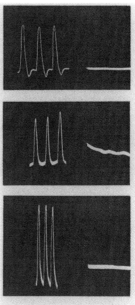

FIG. 5.—Action of poison in abolishing response of muscle (uppermost record), plant (middle record), and metal (lowest record).

metals was tested – tin, zinc, brass, even platinum. So striking was the similarity of response that one day, when Bose was showing his evidence to Sir Michael Foster, the veteran physiologist of Cambridge:

> *The latter picked up one graph of Bose's and said "come now Bose, what is the novelty in this curve? We have known it for at least the last half century".*
>
> *"What do you think it is" said Bose.*
>
> *"Why a curve of muscle response, of course."*
>
> *"Pardon me; it is the response of metallic tin."*
>
> *"What!" said Foster, jumping up – "Tin! Did you say tin?"*

From his experiments, Bose concluded that metals, plants and animals:

All exhibited the phenomena of fatigue and depression, together with possibilities of recovery and of exaltation, yet also that of permanent irresponsiveness which is associated with death.

His next series of experiments aimed to establish whether every part of a plant reacted in the same way as that of an animal. He wrote chapters of comparisons of the "response of animal and vegetable skins" whereby he showed that tomatoes on the one hand and frogs, tortoises and lizards on the other were the same. He also tested the behaviour of specific plants tissues against those of animals and found identical responses. Similarly, Bose looked at the digestive organs of plants. The venus fly trap, which Darwin had brought into great prominence, was tested against the stomachs of frogs, tortoises and other animals, and produced similar results. In fact, every experiment he conducted produced the results that both plants and animals responded in the same way to external influences.

The conclusion Bose came to from his hundreds of experiments was that plants were *behaviourally identical to animals.* This is a vital statement that should not be passed over lightly. It does not mean that plants and animals function in the same way, as they quite obviously do not. Rather, if a plant reacts to light in a positive way, animals and humans will also do so, but via different organs and chemical reactions. But the most amazing idea that can be derived from this principle is that we can learn about the human body from plants! I know this sounds bizarre, but if the principle holds – and it has been proved many times since – then if a plant reacts in a specific way to an external influence, humans will react in exactly the same way. Biologically, the process will be different, but the outcome will be identical.

Theoretically, then, you could get rid of a lot of experiments on animals by using plants, for the simple reason that plants behave in the same way as animals do to most stimuli such as poisons, anaesthetics, electrical stimulation and temperature. If a drug company wanted to know what harmful effects a drug might have, it would be very much easier for them to measure the electrical response from a variety of different plants at different doses of the drug than it would be to experiment on animals to achieve the same results.

One of the problems with experiments on animals is that animal tissue is more easily susceptible to death than plant tissue, as plants can sustain their vitality for a far greater length of time. In animal tissues, the vital conditions are highly complex. In plants, the factors that modify responses can be more easily determined under the simpler conditions that are found in plant life.

In fact, not only can you learn about animals' muscle and nerve behaviour from a plant, but it can also teach us about the behaviour of metals. I would be very interested to know if there are any metallurgists who have looked at Bose's books and used any of his ideas in their study of metals. I would doubt that any sensible person would admit they could determine the outcome of a metal's behaviour from analysing a plant.

EFFECTS OF ELECTRICAL WAVES

Even though Bose was very content with his experiments, he still needed to invent better machines to conduct tests into electromagnetic forces. It was Bose's idea to demonstrate that plants were on the same level as animals in evolutionary terms. In fact, he showed that plants were much more developed than animals and could perform actions that animals were incapable of. One simple experiment that he conducted was to compare the reactions of the human tongue to those of a plant, to see which was the more sensitive.

The tip of the tongue is the part of the human body that is most sensitive to electric currents. European men (I use this example as Bose was very conscious of the regional differences between people at that time) could detect a current as small as 6 micro-amperes, a micro-ampere being a millionth part of a unit of electric current. Indians from Calcutta, however, could detect a current that was only 4.5 micro-amperes, but the plant, on the other hand, reacted to a stimulus of only 1.5 micro-amperes. Thus, from this test, Bose said that the plant was three times more advanced than the Indian and four times more so than the European!

In order to show Bose's idea that plants were susceptible to factors outside the consciousness of human perception, he had to invent yet another machine, one that would report the rate of growth as a visual image, showing growth as a straight line – any deviation from that line would mean that the plant was growing more slowly or more quickly. His machine needed to be so sophisticated that it not only compensated for the movement of the earth, but also took into account the widely varying rates of growth in different plants and also the different rates of growth of the same plant under varying conditions.

Bose solved all of these problems in his invention of a machine that he called the Balanced Crescograph, which could measure the growth rate of plants down to as little as one fifteen-millionth of an inch per second. This was much more than any other machine was capable of doing in its day; for that matter, I am not sure that there are even now similar machines that can achieve the same the result in such a way. How many advanced measuring machines today are programmed to take into account the movement of the earth?

Magnetic crescograph

Later, Bose wanted to conduct more and more research into the growth of plants. What he realised was that the Balanced Crescograph was limited because of the mechanical apparatus it used. He therefore had to re-invent it, and what he came up with was the Magnetic Crescograph, which used electromagnetic force and light to make minute measurements. Bose used his eloquence to describe what his new machine would be capable of:

Our mind cannot grasp magnification so stupendous. We can, however, obtain some concrete idea of it finding what the speed of the proverbial snail becomes when magnified ten million times by the Magnetic Crescograph. For this enhanced speed there is no parallel in modern gunnery. The fifteen-inch muzzle cannon of the Queen Elizabeth throws out a shell with a muzzle velocity of 2360 feet per second or about 8 million feet per hour; but the Crescographic snail would move at a speed of 200 million feet per hour or 24 times faster than the cannon shot. Let us turn to cosmic movements for a closer parallel. A point of the equator whirls round at the rate of 1037 miles per hour. But the Crescographic snail may well look down on the sluggish earth; for by the time the earth makes one revolution the snail would have gone round nearly forty times!

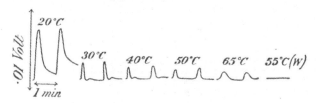

FIG. 38.—EFFECT OF TEMPERATURE ON RESPONSE
The response was abolished at the hot-water temperature of 55° C.

In order to show audiences the power of the magnification and the behaviour of the plants, Bose conducted a series of public lectures in London between 1910 and 1920. During the experiments, he would set up his Magnetic Crescograph in lecture theatres and attach his plant to it. The effects would be shown on a giant three-metre screen by using of a beam of light: any growth would send the beam to the right, and any retardation would show it to the left. Bose's experiment started by adding cooled tap water via a stopcock to the plant. The audience could see that the growth of the plant started to slow down due to the cooled water being introduced, eventually causing the plant to stop its growth completely. As Bose slowly heated the plant chamber, the plant's growth started to renew and gather speed, the greater the temperature reached. Next, another stopcock introduced a depressing agent and the growth again became paralysed – but a dose of stimulant instantly removed the depression. The life of the plant became subservient to the will of the experimenter. He could increase or decrease its growth activity in front of the audience's eyes. Bose said that "it is by the extension of man's power beyond his sense limitation that he is enabled to probe into the deeper mysteries of nature".

This great invention of the Magnetic Crescograph was the subject of intense controversy as its results were so revolutionary.

In the spring of 1920, *The Times* newspaper initiated a debate on the remarkable results achieved by Mr Bose with the high-magnification instruments used to record the automatic pulsations of the plant. In fact, an inquiry was undertaken by such luminaries at the time as Sir William Bragg and Sir William Bayliss, Fellows of the Royal Society. The members of the investigating committee reported later in *The Times* on 4th May 1920 that they were satisfied that the growth of the plant and its response to stimulation were correctly recorded by Bose's instrument at a magnification of one to ten million times.

I often wonder whether, had the First and Second World Wars not stopped scientific studies for forty years, our knowledge of plants would have been significantly more advanced, and the machines that Bose invented would be in every scientific laboratory rather than just in museums. How useful would it be for food development to know how plants react every second to stimulation by fertilisers, electrical waves or sound pollution? Imagine the possibility that you could literally sit and watch the plant grow in front of your eyes and see which fertiliser offered the best results, which water temperature each individual plant preferred and which sounds the plant was stimulated by!

ELECTRICAL RESPONSES

All plants emit electrical responses, and it was this fundamental property of organisms that Bose utilised in his experiments throughout his career. All of his sophisticated machines looked at electrical responses in order to assess the organisms' behaviour. He felt that this response would reflect how the plant was reacting to whatever external stimulus was applied. If the response was positive, the plant was reacting favourably, whereas if it was negative, the plant was reacting negatively. At the point at which the electrical response was so low that no more was emitted, the plant was declared to be dead.

These reactions were essential as they allowed Bose the possibility of conducting experiments to assess the plants' electrical responses. Without electrical responses, it would be impossible to test how a plant behaved as there would be no obvious physical or chemical reaction for such a simple activity as pruning a plant or pinching a leaf. Some reactions of plants are going to be greater than others, and Bose found the variation to be as much as 1 volt. I can only work out how much 1 volt is when I think of batteries that I use for electrical appliances: the smallest ones are the AAA batteries, which are 1.2 volts. So 1 volt is quite a significant amount of current.

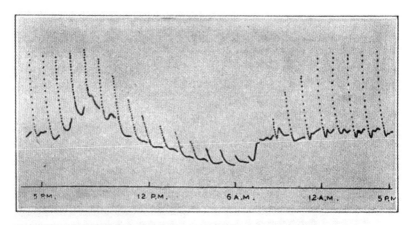

FIG. 1—RECORD OF THE VARIATION IN EXCITA-
BILITY OF A PLANT DURING TWENTY-FOUR HOURS

Is the plant capable of achieving more than humans or animals? Are our "vegetative brethren" superior in any of their abilities? In one area, plants are in fact superior to us, in that they can respond to an infinite number of wavelengths, which is far better than anything an animal or a human can achieve. Scientists say that we can only pick up on few ranges of vibration: sound and light – through our ears and eyes – and tactile vibrations – felt through our skin, which can pick up on very specific vibrations of around 50 Hz and 200–300 Hz. We do not have any other major organs that indicate we have any possibility of picking up other vibrations. But Bose showed that plants can pick up not only sound and light vibrations but every single type of vibration, from the smallest to the largest, from whatever source.

One of the many unusual abilities of plants is to be able to recognise almost all of the known wavelengths and show a reaction to them, from the shortest to the longest. The longest wavelengths are ones that have the longest space between impulses, such as the impulses given off once a year by a circulating planet. Humans can interpret only a very small range of frequencies, the most common being those emitted as light and sound. The plant, on the other hand, recognises them all and reacts accordingly. It can respond to waves that appear only once a year as well as waves that are emitted 500,000 times a second.

Plants also respond to the electrical waves that are generated by all the electrical objects that we use, from mobile phones through to microwave cookers and light bulbs. Not only do plants recognise these wavelengths, but they also respond adversely to them, with a reduction in growth. Although Bose discovered that plants did not like electrical waves, he found that a very small stimulation applied to a plant – in this case a wheat seed – actually caused an increase in growth of that plant. A strong stimulation caused the plant damage, and with a medium stimulation the plant suffered retardation and then recovery, up and down.

In this simple experiment, he measured the amount of growth caused by:

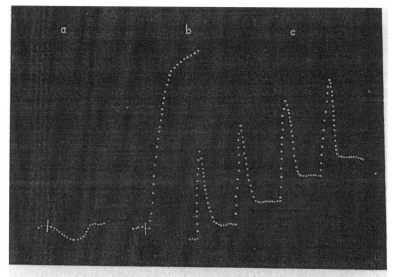

Fig. 113. Record of responses of plant to wireless stimulation. (*a*) Response to feeble stimulus by acceleration of growth ; (*b*) response to strong stimulus by retardation of growth ; (*c*) response to medium stimulation—retardation followed by recovery. Down-curve represents acceleration, and up-curve retardation of growth (seedling of wheat).

1. feeble electrical vibrations;
2. slightly above sub-minimal electrical vibrations;
3. medium-sized electrical vibrations.

In order to measure the effect of electrical vibrations, Bose placed an electric radiator 200 metres from a growing wheat seedling and measured its growth rate. Bose managed to generate feeble vibrations from this radiator by decreasing the energy of the radiator's sparks. This very feeble stimulation led to the plant growing at a very small additional rate.

The slightly above sub-minimal electrical vibrations caused the growth in the plant to become less for a short time before it suddenly put on a growth spurt. This would be a continuous cycle of retardation and growth so that each contraction and expansion would make the plant grow in smaller amounts.

The significant result, however, came from the experiment on the medium-sized electrical output, which was by Bose's definition actually not very large in real terms but a large amount to the plant. What it showed clearly was that the plant did not like the electrical stimulation and reflected this in its immediate retardation and shrinkage.

Is there anything we need to know about this simple experiment? The fact that a small electrical vibration causes a direct effect on a plant should be of historic importance, shouldn't it? Are there not millions of electric radiators in people's houses throughout the world? More to the point, are there not hundreds of millions of other electrical appliances around us all that give out electrical vibrations that are affecting plants? What if they are affecting us as well as plants? If they are, do they affect us in the same way as a plant or are there much more sinister issues that we don't know about? How many of us know that plants can pick up every imaginable vibration, from the smallest to the largest? I certainly didn't. And if they can, why can they? There must be a reason for them to be able to do so, and if they can do it, can animals do it as well? And what else can plants do that we are not aware of?

I will in fact go on to show in the following chapter that there are many things that plants can do that we have ignored simply because they do not fit into our present-day understanding of how everything works together. Acknowledging that plants function at a much higher level than we give them credit for, rather than just being there and looking pretty, is not something that many of us consider. But I will show very shortly that scientists have intentionally chosen to ignore a range of weird and unusual behaviours in plants as it is not to their political advantage.

Remember that Bose was writing from 1902 to 1928 and published his experiments both in India and the UK. He gave numerous lectures to Royal Institutes in London and was often written up in mainstream newspapers. Bose was not an unknown person; his research has been available for scientists to read for over a hundred years now. So why have his ideas not been developed further?

In a chapter in the book "Signalling in Plants", published in 2009, Baluska and Mancuso say the following about how disinterested most botanists are in researching vibrations:

> Despite the fact that the rhythmical behaviour is a
> quintessential pattern of life itself, most researchers still
> treat oscillations in plants as some unwanted physiologically
> unrelated noise.

They go on to say:

> Astonishingly little research effort is currently devoted to high
> frequency oscillations in plant biology.

What a crime. How many millions of pounds-worth of research funding are being wasted when scientists could unlock many of the secrets of plants just by researching vibrational behaviour. It is my contention, moreover, that vibrations are an essential part of life and that we can only understand better our behaviour by understanding these vibrations.

THE DEATH TEMPERATURE OF THE RADISH

This is a strange area of science, particularly as none of us ever thinks about it. What do I mean when I refer to the death temperature of the radish? Surely a radish is dead the moment you pull it out of the ground. Bose proves that this is nowhere near the truth, and the consequences of this fact have, I believe, major consequences for our health and the way in which we choose to cook and eat the food that we think we understand.

What is the highest temperature to which you can subject a radish before its electrical response becomes zero and the plant can be certified as dead? In the case of the radish, Bose slowly raised the temperature in a bath of water in which a radish was floating, and the electrical response of the radish became zero at or around the 55°C level. Bose interpreted this as that the radish had finally met its maker and could be certified as dead. Bose declared that, without any electrical response, all living organisms are dead. He then conducted the same experiment with celery and found that the electrical response died at a temperature of 60°C.

These results were both conducted using a slowly increasing water temperature. What would be the difference, however, if the vegetables were suddenly introduced to a high temperature? Bose discovered that if celery was dropped into water of various different temperatures, it died at 50°C instead of dying at 60°C – 10 degrees less than with slow immersion. So the shock of being dropped into hot water caused the celery to die at a lower temperature.

Unusually, in one experiment on a radish exposed to frost, the electrical response produced was markedly reduced when the radish returned to its normal temperature. The effect of the frost led to a change in molecular structure of the radish so that it could no longer produce its normal response. However, the experiment showed that it was not just the low temperature that was the factor at play, but also how long the radish had been cooled for. If the radish had been cooled for only a matter of minutes, it would show no signs of change after warming and would give out the same electrical response as if it had not been cooled.

Below is a list of plants with good electrical responses that Bose

used to conduct his experiments. Not all plants behave the same –
some offer better results than others:

The root response	Carrot, radish
Stem	Geranium, vine
Leaf stalk	Horse chestnut, turnip,cauliflower, celery, eucharis lily
Flower stalk	Arum lily
Fruit	Egg plant (aubergine)

THE DEATH CRIES OF A CARROT

How long does it take to kill a carrot by steaming it in a kitchen
steamer? Five minutes seems to do the trick. Before that time, the
carrot is managing to cope with the extra heat generated by the
steam. Its electrical response, although somewhat diminished, is
still normal. However, at almost exactly five minutes, the electrical
response fades away and all response returns to zero. I find this a
very fascinating experiment, one that has much more significance
than just the minor amusement of imagining a carrot dying. What
does it say for our method of cooking and its relationship to the
health benefits of a carrot, whether it should be eaten while "alive"
or "dead"? Should we eat all vegetables steamed for less than five
minutes, so that the carrot can stay alive? Or is there no effect, from
a nutritional perspective, of whether the carrot is alive or dead? I can
tell you now that I have tried and tried to find further information on
this matter, but it seems to have been overlooked by every scientist
working in this field for the past one hundred years.

I need to go back to the first experiment conducted by Bose
where he discovered that vegetables actually have a death to show

you what sort of responses his research generated in his day, back in the early 1920s. If similar experiments were conducted today, I am sure the reaction would be similar. But, in fact, I still have no idea why no-one has chosen to re-enact these simple experiments within the food industry so that we can get a better understanding about our cooking habits and identify the best method of eating vegetables with regard to cooking techniques. Could it be that not only the type of vegetable plays a part, but also the way in which it is cooked? Should we roast, boil or steam our vegetables? For what length of time would they have to be cooked and within which temperature range?

Bose showed that a plant emits an electrical current when it dies. In his study of vegetables, he reported that one pea can emit as much as half a volt. If a set of peas were lined up and crushed into an electrical series, the electric pressure would be 500 volts, which might cause even the electrocution of unsuspecting victims. Bose dryly remarked about this experiment, "it is well that the cook does not know the danger she runs in preparing the particular dish; it is fortunate for us that that the peas are not arranged in series!"

In London, Bose demonstrated these death spasms to Mr Bernard Shaw, the famous philosopher – a vegetarian – who was quoted as being unhappy "to find that a piece of cabbage was thrown into violent convulsions when scalded to death". The following quote, from *The Nation* magazine, reads like the description of a modern-day vivisection experiment on a monkey:

in a room near Maida Vale there is an unfortunate carrot strapped to the table of an unlicensed vivisector. Wires pass through two glass tubes full of a white substance; they are like two legs whose feet are buried in the flesh of the carrot. When the vegetable is pinched with a pair of forceps it winces. It is so strapped that its electric shudder of pain pulls the long arm of a very delicate lever which actuates a tiny mirror. This casts a beam of light on the frieze at the end of the room and thus enormously exaggerates the tremor of the carrot. A pinch near the right hand tube sends the beam seven or eight feet to the right and a stab near the other wire sends it as far to the left. Thus can science reveal the feelings of even so stolid a vegetable as the carrot.

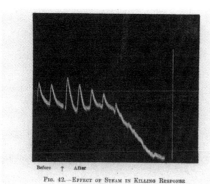

Before ↑ After

FIG. 42.—EFFECT OF STEAM IN KILLING RESPONSE

The two records to the left exhibit normal response at 17° C. Sudden warming by steam produced at first an increase of response, but five minutes' exposure to steam killed the plant (carrot) and abolished the response. Vibrational stimulus of 30° applied at intervals of one minute; vertical line = ·1 volt.

Seriously though, what does that mean when we are eating a piece of carrot? Electrical charges must be going somewhere, and if you bite into a raw carrot, does this not mean you will be collecting the electrical output from the carrot in your mouth?

In one experiment Bose conducted in London on sea kale, he was worried to discover that the kale did not respond as the other vegetables had done, so he asked his vegetable supplier about the delivery and was told that the sea kale had, on its journey to London, been affected by a snowfall. Subsequent deliveries of sea kale showed no negative response. As I read this description in Bose, I thought it was just an interesting anecdote about his time in London; its significance did not dawn on me straight away. It was not until much later that I appreciated its importance. His experiments could imply that, in order to eat healthy food, the carrot, for example, would have to retain a healthy electrical charge that reflected its healthy status. The weaker the carrot, the weaker the electrical charge it would emit. A frozen carrot would emit no electrical charge and would therefore not have any "electrical benefit" to the individual eating it. Imagine if our bodies expect to receive not only vitamins and minerals from our diet, but also electrical stimulation; one could conclude that non-healthy vegetables are not providing all three factors that our bodies need; vitamins, minerals and now also electrical charges!

The more I thought about this idea, the more it seemed to make sense. It seemed to be an important missing link in our understanding of our diet.

But one thing that intrigued me was how you could define the death of a carrot. Does a carrot die when you pull it out of the ground, or when you slice it up for cooking? Does it die only when it has been "poisoned" by the gastric juices in our stomach, or does boiling a carrot so to speak "kill" it? Most importantly, if an electrical discharge were emitted, what part of the body was supposed to collect it, and also what benefit would it be to have this additional voltage?

DIFFERENT DEATHS OF PLANTS

I had to go back to Bose's original work to discover the exact definition of plant death. Luckily, he had thought this process through and had developed many experiments to show exactly when it occurred. Bose was able to develop experiments that looked at four different options, using plants that under normal conditions died at or around 60°C:

1)   *The method of electrical response.* Bose conducted experiments showing that heating a bunch of radishes killed them between the temperatures of 35°C and 55°C. The actual death point, as measured by a lack of electrical response, depended on the individual radish and the season in which the experiment was being done, the death occurring a few degrees lower in winter than it did in summer.

2)   *The method by which the point of death is determined from the occurrence of a spasmodic movement (shock), in a dorsi-ventral or anisotropic organ.* In this experiment, Bose showed that if you drop a plant into a pan of water at 35°C, it will collapse its leaves through the shock of the hot water. If, however, you slowly bring the pan of water up to 35°C, the plant will show no signs of any adverse effect. Sadly, when the temperature reaches 59°C, it hits the death point and the plant leaf is termed dead. Interestingly, when the experiment was conducted with the leaf still attached to the plant, only the leaf that was heated in the water was killed while the rest of the plant was unaffected.

3)   *The method that depends on the sudden expulsion of water at the moment of death from a hollow organ, previously filled with liquid.* This investigation reported that, in the throes of death, a plant will expunge water from itself as a final act. The plant in this case was an allium. It was shown that temperatures of 59°C in a young plant and 63°C in an older plant were those at which the plant died, causing a sudden expulsion of water.

4)   *The method in which the death point is determined from the sudden reversal of a thermomechanical response curve.* Bose went into great detail to describe this experiment and the apparatus upon which his experiments were conducted, doing this to demonstrate that his

results were irrefutable. He showed, using photographic paper, that he could obtain the same results as were obtained by measuring the electrical response. The molecular change that was visible on the photographic paper was caused by the increase in temperature of the *Passiflora* plant and was the cause of the plant's death, specifically at 59.6°C.

FATIGUE

Imagine you had to lift a very small weight over and over again, as you might do in the gym. The more you do it, the harder it gets, and your muscles start to show signs of fatigue. Without this fatigue, you would be able to carry on regardless and increase your muscles to any size in just a matter of weeks. However, as anyone who has tried to get fitter knows, you have to put in the work and train your muscles to get stronger so that the fatigue takes longer each time to kick in. Plants behave in exactly the same way as animal muscles: too much stimulation causes them fatigue. This is a very important point, one of many fundamentals of science that seems to have been forgotten by most scientists conducting experiments on plants. If you knew this simple fact, why would you experiment on a plant and subject it to impulses that lasted twenty-four hours a day, seven days a week, and not expect the plant to show signs of fatigue? This would reduce your scientific results to complete meaninglessness.

But if, on the other hand, you can give the muscle enough rest between each exercise, it is possible to continue the exercise for a very long time. The point to grasp here is that it is not the repeated exercise that is the key to muscle fatigue, but the frequency of exercise that is important. One lift every 20 minutes for example can be carried on all day; one lift every 10 seconds will be maintained for only a matter of minutes.

In one of Bose's experiments, a cauliflower was stimulated by a vibration of forty-five times per second at one minute intervals and reacted positively; the vibration was then doubled for the next three consecutive stimulations and then reverted back to the forty-five per second stimulation. As a consequence of the overexertion caused by the ninety per second impulse, the plant showed signs of fatigue. With a fifteen-minute rest, the plants then responded normally

Another experiment was carried out on the carrot. In this case, a two-minute stimulation was followed by a two-minute rest, with a vibration rate of fifty per second. There was a significant initial response followed by fatigue, in a constant cycle, up and down. When, however, the carrots were given a five-minute rest after two sets of stimulation, the resulting response was significantly greater.

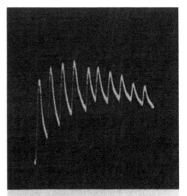

FIG. 3.—Electric response of metal showing fatigue (tin).

So imagine if you did one set of weights for two minutes and then rested for another two minutes – you could do the same amount of exercise each time. However, if you then gave yourself a five-minute rest, you could actually lift more weights than you had done in the two previous two exercises.

Of course, this idea is purely based on the electrical response shown by the stimulation of a plant. I am not suggesting that you go out and follow this new style of exercise, but it would be interesting to know why there are no exercise classes in gyms that get you to do exercise slowly rather than getting as much as you can done in one hour. Maybe it's another case of science not telling us the facts because it would then not be in anyone's interest to exercise over a long period of time, whereas all the exercise books and classes seem to want to get you to do everything in arbitrary amounts of time such as thirty minutes and one hour. These are not times that your body is aware of. It would be more beneficial to do half the number of exercises in twice the length of time.

Bose's interpretation of what is happening is based on equilibrium. The body always likes to maintain equilibrium in every function; when the body is out of equilibrium, we show signs of fatigue or illness. The body then reacts accordingly and tries different means to restore that equilibrium. In the muscle, Bose suggested that the molecules are thrown out of their state of equilibrium, and this is demonstrated by the change in electrical response. The greater the molecular distortion produced by the stimulus, the greater is the electrical variation. Therefore, the electrical response is shown to be the expression of the molecular disturbance produced by a stimulus of some kind.

An interesting issue arises when you compare tapping to vibrating. Tapping a plant, firstly with one tap followed by an interval and then with two taps and an interval, then three taps an interval, etc., produces increasing responses in the plant after each set of tapping – the responses actually get bigger each time. If you do the same with a vibration, increasing the vibration after every rest period, the electrical response does not increase significantly but comes to a maximum very quickly. This occurred very clearly in one of Bose's experiments on a turnip. Would it not be very interesting to analyse this tapping effect in a lot more detail because Bose's experiment implies that it is possible to stimulate plants more by tapping than is possible using vibration. Could this effect be similar in humans? Would tapping on different parts of our body stimulate any chemical reaction that would prove to be beneficial to our health? Some form of complementary therapies use tapping as a procedure; maybe Bose has shown that there is a scientific basis for this after all.

One experiment on the radish showed that if the stimulus was very small to begin with, the radish would elicit no response until the stimulus rose to a certain point, after which there would suddenly be a maximum response past which it was impossible to go. This is the same in cardiac muscle. In Bose's time, this was known as the "all or none" principle; it says that there is a certain minimal intensity that is effective in producing a response, but further increases in the stimulus do not produce any more increase in response.

If you take a stale radish – you know the sort, the one that has been at the bottom of the fridge drawer for too long and is tucked away in the back corner – this radish will actually show a lower electrical response as it is stale. Initially, it will respond to a stimulus negatively, but then it will show improved signs of a response after a couple of increases in frequency, but not up to the level of a fresh radish. What does this tell us about the radish? It suggests that stale food has different properties from fresh food, properties that might have an effect on the nutritional qualities and behaviour of these foods within our digestive system.

GROWTH OF PLANTS

Of even more significance to modern science are the experiments that Bose conducted on the growth of plants and how they were affected by electrical stimulation. The salamander is well known as an animal that can regrow lost limbs, and it has been found that it does this by electrical stimulation. If Bose were to show that a plant can grow over and above its normal level via electrical stimulation, could the human body also regrow organs or bones through additional electrical stimulation?

The growth of plants is more significant, however, as plants provide a large part of our daily food intake, and if it were possible to increase production using any non-chemical means, any scientific research would be hugely significant and important. Or so you would think. But it appears that this is not always the case. Bose made a few critical discoveries that should have been used in our food production methods eighty years ago but are still not being introduced. He showed that you can increase yields in wheat by up to 50% utilising electrical vibrations to stimulate wheat seeds. I know that it seems ridiculous to be told this as we always are worried about the world's ability to feed itself, but although this simple experiment has been reproduced numerous times, its results have still not been put into use.

When conducting any experiment into the growth of plants, it must be remembered that some plants grow very slowly. In the time it takes us to take one step, mimosa plants grow just by the length of half a single wave of light. So imagine what sort of technology is required in order to measure this minute change in growth. At the time Bose was working on his ideas, the only machine available was the "auxometer", which produced only about twenty times magnification. Several hours would have to elapse using this machine before the increase in growth became perceptible. It was so difficult to obtain enough magnification to make any investigation worthwhile that it took eight years of invention to overcome the problem. It forced Bose to create the "High Magnification Crescograph", a triumph of invention. The machine not only allowed him to see the plant growth in minute detail, but was also capable of keeping automated records.

What Bose's initial studies of plants using the Crescograph showed was that plants do not grow in a steady and continuous pattern, but grow in rhythms. In Calcutta, where these experiments were conducted, the plants' growth cycle was about three growth pulses per minute. Each growth pulse showed a rapid uplift and then a slower partial recoil, amounting to a recession of about 0.25 of the distance first gained. So each pulse generated a total growth rate of 0.75 of the initial burst.

Some of Bose's studies made for uncomfortable reading amongst the biologists of his day. Frighteningly, some of the results still seem to scare scientists and seem to have been ignored. What would you say if the results suggested that touching an unhealthy plant actually helped to heal it, that physical stimulation made it better? But conversely, what if touching a healthy plant induced an immediate retardation of its growth, making it ill. Bose discovered, by using his Crescograph, that both these propositions were true.

One other piece of science that Bose reported is related to temperature. One of the obvious facts we all know is that temperature will affect the growth of a plant – sunny days are preferable to colder ones. But what we might not know is that cooled water applied to a plant will actually slow its growth rate, whereas hot water will in fact increase its level of growth, even by many times until it reaches an optimum level. So to all you gardeners out there, try sticking your elbow in the water to make sure it is not too cold before you give it to your plants if you want to get the best out of them.

HAPPY AND SAD RESPONSES

Yet again, Bose was to discover universalities that seem to have passed unnoticed in today's experiments. The very notion that you can have positive and negative responses to the same stimulation that then travel along the nervous system at different speeds is unparalleled. His investigations proved that if a plant was given an external stimulus such as heat, it would create two simultaneous impulses, negative and positive, which then travelled through the plant at different speeds. The positive response travelled faster and arrived at the point of reception a considerable time before the negative response. But the negative wave, with its slower speed of transmission, was much the stronger of the two. In consequence, if the two impulses reached the responding point at about the same time, the positive stimulus would be completely masked by the predominant negative one.

Weird but true. If you create a stimulus at a long distance from the plant, the positive response is stimulated before the negative. If the distance is great enough, the positive effect will reach the receptor so far ahead of the negative response that the negative one fails to reach the receptor point. Conversely, with the same stimulus, if it is applied too near the plant, the negative effect alone is stimulated at the receptor, the positive being masked by the more powerful negative effect. To show this, Bose used heat as his stimulus.

Obviously, the quicker the nervous system can transfer the stimulus, the greater the effect. The stimulus travels slowly in a plant stem, and therefore the positive effect will be more pronounced if the stimulus is applied in the leaf area, where the communicating system is much faster. As an example, if a heat source was placed 10 mm from the plant's stem, the positive effect arrived after 3 seconds and the negative one 21 seconds later. If the heat was moved further away, thus creating a smaller amount of heat stimulation, the effect still occurred at 3 seconds for the positive, but now 27 seconds for the negative, response. What Bose's experiments showed is that the smaller the heat stimulation and the greater the distance from the plant, the larger is the positive response – less is more.

I don't know how many scientists are aware of this, but I am pretty certain that most non-scientists have never heard of this idea in plants. Let alone that these impulses are the same in animals and therefore in humans. These double impulses were found by Bose to be exhibited in both plants and animals; we all have a positive and negative impulse racing around us at different speeds – how peculiar. But what are the implications? Is there any area of our bodies in which the impulses travel more slowly so that if we receive a feeble impulse, it should have a more positive effect than a strong impulse? This idea does not seem logical, yet Bose proved that animals respond in the same way as plants.

LIGHT

Light is important in any experiment because it determines the growth of a plant. But not just any old light; it has to be the right sort of light. As I mentioned before, everything vibrates, including light. Our eyes are capable of picking up different colours of light because, for example, the colour red vibrates at a different rate from the colour yellow. Our eyes are very sophisticated pieces of equipment that can differentiate between minute differences in the frequency of vibrations. Light waves vibrate incredibly quickly, the quickest being infrared. The factor that is also important is the length of each vibration; some vibrations are extremely fast, many thousands per second, while other vibrations might take place only once a year. Some of the longest vibrations are electrical vibrations which can be fifty million times longer than the vibrations in ultraviolet light.

Light affects plants depending upon its intensity; however, too much light slows the growth of plants. Plants grow best when the light is at a lower level rather than at a maximum; in fact, a too intense a level of light causes the level of growth within the plant to stop. The only analogy I can think of is sun tanning. The best way to get a good suntan is to get a small amount of sun over a longer period, rather than sitting infrequently under the sun for long periods. For any of us who have attempted the latter, we know it only causes a lot of pain, trips to the chemists and sometimes sunstroke. So the level of the amount of sun we receive and its strength affects us, just as it seems to affect plants.

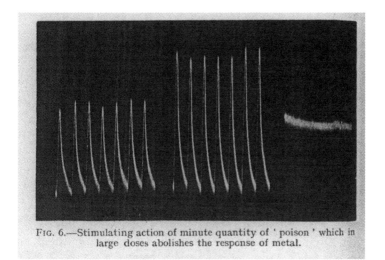

FIG. 6.—Stimulating action of minute quantity of ' poison ' which in large doses abolishes the response of metal.

PROVING THE THEORY OF LESS IS MORE

Bose was able to watch over the space of just a few minutes the effect that chemicals, drugs and poisons had on plants' behaviour. Up until then, the level of knowledge of chemical and electrical stimulation had been very mixed; some experiments showed one result, whereas similar ones showed completely the opposite. With high magnification as well as Bose's intellect and methodology, he was able to explain all of the contradictions at the same time as laying out the groundwork for a new science.

Bose made the remarkable discovery that while a particular level of electrical current stimulated growth, any excess amount had the opposite effect. The same was true of chemical stimulants – minute doses of certain poisons that would normally kill a plant instead acted as a stimulant, the plants growing more vigorously and flowering early. Moreover, these plants chemically treated with minute levels of poisons resisted "insect blights" more successfully.

Amazingly, one other experiment highlighted additional factors that should be investigated further to help our understanding of how homeopathy works. Bose conducted an experiment using a set batch of seedlings and divided them into three groups: one was kept in normal conditions to act as the reference point, another was depressed to a less favourable state by using subnormal conditions, and the third was put in optimum conditions. Minute doses of poisons that normal plants could just survive after a period of struggle were found to produce immediate death in the depressed plants; however, the same dose actively stimulated the growth of the plants held in the optimum conditions.

Maybe it is no wonder that scientific experiments on humans produce such conflicting results as the state of health of each individual taking a particular drug is NEVER taken into account. In fact, most people who enter into drug experiments are, by definition, unwell in the first place. Maybe if all drug experiments were conducted on only healthy people, it would be possible to generate a better idea of which drugs work and which ones don't.

"THUS THROUGH THE PLANT IT MAY BE POSSIBLE TO ALLEVIATE THE SUFFERINGS OF MAN"

Scientific experiments have clearly shown that measurement of the electrical response provides a faithful reflection of the physical behaviour of plants. Bose showed that the life reactions of plants and humans are alike. He waxed lyrical a bit in the following prose he wrote for one of his lectures at the Royal Institution in London:

> *In realising this unity of life, is our final sense of mystery deepened or lessened? Is our sense of wonder diminished when we realise in the infinite expanse of life that is silent and voiceless the foreshadowing of more wonderful complexities? Does not each of her new advances (science) gain for us a step*

in that stairway of rock which all must climb who desire to look from the mountain tops of the spirit upon the promised land of truth?

When a passing cloud is shown to decrease the electrical response of a mimosa plant for the few moments that the cloud is covering the sunlight, can we wonder that Bose said this?

CUTTING A PLANT

How does a plant behave when you prune it? The simple answer is initially not very well. It does not like it, which is not really surprising. When a leaf was cut off the mimosa plant mentioned above, the plant did not react to any outside stimulus for several hours; it had a paralysing effect. But then the plant recovered to its initial state. The detached leaf also recovered its responses in a couple of hours, but this lasted for only a day, after which a curious change crept in – the strength of its responses began rapidly to decline and it finally died. Its life could be extended by immersing the leaf into a solution of nutrients, but it would still die after a week:

> *we find that the plant is not a mere mass of vegetative growth, but that its every fibre is instinct with sensibility. We find it answering to outside stimuli, the responsive twitches increasing with the strength of the blow that impinges on it. We are able to record the throbs of its pulsating life and find these wax and wane according to the life conditions of the plant, and cease with the death of the organism. We find the different parts of the plant are connected together by conducting threads, so that the tremor of excitation initiated at one place courses through the whole, this nervous impulse, as in man, being accelerated or arrested under the several actions of drugs and poisons. In these and in many other ways the life reactions of plant and man are alike; thus through the experience of the plant it may be*

possible to alleviate the sufferings of man.

Indeed, the response caused by different temperatures in plants is exactly the same as the response shown by muscle and nerve responses in animals.

SUMMARY

There is no doubt that Bose was a man of genius. His findings should have been granted the magnitude of those of other great scientific minds, such as Darwin. It is a tragedy that his discoveries have not yet been understood or realised in current mainstream science. How many of today's experiments take into account a plant's level of fatigue, the time of year the experiment takes place, the level of the plant's health or the temperature of the water it is being fed? How many medical or nutritional experts have ever considered that our bodies might be missing an essential element in our diet – electrical impulses – resulting from the electrical expulsion caused by the final death of a vegetable? I feel very privileged that I have had access to all of Bose's books and have managed to take a glimpse into the world of this incredible man.

INTRODUCTION TO
PLANTS

" *Despite the fact that the rhythmical behaviour is a quintessential pattern of life itself, most researchers still treat vibrations in plants as some unwanted physiological noise* ".

SERGEY SHABALA,
"COMMUNICATION IN PLANTS" 2009

I am going to start by telling you about a controversial book that was written in 1973 called the *Secret Life of Plants*, by Peter Tompkins and Christopher Bird. This one book, a US bestseller, was, I believe, the reason why major research into plant behaviour was halted for more than forty years. The ideas in that book were so radical that it is only recently that scientists have finally been able to stick their heads above the parapet and attempt to investigate the behaviour of plants without being open to peer group ridicule.

Why did this book cause such a major problem? The most significant idea was that plants can react to human emotions. It was alleged that plants were able to react to events even before they happened. For instance, if you were walking over to a plant to prune it, the plant would be aware of this before you had actually started to make any physical cuts to the plant itself. It was as if the plant could read your thoughts. This of course, reeked of extrasensory perception, which scientists in all walks of life no doubt dismissed as sci-fi nonsense. How could it be possible that plants, with no central nervous system, could recognise emotions in a human?

As crazy as it now seems, I seriously believe – simply from the scientific discoveries that I have written about in this book – that plants are capable of achieving this amazing feat. I also have to believe that if plants can do it, so can we, by the very fact that we are behaviourally the same, the only difference being that we are not consciously aware that we are picking up on other people's emotions and intents. Have you ever recognised emotions such as depression or happiness in other people when they have simply walked into the same room as you? I am sure most scientists would say that it was merely visual clues that you are recognising, but maybe there is a possibility that you are picking up on other subconscious ones as well. Gut instinct might be all about recognising vibrational patterns in other people or surrounding areas. As might fear as well. These are areas for other people to discuss in other books, but for me they are all distinct possibilities based on the ideas that I have already mentioned.

The most significant ideas that were discussed in *The Secret Life of Plants* were based on scientific studies conducted from 1966 onwards by Cleve Backster, who was simply taking the ideas of J.C. Bose one stage further. If you recall from Chapter 7, Bose conducted his experiments on plants by measuring their electrical response to a number of different stimuli and proved beyond doubt that plants' growth behaviour could be measured using this methodology. Backster developed on Bose's ideas, using much more sophisticated electronic measuring devices than had been available to Bose sixty years earlier.

Backster worked for the CIA, specialising in interrogation. He was an expert in the use of polygraph machines to interrogate applicants who were looking for employment in the CIA. As a young and innovative man, Backster found that this work became less and less stimulating and decided to go freelance, setting up his own school to teach polygraphic techniques in New York in 1965 and calling it the "Backster Research Foundation". It was during a quiet night in the office that Backster decided to investigate the behaviour of plants and the speed at which water rose from the root to the leaf area. He happened to have a large *Dracaena* plant in a pot in the corner of the office that he thought he would experiment on, and he wired it up to his polygraph machine.

The first reaction produced surprising results, completely opposite to what Backster had expected, but exactly the results that Bose had shown seventy years previously. Plants do not like being fed cold water; they go into shock and take time to respond positively, and this is exactly what the lie detector graph showed.

The initial tracing moved in a downward direction, but one minute after feeding, the tracing exhibited a "short term change in contour similar to a reaction pattern typical of a human subject who might have been briefly experiencing the fear of detection".

For some unknown reason, Backster decided to challenge the plant because the unexpected human contour pattern seemed to bring out his competitive nature. He seemed to be saying, if that is how you are going to behave, then let's see what you do when I do something that a human would react very strongly to, like being punched in the face. The only equivalent idea that Backster had, other than actually punching the plant, was to hurt it by burning it with his cigarette lighter. Imagine this moment. It must have been like one of those really scary scenes in a horror movie, when the audience is aware that something terrible is about to happen, but the unsuspecting doctor has no idea. I can almost hear the music to *Jaws* in the background.

The room was small, it was close to midnight and there was no-one around in the building, just Backster and the *Dracaena* plant. While Backster was searching for his cigarette lighter, knowing he had the idea of burning the leaf attached to his polygraph, his ears picked up something strange that stopped him in his tracks – the

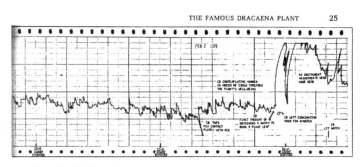

Figure 1D – Plant Reaction at Imaged Intent to Burn Leaf

288

polygraph machine was showing extreme movements. "The very moment the imagery of burning that leaf entered my mind, the polygraph recording pen moved rapidly to the top of the chart! No words were spoken, no touching the plant, no lighting of matches, just my clear intention to burn the leaf". I don't know about you, but I think I would have immediately run out of the room screaming in terror. The image of this reaction can be seen in the graph above, the intent being shown by the huge jump at the right of the chart.

This was the first time in history that a recording of someone's intent had been captured graphically on paper. Of course, Backster did not stop there. Once he had understood the significance of his discovery, he continued to make polygraph recordings. It soon became obvious that the plant had a strong connection with Backster, maybe because he worked in the same room, maybe because he was the one who watered it, or maybe it was for a completely different reason that science is not aware of. But regardless of why, Backster proved that no matter how far from the plant he was, the polygraph machine showed a reaction from the plant. In order to test his theory, Backster left the plant permanently attached to the polygraph and then, using of a stopwatch, timed his movements and thoughts and then compared them with the images and times on the graph paper. It soon became very apparent that when he was out of the office, any spontaneous thoughts that he had, such as returning early to the office, were picked up by the plant.

Here's a question. If the plant picked up on Cleve Backster's thoughts, what other living organisms would the plant be in tune with, and why should they only be human? It appears that it is every life form, from bacteria through to elephants (I use elephants under dramatic license as Backster did not experiment on them). In one accident, he poured boiling water down the dirty drain in the sink of the office having made a cup of tea. The graph spiked as if the plant had heard the screams of the billions of tiny bacteria being killed simultaneously.

So why don't we know about all of this? Why is it not general knowledge? This is probably because, in science, it is necessary before proving a theory to have it tested by others, and then and only then can the results be confirmed. But similar results were not seen when other institutions tried to test Backster's findings, and it took thirty years before someone else managed to replicate his experiments. In Backster's defence, he argued that the other researchers had no idea how to do an experiment that involved intent. For example, in one of his experiments that he presented to the manufacturer of the polygraph machine, the plant was very aware in the experiment when the scientist intended to drop an orange on the plant and when it intended to miss the plant.

There are no textbook studies to offer advice on how to set up such an experiment. Backster claimed that no-one managed to replicate his very sophisticated randomized automated experiments that did not involve human emotion. Although, when I say no-one, I mean no-one in America. The Soviets easily repeated the experiment, but instead of using randomized machines they used hypnotised people who had no thoughts of intent except for those suggested by the person who had hypnotised them. These tests were, according to Backster, accurate every time, but back in 1972 the Cold War was still on and any Soviet scientist's results were not felt to be up to the standard of their American counterparts, and were thus dismissed.

Once Backster had conducted experiments on plants, he went on to test the reactions of other living organisms such as the bacteria found in yoghurt. When samples of the yoghurt were hurt or damaged in an adjoining room, he had no trouble showing that the yoghurt bacteria reacted in the same way as the plants. His experiments continued with the use of male sperm, and he showed that if the donor of the sperm cut himself in a room thirty metres away, the sperm would show a reaction when the sample was wired up to the machine. In fact, Backster experimented with lots of different cellular structures and found that every single one of them had a connection with its original host.

It is perfectly clear that all of this is possible. Each cell within a human vibrates at a unique level, and any change in the vibration caused by thoughts, pain, happiness or whatever will be transmitted to the surrounding area. Any vibration in the air will have a direct effect on the cell, and if it is tuned to that vibrational wavelength it will emit a response – if a single cell from that organism has been wired up to a polygraph that measures the electrical change in the cell, the machine will pick this up. It is no different from a radio signal, where your personal radio is tuned to the correct wavelength for each station: any change in the wavelength and you will not be able to listen to your programme.

It is all about vibrations and how living organisms react to each other's vibrations. It would seem that the cell is perfectly aware of its own natural vibration, and the electrical characteristics of the electrons within the cell change when its natural vibration is altered, which is reflected in the polygraph's trace. There is no requirement for either intelligence or a central nervous system for this response to be engendered within a single cell; it is simply the electrons and the nucleus of the cell that react to the vibrations. When a vibrational disequilibrium occurs, the electrical balance changes. If you can accept that this is what happens, the unique properties of plants become all too obvious and what might have been extraordinary to you before will, I hope, become very logical.

In 2003, Backster finally wrote his own version of events and published his book *Primary Perception*. This goes into much more personal detail than the *Secret Lives of Plants* and is much more authoritative. However, what no doubt was frustrating for Backster was that, for thirty years, his ideas had received only ridicule and abuse. He was to most scientists a laughing stock.

PLANTS AND ANIMALS ARE THE SAME

In the very early stages of cell development, the first advanced organisms were the plants. From these developed insects, birds, fish and finally humans, a natural progression over millions of years. So in one respect it is possible to say that we all come from plants if we look back that far, although that view is not so easy to accept. If I were to say that we are similar to fish, is that any easier? If you can make that leap, it is not hard to assume that wherever fish came from, so did we.

In the book *Your Inner Fish*, the author, Neil Shubin, explains that as a lecturer in anatomy his background in palaeontology is a huge advantage when teaching human anatomy. In order to show his students how the human body functions, he turns to the structure of fish. If he is lecturing on the nerve paths in the brain, the most effective method of showing these is to analyse a shark, and with limbs the best road map is fish. The reason Shubin gives for this is that the "bodies of these creatures are often simpler versions of ours". If this is the case, Bose's assertion that plants and animals are behaviourally the same implies that plants and humans are the same, if you can accept that we are just overly developed fish. If that is true and you make a list of the behaviours of humans, you will find that the list is very similar to one showing the behaviour of plants.

So what do you think the following list is describing – is it fish, plants or humans?:
- Has an ability to communicate with others.
- Can recognise family members.

- Has the capability to remember things.
- Shows signs of fatigue when overstimulated.
- Contains a nerve system.

Well, these are in fact five common features of plants. Other behavioural habits include:

- a response to every wavelength from the long wavelengths emanating from distant planets to the ultrafast waves of ultraviolet light;
- an increase in growth when stimulated by sound;
- a growth in height before a lightning storm.

It has finally been realised that plants are not just passive objects that work solely on the basis of chemical reactions, but are much more complicated than that. Research conducted within the last few years has finally turned to the unusual behaviour of plants and has shown that plants do in fact have memory, planning abilities, learning capabilities, complex plant behaviour and even cognition.

In recent scientific research, it has been shown that plants and animals have the following shared patterns of behaviour:

1. Plants and animals use identical sexual processes.
2. Plants develop immunities using processes and mechanisms that correspond identically to those in animals.
3. Animals and plants use the same molecules and pathways to drive their own biological clocks.
4. Plants perform complex information-processing via cell-to-cell communication.
5. All cells and parts of a plant respond in exactly the same way to electrical stimulation as animals do.

6. Plants can memorise stressful experiences and can conjure up these memories when needing to make decisions about future activities.
7. Plants recognise their siblings.
8. Plants anticipate future conditions by accurately perceiving and responding to reliable environmental cues.
9. Plants have the potential to make decisions based upon responses to gravity, light, moisture and touch.
10. Amino acids are essential elements for both animals and plants. They are involved in several functions such as protein synthesis, hormone metabolism, nerve transmission, cell growth, production of metabolic energy, base synthesis for the nuclear material, nitrogen metabolism and urea biosynthesis.
11. Plants communicate with other plants and herbivores.

Why, then, do they have similar behavioural characteristics? The only conclusion that I can draw is that they all come from the same cellular development processes that first started life on Earth, and they all developed the same basic behaviours to stimulation from light, sound, temperature, atmospheric changes and electromagnetic forces. As a consequence plants, fish and humans have a good deal in common.

PLANTS TALK TO EACH OTHER

It is surprising to learn that most botanists have only recently woken up to the fact that plants communicate with each other. In 1983, one of the first studies was undertaken to show that, in times of crisis, plants of similar species communicate information immediately to each other so that they can put up a collective defence. An experiment was conducted on young poplar trees in one room in which a few leaves from a sample group of fifteen trees were physically damaged. Fifteen more, but undamaged, poplar trees in another room showed a change in their chemical content in response to the damage that had accrued in the first set of trees. As one of the scientists was heard to exclaim when he analysed the chemical changes, "Hey – poplars talk."

Of course, no-one has yet been able to furnish an understanding of how plants communicate. All of the science in this area of communication refers to chemical signals between plants. It is suggested that chemicals somehow float in the air and are collected in an unknown way by other plants. My simple alternative suggestion is this: do you really think nature would develop such an inefficient method of communicating? What would happen on a blustery day when the wind was blowing in the wrong direction? It would be impossible to communicate danger to plants upwind using this method. No, the answer to this riddle lies in the properties of vibrations. A damaged leaf emits a vibrational signal that other plants which have the same base vibrational wavelength recognise, and this change in vibration stimulates a chemical change in every similar plant in the area – a very simple and incredibly efficient method of communication, one that I believe is one hundred per cent reliable. I would argue that this is a perfect system of communication and would have dominated evolutionary development.

PLANTS RECOGNISE THEMSELVES

Research by Richard Karban of the University of California and Kaori Shiojiri of Kyoto University in Otsu, Japan, has revealed that some plants are capable of recognising themselves. Experiments have shown, using a genetically identical sagebrush plant, that two clones communicate and cooperate with one another. This confirms that plants, just like animals, prefer to help their relatives

Sagebrush

over unrelated individuals:

Somehow, the clipped plants appeared to be warning their genetically identical neighbours that an attack was imminent, and the neighbour should somehow try to protect itself. But clipped plants didn't warn unrelated neighbours.

Karban says he was "pretty surprised" at the results – "It implies that plants are capable of more sophisticated behaviour than we imagined." Golly gosh. This discovery was made only in 2009. I fear it is going to be hard to change mainstream teaching towards accepting that plants are so much more sophisticated than scientists will readily accept.

Sadly, Karban and Kaori believe the plants are communicating using chemicals:

When one plant is clipped, or comes under attack from herbivores, it emits these chemicals into the air, warning those around it to put up a defence, either by filling their leaves with noxious chemicals, or by physically moving their stems or leaves in some way to make themselves less palatable.

What is even more depressing is that this research has proven that plants recognise each other, but because other scientists do not understand the mechanism for the exchange of this information, they remain sceptical that this relationship exists in the first place.

PLANTS RECOGNISE THEIR SIBLINGS

Thanks to Darwin, we all know that plants compete with each

other – survival of the fittest. However, what we might not have been aware of is that plants do not compete with their own siblings. Their relationship is very similar to that of animal species, where the parents help and nurture their offspring in the hope that they will develop into adulthood. It seems that, in this behavioural case, plants are again just like animals.

In a paper by Dudley and File in 2007, it was shown that the plant *Cakile edentula* was able to identify its kin in competitive settings and react by competing less aggressively against a close relative. When individuals were grown in pots with close relatives, root biomass was lower than in individuals grown in the vicinity of strangers.

Cakile Edentula

This would mean that kin recognition and the subsequent reduction in root growth facilitates the development of relatives that occupy the neighbouring space. So the parent plant does not maximise its growth potential while being surrounded by its kin. Other research following on from this paper showed that plants surrounded by strangers grow significantly more than those surrounded by kin. This seems logically obvious. If scientists had investigated vibrations a lot earlier, this would all have been seen as common sense: plants behave just like animals, nurturing their young and fighting off competition. Plants have yet again been shown to be the same as animals.

In order to provide solutions to this problem, scientists believe that it is root development that allows plants to identify their kin to each other. How can this be? Why do they assume that plants recognise each other's roots? What is there in a root that is recognisable? As I have said countless times in this book, it is almost impossible not to come to the conclusion that plants recognise each other through their own individual vibrational signal rather than anything else.

Why have there not been any scientific experiments on plants' vibrational communication? In a paper in 2007, Günther Witzany makes a typical statement that seems to be a universally accepted interpretation of how plants communicate. He says:

Chemical molecules are used as signs. They function as signals, messenger substances, information carriers and memory medium in either solid, liquid or gas eous form, in order to guarantee coordination and organisation processes.

What he should have said is that some plants and some animals use chemicals as a form of communication between themselves – obvious uses are for finding a mate or for defence purposes, some leaves emitting toxins that deter pest infestations. What is missing is the fact that this simple answer fails to resolve the fact that plants also communicate with each other and with insects and animals at distances that are not capable of being achieved via chemical emissions, particularly when it is windy. No plant would evolve that was dependent solely on favourable wind conditions.

Another quote shows the logic behind current scientific thought :

In Lima beans, various coordinated defence strategies against mite infestation have been discovered. First, they change their scent to make them unattractive to the mites, then the plants emit scents that are perceived by other plants, which then do precisely the same thing to warn surrounding lima beans before the mites even reach them. Some of the emitted substances

*have the effect of attracting other mites that eat the attacking
red mites.*

I have no doubt that lima beans emit chemicals to fight off mite infestation, but what I find very difficult to accept is the simple assumption that the whole process is carried out exclusively via chemical communication between plants, and even more extraordinary is the idea that emitting this chemical scent seems to attract other competing mites who must again then be living upwind of the plants. I have read numerous papers all saying that plants communicate exclusively via chemicals, yet insects and animals communicate sometimes with chemicals and sometimes with vibrations. Where is the research that acknowledges that they communicate both chemically and via vibrations? As I have shown in earlier chapters, it is indisputable that plants and animals are basically similar in behaviour terms, so if animals and insects behave in a certain way, then, by definition, so do plants.

Other research papers have shown that when you move a plant and place it elsewhere, it will remember the identity of its former closest neighbours for several months. One interpretation was that these plants recognise patterns in neuronal-like networks. However, almost twenty years after this research, no-one seems to have put two and two together and said that plants recognise the vibrational pattern of the plant that they used to be next to. One answer lies in the following quote that was published recently in the book *Rhythms in Plants 2009*. The authors, Shabala and Mancuso, reflect in their introduction on the fact that there is very limited research into plant oscillations (vibrations), for which they give the following explanation:

> *Despite the fact that the rhythmical behaviour is a
> quintessential pattern of life itself, most researchers still treat
> oscillations in plants as some unwanted "physiological noise".*

More fool them.

PLANTS TALK WITH THE ANIMALS

How does an insect that is no bigger than two millimetres in length project its voice against the elements, when the sounds that the insect itself can make may be drowned out? The answer is to use vibrations. Instead of vibrations through the air in the form of sound, insects use vibrations that utilise the mass of organic matter around them. Imagine that you are in a crowded square with thousands of people around you and you need to communicate a message to a group of people at the furthest corner of the square – what options do you have if you can't use your voice? As long as they were aware that you were going to try some other form of communication, all you would have to do would be to bang your shoes hard on the ground and your listeners could, simply by placing their ears to the ground where they were standing, pick up the vibrational waves caused by you hitting your shoes on the paving. And this is in principle how small insects communicate over long distances. They simply vibrate the leaves or stems of the plants they are sitting on, the vibration travels into the ground and along the earth, and it is then picked up by all of the plants and vegetative growth in the surrounding area. Importantly, studies have also shown that the signal characteristics of the insects receiving the information stay the same irrespective of the type of plant the sender is resting on. Therefore, it does not matter to the insect what type of leaf or plant stem it is sitting on as it will always receive the information.

All plants give off their own distinctive individual vibrations, and it appears that every insect is aware of these differences. It is estimated that 195,000 different insect species use vibrations to communicate. Notwithstanding that, the frequency the insects

Vibrating the leaf to communicate

use varies depending upon the type of plant they are resting on. In the case of the stink bug (*Nezara viridula*), an insect that is often used in experiments, the difference is significant as the vibration can range from 1 to 500 Hz on Bladderpod leaves, whereas on London rocket leaves it ranges from 100 to 1000 Hz.

Insects must somehow be able to understand what type of leaf they are resting on to adapt their own individual vibration to that of the plant. It has been shown that specific vibrations of the plants will closely match those of insects, and for the stink bug the plant's natural vibrations and those of the insect work best at 100 Hz. At different stages of its development, the insect will utilise different frequencies: the young treehopper will use short signals to solicit maternal care, but the adult will produce complex frequency- and amplitude-modulated signals while searching for a mate.

Tree frog

Tree frogs have been shown to use vibrations to communicate with other tree frogs in neighbouring trees. In fact, it is likely that most vertebrates communicate using vibrations, but very little research has been done in this field as most of it is focused on sound communication. In one of the few experiments on vertebrates, it was found that the tree frogs use vibrations much more than they use sound. They use the power of trees and their ability to transmit vibrational signals over great distances to communicate aggression in conflicts between two opposing male frogs. Other vertebrates that use vibrations include the chameleon, which produces at least three distinct patterns of substrate vibration when in the presence of a female. Tree frogs from South Asia rhythmically tap their toes on plants above breeding sites, which appears to attract males.

THUNDERSTORMS

Nature has developed unusual behavioural characteristics in plants for a reason, but what that reason is, however, is not always obvious. The opposite is true during a thunderstorm. If you analyse a plant's behaviour then, it makes complete sense, but the "how it does it" question is not as easy to answer.

I'm sure I don't need to describe a thunderstorm; we all know what one is. We have been around many people during one who all seem to respond quite differently, some being scared, others taking it in their stride. But what do plants do in a thunderstorm, and if their behaviour changes, how do they know that a thunderstorm is coming? Let's imagine there is a big storm in the distance, the light in the air is getting darker, the atmosphere is getting oppressive, and it slowly starts to spit with rain. At some point over the next few minutes and hours, you know that the electrical charge is going to build up so much that a loud bang will emanate from the clouds, and if the charge is large enough, that energy will be dissipated in the form of lightning. The heavily saturated clouds will then discharge their moisture in the form of rain.

Now, if I were a plant, I would like to know that a large amount of water was coming my way because plants like water, and they need to absorb it to sustain themselves. Ideally, they want to absorb as much as possible. Imagine then that, at the same time as they picked up the fact that a thunderstorm was on the way, they instantly started growing to increase their capacity for water absorption. This would allow them to absorb more water than before the storm was coming, a very, very clever piece of plant biology. And this actually happens. Plants do grow just before a thunderstorm in order to be able to gorge on the extra water available. How useful would it be for us if, when we were starving hungry, we could somehow increase the size of our stomachs in order to allow more food to be absorbed at one time, just in case there was no more food expected for the next few days.

So how do plants know that a thunderstorm is coming? Obviously, they must be able to pick up on the changes in the electrical vibrations in the atmosphere. As I mentioned previously, they can recognise every wavelength from the smallest to the largest. So a huge change caused by an electrical storm would be easy to recognise. How do they pick up on these huge electrical discharges? The answer is through their water content, which immediately transfers information throughout the plant, stimulating growth chemicals and causing the stem and roots to enlarge. These plant transformations can be rapid. For some reason, scientists have thought of the plant as being slow and docile in the way in which it reacts to external stimuli, but certain plants have a reaction time that is faster than that of any animal. This is particularly the case with the venus fly trap, whose trap shuts in a response time of under a tenth of a second.

TALKING TO PLANTS

Most people would laugh at the possibility that talking to a plant is of any use to the plant. I certainly did before I started researching the effect that sound waves have on plants, and now that I know a lot more about the subject, I find it hard to believe that I took such a negative stance, one that was born out of ignorance and prejudice. Ignorance of the science, but prejudice towards those believers whom I thought were impressionable people who followed all of the quackery science that was being peddled by alternative groups. Ones that preached a certain New Age lifestyle and belief system. Now that I am not so ignorant or prejudiced, the joke is on me. The importance of sound should not be underestimated.

If I were to set up a sound system in a field in the countryside and play, for argument's sake, the Beatles' greatest hits at a volume that could be heard throughout the field, do you think that the plants would react in any way? I would imagine that no-one would be easily convinced that this sound could affect the plants significantly. But, in fact, a plant reacts to the music in many different biological ways. Firstly, its level of potassium and calcium will be changing, cell growth will be stimulated, and there will be alternations in the level of ATP (the plants' energy content), the amount of nucleic acid, the quantity and quality of RNA (involved in protein and DNA synthesis), the content of soluble proteins and the activity of the enzyme IAA oxidase . In all, many, many factors are changing in the plant because of the music that is being played.

But if this is the case, why is it not common knowledge? Why are farmers not looking into this possibility in helping to grow their crops? These questions I can't answer. All I can say is that the science is there for anyone who wants to go and investigate it. Which is what I did, and now I can say quite categorically that playing music to plants affects them directly – not always positively, but it stimulates them both positively and negatively depending upon the frequency (Hz) and strength (the volume or decibel level) of the sound signal.

Ultrasound, which comprises extremely high-frequency sound waves that are not audible to human ears, are already extensively used in many different areas, for instance to successfully treat some forms of cancer. Ultrasound is also used in welding, cleaning and chemical and biological processing. And it is used in hospitals in visual imaging, particularly on pregnant women – any parent will remember seeing their first three-dimensional, black and white, living ultrasound image of their developing child.

Scientific experiments into the benefits of ultrasound on plants are numerous. They have shown that ultrasound waves are very efficient at maintaining the shelf-life of fruit and vegetables as they can eradicate some harmful bacteria that encourage the fruit or vegetable to perish. Obviously, any experiment that can benefit the supermarkets will generate good funding, and as this area of science has proved to have a commercial basis, there appears to be lots of funding and scientific experiments relating to it.

The earliest experiments involving audible, that is, slower, sound waves and their effect on plants go back to Bose in 1907, where he clearly discovered that plants are stimulated by sound. Between 1907 and 2001, there were virtually no scientific studies of any significance on this topic, and then in 2001, scientists working in China and Korea wrote a clutch of five significant papers on the different effects that sound waves had on plants. Why was there a gap of almost one hundred years for a number of papers to be published? The reason is that it was considered to be crazy science.

If I were to ask you this question, what would be your first reaction – does talking to plants help them grow? I'm sure the answer would be a resounding no, because it implies that you are somehow creating an emotional response that the plant can pick up on, responding according to your attitude towards it. However, if you look at the question in a different way and ask whether a sound vibration can affect the behaviour of plants, the question is completely different and the effect can be measured scientifically. Imagine discovering that sitting next to a plant for a few minutes a day whispering sweet nothings into the leaves actually helped the plant to grow. My common sense also tells me that we all like different sounds; some we find jarring, others we find incredibly soothing. I know that I react differently to sounds; I don't need a scientific paper to tell me I do. And based upon the fact that plants and humans are behaviourally the same, it seems logical that plants will respond to sound in positive or negative ways.

I find it very surprising that one of the first modern experiments into sounds and plant growth was conducted only late in the 1950s by the Indian botanist T.C. Singh, who first looked at the effects of music on plants. Singh used a microscope to view the protoplasmic streaming in an Asian aquatic plant and discovered that he could induce this streaming at different times of the day by activating an electrically driven tuning fork. He then experimented with recorded South Indian violin music with frequencies in the range of 100–600 Hz range, and demonstrated that these frequencies resulted in increased plant growth.

The concept of music affecting plants was later popularised by an American housewife, Dorothy Retallack, in her book *The Sound of Music and Plants*, published in 1973. Retallack noticed that the plants in her living room, which were exposed to rock music, were not growing as quickly as the other plants in her house. She subsequently conducted a series of experiments whereby a selection of household plants were exposed to three different types of music: rock, jazz and semi-classical. The experiments were controlled under strict scientific conditions, with all the plants were kept in Perspex cabinets with the temperature and light strictly regulated. For three hours a day, music of different types was played into the boxes, and the plants' growth was then measured after four weeks. Later experiments showed that the most beneficial music for Retallack's plants was Indian devotional music, which caused the plants to grow two inches taller than the plants left in silence. These plants also leaned towards the speaker.

Common sense suggests that if I were in an enclosed room listening to loud rock music that I was not familiar with for three hours every day, I would certainly be trying to break the door down to escape. It's not that I don't like loud music or rock music, it's just that having unfamiliar rock beats forced upon me would not be a pleasant experience. I can imagine that my behaviour would definitely change and my mood would almost certainly become affected by the sounds. On the other hand, three hours of classical music, even though I admit to not ever having bought a classical record, would not result in such a change of behaviour because the tones of the music do not affect my behaviour in the same way. I like listening to some classical music as much as any popular music. In fact, some music performed by the cello, violin and saxophone affects me in an incredibly positive way, irrespective of the genre it is part of. It's obvious when I think about it – some music really relaxes me, makes me feel good and can completely change my mood. But why does it do this? Where is the science that proves to me something that I subconsciously already know?

An experiment in 2007 looked at the effects of different musical elements on the root growth of onions. The researchers looked at specific elements of music such as rhythmically dynamically changing lyrics or rhythmic classical music and compared their effects on onion roots. The onions in group 1 listened to Wagner and Mussorgsky, and the onions in group 2 listened to Mozart, Chopin, Schubert and Tchaikovsky. The onions were subjected to the music for six hours a day for ten days. The results concluded that both sets of sound improved root elongation, but in both groups the sounds that involved lyrics increased growth the most.

THE HEALTH BENEFITS OF PLANTS

There are hundreds of scientific papers proving that plants make you healthier. I am not referring to herbal treatment here, but proof that simply being around plants can have positive health benefits. These are not small studies that investigate small-scale tree-hugging; quite the opposite – these are major international studies. You might ask, therefore, that if there are so many benefits, why do we not know about them? Why didn't I know that a plant can have any benefits? The answer, as in so many other instances, is that the scientists do not know they have proved it – in fact, they would probably run a mile if they thought that there was any science in this at all. How could they raise funding for future projects if their research were in any way mixed up with the idea of tree-hugging? But let me give you an example of a study that I believe points towards the idea that trees help people who are ill.

The title of this research gives it all away – "Children with attention deficits concentrate better after walk in the park". This paper, written in 2009 by Taylor and Kuo, can suggest one of two things: either that there is something about going to a park that helps to restore the children's attention, or that objects within the park are creating an environment that somehow stimulates the body to improve its concentration levels. It is pretty obvious which hypothesis all the scientists choose – the first one, the safer option. I am going to propose a different interpretation of the study's findings, and I hope you will agree that my solution fits the facts. I hope my interpretation will change people's opinion of the role of nature in health and will in fact lead, in the future, to free health treatment for millions of people simply by making sure they are near to plants.

Taylor and Kuo's study was incredibly methodical in its design. Seventeen children aged seven to twelve who were all clinically diagnosed with ADHD experienced three environments: a city park, a downtown walk and a neighbourhood walk. Each walk lasted twenty minutes, and their walks in the different environments were spaced one week apart. After each walk, the children's concentration levels were measured using approved measuring techniques for children with ADHD. The conclusion of the study was that twenty minutes in a park setting was sufficient to elevate attention performance relative to the other walks, and that "'Doses of nature' might serve as a safe, inexpensive, widely accessible new tool in the tool kit for managing ADHD symptoms."

If there is this positive affect for children with ADHD, do you not think it would work for everyone? I would argue that all school children should have some of their classes outside, amongst the plants, to improve their concentration levels. One study of forty schools with more than four hundred students found that "environmentally based curricula were linked with a whole range of benefits, including increased engagement and enthusiasm for learning and higher scores on standardized tests in reading writing, maths, science and social studies".

Of course, the ADHD study proves nothing in terms of an underlying mechanism; I use it only to introduce an idea. The park in question was not described so I have no idea what was in it – whether it was a wooded park, one with just grass or a combination of the two. But the study does say that the children just walked in the park. The authors are very specific about this – there was no running around, no exercise, just walking. So there must be something about the park that was causing the children's behaviour to change. The only obvious difference between the three settings is the fact there are a lot of plants in a park, but this of course does not prove one thing or another. It could simply be the fact that the park stimulated a psychological change in the children's attitude, and the power of the brain then changed their biological make-up, allowing them to have an increased concentration level. It could also be that the colour green somehow affected the children's mood as it has been shown that colour significantly affects behaviour.

So, in order to narrow the choices, let's look at a number of other studies into the effect that changes in the environment can have on mental illness. One large public health report that investigated the association between green spaces and mental health concluded that "access to nature can significantly contribute to our mental capital and wellbeing". But what is meant by "nature"? In the study, the authors refer to nature as simply being a park or grassy area within an urban environment. They state that access to such as area has wide-ranging benefits on our health because "a safe, natural environment can be a break from our busy lives – a place to get some fresh air, to exercise or play – a place to go and relax".

Yes, that is all true, but it does not say why the green space? What is it about it that is better? The authors' conclusion is therefore that the benefits of the park derive from the ability to relax in a safe and peaceful environment where the air quality is better, and I have no doubt that these are all beneficial qualities. It would be interesting to analyse the level of mental health issues of those people who work as gardeners in parks, so that we could consider all of the above issues to see which factors play the most significant role. Supposing it was discovered that these workers did not suffer from any mental health problems; one could then conclude that the benefits of the park were nothing to do with the peaceful environment as the gardeners would obviously be doing strenuous and noisy work. It would have to be something else completely.

Irrespective of the reasons why for the moment, the report does agree that "safe, green spaces may be as effective as prescription drugs in treating some forms of mental illnesses". In England, prescribing of drugs for ADHD to under 16s went up by 33% between 2005 and 2007. Maybe doctors need to consider other solutions to this condition such as recommending a walk in the park –ADHD levels would be improved, and everyone would benefit. But obviously doctors can't just recommend this as there is no science to explain it. Who would believe that plants could be the factor making the difference? The science showing an effect is clearly there, but the explanations are definitely not.

One possible answer is provided by psychologists in the study entitled "The cognitive benefits of interacting with nature". This was a thorough review of the health benefits that nature can provide, and it quoted from many past studies that have clearly proved this. However, these scientists turned to psychology to provide the reasons why nature is so beneficial. According to Attention Restoration Theory (ART):

> *interacting with environments rich with inherently fascinating stimuli (e.g., sunsets) invoke voluntary attention modestly, allowing directed-attention mechanisms a chance to replenish ... So, the logic is that, after an interaction with natural environments, one is able to perform better on tasks that depend on directed-attention abilities.*

Because nature is so successful in providing us with health benefits, it has created a whole gamut of lectures, books, articles, conferences, discussions, contracts, theories and professorships in psychology alone. It is going to be hard to convince those involved that the answer lies simply in vibrations and has nothing whatsoever to do with psychology – particularly as this theory is already thirty years old and still going strong. But, irrespective of the reasons why the natural environment improves our behaviour, this study confirmed yet again that walking for only thirty-five minutes amongst trees improved the participant's memory abilities by 20%. By comparison, those subjected to a busy street did not improve at all.

Countless studies have shown that children show significant psychological and physiological effects in terms of their health and well being when they interact with plants. They demonstrate that children function better cognitively and emotionally in green environments and have more creative play in green areas. So what is it about nature that can have these significant effects? Sadly no-one provides any answer for this besides the ones I have already mentioned.

Is it possible to prove that this effect is caused primarily by plants themselves? Yes, and very simply. If you take all of the other factors out and just measure only the effect of plants on behaviour, this should leave no area of doubt that the plants – and nothing else – are the cause. So how do you do a study of this sort? Very easily, I am pleased to say, simply by using indoor plants. At least thirty different studies over the past fifteen years have all investigated the relationship between plants and behaviour. There have been tests related to word associations, pain tolerance, stress recovery, task performances, etc. And the majority of them have found a distinct relationship.

In 1976, fifteen people with severe psychopathology had a geranium plant placed on their dining table while they had their lunchtime meals. Over four weeks, there were significant changes in the amount of conversation that took place between the patients, a significant increase in mean time spent in the dining room and an increase in the amount of food consumed. In 1996, a study involving ninety-six subjects analysed the changes that seventeen plants brought about when placed in a computer laboratory. The treatment

Geranium plant

group, although only exposed to the laboratory for fifteen minutes, showed a 12% improved reaction time, lower stress reactivity and a faster stress recovery. They reported higher attentiveness levels and less fatigue. Overall, they had a 21% lower total symptom score than the unexposed group. Similar levels of response were found in a study that placed twenty-three plants in a radiology department; the mean symptom score of the staff was reduced by 25.6%.

I won't go through all the different studies that I have found, as that would become too boring to read, but you will have to take my word for it that many different studies show a relationship between indoor plants and behaviour very similar to what has been reported in the experiments showing the benefits of walking in the park. I will not say that it proves the plants that are the cause, but for me it strongly suggests that plants affect our behaviour and our health. There is no doubt in my mind that the benefits of being close to nature are produced by the plants themselves somehow affecting our biological make-up, and that this can only be achieved if their vibrational element is affecting ours via the our body's water content.

HOW DO TREES AFFECT US?

As there is no actual proven scientific explanation for the health benefits of a tree, I had to turn to the man who gave me the initial idea in the first place, the strange healer whom I mentioned in my

Introduction. He explained it to me in very simple terms that made complete sense once I understood the nature of vibrations. He used the example of a headache to explain how trees affect our health. He said that the trees give us a "human reboot" – just as we turn the computer on and off when it does not work, so the tree does the same to our body. In the healer's terms, a headache is simply a pain caused by a misaligned vibration sitting next to a normal vibration, the pain being caused by the mismatch between the vibrations. In order to get rid of the pain, all that is needed is to realign the two vibrations to be the healthy one.

And this is exactly what the tree does; it synergises the vibrations by altering every vibration in our body. So when you approach a tree, the vibrations it sends out immediately start to change the vibrational element of the water in your body, which then changes all of the vibrations that are causing the pain. For arguments sake, let's say that the tree vibration increases the speed of all of the vibrations in the body so that both the normal and abnormal ones speed up. All of the vibrations are then taken to a new level in parity with each other, so that there is no misalignment in the vibrations and therefore no pain. Once you walk away from the tree, the vibrations return to their natural level, but the incorrect, misaligned ones have been re-booted back to their healthy level. This is, however, not necessarily going to get rid of the cause of the problem – it just gets rid of the pain.

Obviously, I am not suggesting that trees can cure all illnesses as some viral vibrations might be of such a frequency that the tree cannot affect them, but in the simple case of a headache, the vibrations must for some reason be such that the tree has an effect. It would be very interesting to test out many different illnesses with a large group of volunteers to see which illnesses trees can help. Probably, however, such research is not necessary as all that is required is for historians to delve into the archives to see what the ancient civilisations discovered and use their knowledge instead. It would not surprise me to learn that many South American Amazonians might already know the answer to this without having to read a book; it is probably common knowledge to them in their everyday treatments.

My book has now gone full circle. If you remember, in the Preface I described my son's experience of touching a tree and how it made him feel sick. That initial reaction was the catalyst for this book, and as a result I started to research all that there was to know about trees and their effect on us. As you might have noticed, I have not quoted from any study on that subject because, as far as I can make out, none has yet been conducted. My advice to anyone who might be considering initiating research into the relationship between trees and health is that they need to know the following:

1. Do not assume that men's, women's and children's reactions will be the same.
2. Every plant is different, so choose each plant for a reason.
3. Plants have a lunar cycle, so some plants behave differently at particular points in the lunar cycle.
4. Choose big, healthy examples as using sick plants might affect the results.
5. Keep away from plants that are near stagnant water.
6. Don't look at health issues that have been conducted in the past; look for new ones. There is no reason why trees cannot be beneficial for a range of different illnesses and not just the minor ones that have been researched so far.
7. Make sure that the study takes place over a long period rather than just a few weeks.

These ideas might seem obvious to anyone who works with plants, but I have not found the majority of them mentioned in any scientific paper over the last fifty years. All of them seem like concepts that we would take for granted, but it seems that none of the scientists involved in plants behaviour acknowledges that plants are incredibly sophisticated and have to be handled accordingly, just as with a specific species of animal.

HOW YOU CAN GET INVOLVED

I would like to end this chapter on an anecdotal story, provided by my stepfather, Michael Miles. He was brought up on a farm in Somerset, England, owned by his father, that had been in the family for generations. Michael had never been a farmer, but every six months or so while writing this book, I would go down and visit my mother and stepfather in their cottage in Somerset. I would often recount to them the different ideas I had encountered, particularly those related to trees, to see what reaction they had to my ideas. What shocked me more than anything was that absolutely nothing that I told Michael was new to him. Very early on in my research, I told him that each tree had a planetary relationship associated with its growth cycles. He told me, very matter of factly, that he knew this and that he personally was quite aware he had a special relationship with beech trees that went beyond anything I had told him.

When I had finally finished the book, I happened to visit them and described the outline of this chapter. What Michael told me that weekend came as a bolt of lightning. As we were sitting round the table having dinner, he told me that when he was young, his mother used to tell him that if he had a headache, it was very easy to cure – all he had to do was take a walk in the local woods. At this point, I was a little bit speechless. This was an aspect of trees that I was fully aware of, but as there were no scientific studies to prove it, I was not going to include it in this book. However, as Michael readily came forward with this information, I thought why not?; maybe there are lots of other people who know about this already, and all it will take is a bit of confirmation from others before they publicly acknowledge it, having previously tried to avoid any ridicule. Michael told me he had never expressed his ideas to anyone else as he assumed that it was common knowledge. Maybe like so many ideas that have disappeared, this knowledge has gone underground and been all but forgotten. It occurred to me that it was possible for everything I thought I had discovered to in fact be old news, something known about for generations. Yet for some reason, contemporary society had ignored it and chosen to erase it from our way of thinking.

So, in order to reintroduce these old ideas into mainstream thinking, I want to attempt to get as many people as possible to participate in a study on trees. I intend to include a section on my website, www.blindedbyscience. co.uk, where everyone can

Touching a tree can remove headaches

plot on a map an individual tree in a park or public space that they feel has helped them in some way. Maybe it has made them feel happy, it has looked beautiful, has helped cure a headache, restored or improved their attention, or anything that they want to write. In this way, maybe if we can get enough people involved, we can show scientists that there is overwhelming anecdotal evidence that plants and trees can be part of every doctor's health treatments for people with, for example, depression or ADHD. Maybe even those people who suffer from hangovers or migraines might also want to participate and see what the results are. Wouldn't it be wonderful if we could start to think like those ancient wise men who knew so much that now seems to have been forgotten?

I also plan to introduce a similar section on sleep disorders on the website as I am convinced that we all sleep differently during the different lunar cycles and that our sleep patterns are definitely disturbed by a full moon. If everyone could keep a sleep diary, it would be possible to publicise this fact and change the way that we look at sleep and the lunar cycles, for if these can affect our sleep, what else might they be able to do?

BIBLIOGRAPHY

Introduction

Becker R, Selden G (1985) *The Body Electric*. Harper Paperbacks.

Chapter 1: Vibrations

Adey WR (2004) Potential therapeutic applications of nonthermal electromagnetic fields: ensemble organization of cells in tissue as a factor in biological field sensing. In: Rosch PJ, Markov MS (eds) *Bioelectromagnetic Medicine*, pp. 1–5. Informa Healthcare.

Aon M, Cortassa S, O'Rourke B (2008) Mitochondrial oscillations in physiology and pathophysiology. In: Maroto M, Monk N (eds) *Cellular Oscillatory Mechanisms*, Chapter 8. Landes Bioscience and Apringer science + business media.

Bennet-Clark H (1998) Effects as constraints in insect sound communication. *Philosophical Transactions: Biological Sciences*, 353, pp. 407–419.

Benveniste J (2004) A fundamental basis for the effects of EMFs in biology and medicine: the interface between matter and function. In: Rosch PJ, Markov MS (eds) *Bioelectromagnetic Medicine*, pp. 207–211. Informa Healthcare.

Casas J, Bacher S, Tautz J, Meyhofer R, Pierre D (1998) Leaf movements and air movements in a leafminer-parasitoid system. *Biological Control*, 11, pp. 147–153.

Cocroft RB, Shugart HJ, Konrad KT, Tibbs K (2006) Variation in plant substrates and its consequences for insect vibrational communication. *Ethology*, 112, pp. 779–789.

Cokl A, Zorovic M, Millar J (2007) Vibrational communication along plants by the stink bugs *Nezara viridula* and *Murgantia histrionica*. *Behavioural Processes*, 75, pp. 40–54.

Cremer L, Heckl M, Petersson BAT (2005) *Structure-borne Sound*, 3rd edn. Springer.

Crile G (1926) *A Bipolar Theory of Living Processes*. Macmillan.

Crile G (1936) *The Phenomena of Life*. Heinemann.

Engstrom S (2004) Magnetic field generation and dosimetry. In: Rosch PJ, Markov MS (eds) *Bioelectromagnetic Medicine*, pp. 39 – 40. Informa Healthcare.

Ewald PP, Pöschl T, Prandtl L (1936) *The Physics of Solids and Fluids.* Blackie & Son.

Hankey A (2004) Are we close to a theory of energy medicine? *Journal of Alternative and Complementary Medicine,* 10, pp. 83–86.

Kane S (2002) *Introduction to Physics in Modern Medicine.* CRC Press.

Lakhovsky G (1925) *The Waves that Heal. An Account of the Theories of M. George Lakhovsky.*

Liboff AR (2004) Signal shapes in electromagnetic therapies: a primer. In: Rosch PJ, Markov MS (eds) *Bioelectromagnetic Medicine,* pp. 17–19. Informa Healthcare.

Loomis W (2008) cAMP oscillations during aggregation of dictyostelium. In: Maroto M, Monk N (eds) *Cellular Oscillatory Mechanisms,* Chapter 3. Landes Bioscience and Apringer science + business media.

Lutkenhaus J (2008) Min Oscillation in Bacteria. In: Maroto M, Monk N (eds) *Cellular Oscillatory Mechanisms,* Chapter 4. Landes Bioscience and Apringer science + business media.

Miklavcic D, Kotnik T (2004) Electroporation for electrochemotherapy and gene therapy. In: Rosch PJ, Markov MS (eds) *Bioelectromagnetic Medicine.* Informa Healthcare.

Mitchell, E (2004) Quantum holography: a basis for the interface between mind and matter. In: Rosch PJ, Markov MS (eds) *Bioelectromagnetic Medicine,* pp. 153–159. Informa Healthcare.

Oschman JL (2004) Recent developments in bioelectromagnetic medicine. In: Rosch PJ, Markov MS (eds) *Bioelectromagnetic Medicine,* pp. 77–90. Informa Healthcare.

Palmeirim I, Rodrigues S, Dale J, Maroto M (2008) Development on time. In: Maroto M, Monk N (eds) *Cellular Oscillatory Mechanisms,* Chapter 5. Landes Bioscience and Apringer science + business media.

Prato FS (2004) Image-guided electromagnetic therapy. In: Rosch PJ, Markov MS (eds) *Bioelectromagnetic Medicine,* pp. 51–53. Informa Healthcare.

Rougemont J, Naef F (2008) Stochastic phase oscillator models for circadian

clocks. In: Maroto M, Monk N (eds) *Cellular Oscillatory Mechanisms*, Chapter 10. Landes Bioscience and Apringer science + business media.
.

Saxton-Burr H (1972) *Blueprint for Immortality*. Neville Spearman.

Shabala S, Shabala L, Gradmann D, Chen Z, Newman I, Mancuso S (2006) Oscillations in plant membrane transport: model predictions, experimental validation and physiological implications. *Journal of Experimental Botany*, 57, pp. 171–184.

Thul R, Bellamy T, Roderick H, Bootman M, Coombes S (2008) Calcium oscillations. . In: Maroto M, Monk N (eds) *Cellular Oscillatory Mechanisms*, Chapter 1. Landes Bioscience and Apringer science + business media.

Travassos M, Pierce N (2000) Acoustics, context and function of vibrational signalling in a lycaenid butterfly–ant mutualism. *Animal Behaviour*, 60, pp. 13–26.

Volkov A, Carrell H, MarkinV (2009) Biologically closed electrical circuits in venus flytrap. *Plant Physiology*, 149, pp. 1661–1667.

Waller M (1961) *Chladni Figures, a Study in Symmetry*. G. Bell & Sons.

Wood AB (1941) *A Textbook of Sound*. G. Bell & Sons.

Chapter 2: Water

Alexandersson O (1976) *Living Water: Viktor Schauberger and the Secrets of Natural energy*.

Andocs G, Vincze GY, Szasz O, Szendro P, Szasz A (2009) Effect of curl-free potentials on water. *Electromagnetic Biology and Medicine*, 28, pp. 166–181.

Ayrapetyan SN (2006) *Cell Aqua Medium as a Primary Target for the Effect of Electromagnetic Fields*. Bioelectromagnetics Current Concepts. Springer.

Batmanghelidj F (1983) A new and natural method of treatment of peptic ulcer disease. *Journal of Clinical Gastroenterology*, 5, pp. 203–205.

Bellavite P, Signorini A (2002) *The Emerging Science of Homeopathy: Complexity, Biodynamics and Nanopharmacology*, 2nd edn. North Atlantic Books.

Beloussov LV, Voeikov VL, Martynyuk VS (eds) (2007) *Biophotonics and Coherent Systems in Biology*. Springer.

Burns JT (1997) *Cosmic Influences on Humans, Animals and Plants: An Annotated Bibliography*. Scarecrow Press.

Capel-Boute C (1990) Water as receptor of environmental information: a challenge to reproducibility in experimental research. the Piccardi effect. In: Tomassen GJM, de Graaf W, Knoop AA, Hengeveld R (eds) *Geo-Cosmic Relations: The Earth and its Macro-Environment*. PUDOC.

Coats C (1996) *Living Energies: Viktor Schauberger's Brilliant Work with Natural Energy Explained*. Gateway Books.

Cooke R, Kuntz I (1974) The properties of water in biological systems. *Annual Review of Biophysics and Bioengineering*, 3, pp. 95–126.

Del Giudice E, Preparata G (1988) A new QED picture of water: understanding a few fascinating phenomena. In: Sassaroli E, Srivastava Y (eds) *Macroscopic Quantum Coherence*, pp. 108–129. World Scientific.

DeMeo J (2009) Water as a resonant medium for unusual external environmental factors. Lecture at the Fourth Annual Conference on the Physics, Chemistry and Biology of Water, Mount Snow, Vermont, USA.

Elia V, Napoli E, Germano R (2007) The memory of water: an almost deciphered enigma. Dissipative structures in extremely dilute aqueous solutions. *Homeopathy*, 96, pp. 163–169.

Emoto M (1999) *The Message from Water*. Vol 1 Hado publishing

Emoto M (2004) *The Healing Power of Water*. Hayhouse.

Emoto M (2006) *The Secret life of Water*. Beyond words publishing

Emoto M (2006) *Water Crystal Healing: Music and Images to Restore Your Well Being*. Atria.

Emoto M (2007) *The Miracle of Water*. Beyond Words.

Foletti A, Lisi A, Ledda M, de Carlo F, Grimaldi S (2009) Cellular ELF signals as a possible tool in informative medicine. *Electromagnetic Biology and Medicine*, 28, pp. 71–79.

Gant N, Stinear CM, Byblow WD (2010) Carbohydrate in the mouth immediately facilitates motor output. *Brain Research*, 1350, pp. 151–158.

Giudice E, Tedeschi A (2009) Water and autocatalysts in living matter. *Electromagnetic Biology and Medicine*, 28, pp. 46–52.

Glasgow RDV (2009) *The Concept of Water*. R. Glasgow Books.

Gohar IM, Barkdoll BD (2001) Particle transport in vertical vortex flow. Proceedings of the Water Resources Engineering 2001 Conference of the American Society of Civil Engineers, Orlando, Florida, USA. Section: 1, Chapter: 330. http://cedb.asce.org/cgi/WWWdisplay.cgi?0104729

Gorbaty YE, Demianets YN (1985) An X-ray study of the effect of pressure on the structure of liquid water. *Molecular Physics*, 55, pp. 571–588.

Grigioni M, Daniele C, Morbiducci U, Del Gaudio C, D'Avenio G, Balducci A, Barbaro V (2005) A mathematical description of blood spiral flow in vessels: application to a numerical study of flow in arterial bending. *Journal of Biomechanics*, 38, pp. 1375–1386.

Hitoshi T, Yoshihiro O, Nobuhiro I et al. (2004) Clinical significance of clockwise spiral blood flow in abdominal aortic aneurysm observed by ultrasound Doppler imaging. *Journal of Medical Ultrasonics*, 31, pp. J239–J247.

Houston JG, Gandy SJ, Sheppard DG, Dick JBC, Belch JJF, Stonebridge PA (2003) 2-Dimensional flow quantitative MRI of aortic arch blood flow patterns: effect of age, gender and presence of carotid atheromatous disease on the prevalence of spiral blood flow. *Journal of Magnetic Resonance Imaging*, 18, pp. 169–174.

Houston J, Gandy S, Milne W, Dick J, Belch J, Stonebridge P (2004) Spiral laminar flow in the abdominal aorta: a predictor of renal impairment deterioration in patients with renal artery stenosis? *Nephrology Dialysis Transplantation*, 19, pp. 1786–91.

Jahnke T, Sann H, Havermeier T et al. (2010) Ultrafast energy transfer between water molecules. *Nature Physics*, 6, pp. 139–142.

Janin J (1999) Wet and dry interfaces: the role of solvent in protein–protein and protein–DNA recognition. *Structure*, 7, pp. 277–279.

Knight D, Stromberg J. Centre for Implosion Research. www.implosionresearch.com

Linton J (2010) *What is Water? The History of a Modern Abstraction.* University of British Columbia Press.

Lo S, Li W, Huang S. Water clusters in life. *Medical Hypotheses*, 54, pp. 948–953.

Ludwig W. The memory of water. www.magnetotherapy.de

Martensson L, Wallin G (2008) Sterile water injections as treatment for low back pain during labour: a review. *Australian and New Zealand Journal of Obstetrics and Gynaecology*, 48, pp. 369–374.

Mates R (2010) Hunger and thirst: issues in measurement and prediction of eating and drinking. *Physiology and Behaviour*,100, pp. 22–32.

Ostrander S (1972) *Astrological Birth Control.* Prentice-Hall.

Park JB, Santos JM, Hargreaves BA, Nayak KS, Sommer G, Hu BS, Nishimura DG (2005) Rapid measurement of renal artery blood flow with ungated spiral phase-contrast . *Journal of Magnetic Resonance Imaging*, 21, pp. 590–595.

Paul MC, Larman A (2009) Investigation of spiral blood flow in a model of arterial stenosis. *Medical Engineering and Physics*, 31, pp. 1195–203.

Pfeiffer E (1935) *Practical Guide to the Use of the Bio-dynamic Preparations.* Rudolf Steiner Publishing.

Pfeiffer E (1947) *Soil Fertility, Renewal and Preservation.* Faber & Faber.

Piccardi G (1962) *The Chemical Basis of Medical Climatology.* Charles Thomas.

Popp F-A (2002) Biophotonics – a powerful tool for investigating and understanding life. In: *What is Life? Scientific Approaches and Philosophical Positions.* Series on the Foundations of Natural Science and Technology, Volume 4, pp. 279–306. World Scientific Publishing.

Reich W (1973) *The discovery of the orgone Vol.2 : The Cancer Biopathy.*New York : Farrar, Straus and Giroux Inc., 1973.

Roy E, Tiller WA, Bell I, Hoover MR (2005) The structure of liquid water: novel insight from materials research; potential relevance to homeopathy. *Materials Research Innovations*, 9, pp. 78–103.

Roy, R. et al. The Structure Of Liquid Water; Novel Insights From Materials Research; Potential Relevance To Homeopathy MATERIALS RESEARCH INNOVATIONS VOL 9; NUMB 4, ; 2005, 98-102 -- SPRINGER -- 2005

Rubik, B. Studies and Observations on Frequency-Treated Water, Electrolyzed Water, and Human Blood, Abstract for Water Conference, August, 2010

Schauberger V (1998) *Nature as Teacher*. Gateway Books.

Schauberger V (1998) *Water Wizard*. Gateway Books.

Schauberger V (2000) *The Fertile Earth: Nature's Energies in Agriculture, Soil Fertilisation and Forestry*. Gateway.

Schauberger V (2001) *The Energy Evolution* (translated by C. Coats). Gateway.

Schiff M (1995) *The Memory of Water: Homeopathy and the Battle of Ideas in the New Science*. Thorsons.

Schwenk T (1965) *Sensitive Chaos: The Creation of Flowing Forms in Water and Air*. Steiner Press.

Szent-Györgyi A (xxxx) Biology and pathology of water. Perspectives in Biology and Medicine, Winter 1971, 239-249?

Szent-Györgyi A (1968) Biolectronics. Science, 161, 988-990?

Tiller W. Psychoenergetic science: expanding today's science to include human consciousness.

Treven M, Talkenberger PP *Environmental Medicine. A New Age of Medicine*. Moewig Verlag.

Vermassen F, Dick J, Houston JG, Stonebridge PA (2008) Spiral laminar flow: an examination of this critical blood flow pattern and the early results of a first in man study. Poster presentation at XXII European Society for Vascular Surgery meeting, Nice.

Voeikov VL (2007) *Fundamental Role of Water in Bioenergetics.* Biophotonics and Coherent Systems in Biology. Springer.

Wilkes J (2003) *Flowforms: The Rhythmic Power of Water.* Floris Books.

Chapter 3: The Sun and The Moon: Madness, Menstruation and Manure

Ahmed F. Quinn T, Dawson J, Walters M (2008) A link between lunar phase and medically unexplained stroke symptoms: an unearthly influence? *Journal of Psychosomatic Research,* 65, pp. 131–133.

Ali AA (1993) *Rhythms in Fishes.* NATO Science Series A. Springer.

Ali Y, Rahme R, Matar N et al. (2008) Impact of the lunar cycle on the incidence of intracranial aneurysm rupture: myth or reality. *Clinical Neurology and Neurosurgery,* 110, pp. 462–465.

Allen E (1933) The irregularity of the menstrual function. *American Journal of Obstetrics and Gynecology,* pp. 705–9.

Babayev E, Allahverdiyeva A (2007) Effects of geomagnetic activity variations on the physiological and psychological state of functionally healthy humans: some results of Azerbaijani studies. *Advances in Space Research,* 40, pp. 1941–1951.

Barnwell FH, Brown FA (1964) Organismic responses to very weak magnetic fields. *Proceedings of the 1st Biomagnetics Symposium.*

Beauchamp D, Labrecque G (2007) Chronobiology and chronotoxicology of antibiotics and aminoglycosides. *Advanced Drug Delivery Reviews,* 59(9–10), pp. 896–903.

Beran G (1972) Blood coagulation studies at different localities and correlations with the chemical test of Piccardi. *Journal of Interdisciplinary Cycle Research,* 3, pp. 207–208.

Bhattacharjee C, Bradley P, Smith M, Scally AJ, Wilson BJ (2000) Do animals bite more during a full moon? Retrospective observational an analysis. *BMJ,* 321, pp. 1559–1561.

Brock M (1983) Seasonal rhythmicity in lymphocyte blastogenic responses of mice persists in a constant environment. *Journal of Immunology,* 130, pp.

2586–2588.

Brown FA (1962) Responses of the planarian, *Dugesia* and the protozoan, *Paramecium*, to very weak horizontal magnetic fields. *Biological Bulletin*, 123, pp. 264–281.

Brown F, Chow C (1973) Interorganismic and environmental influences through extremely weak electromagnetic fields. *Biological Bulletin*, 144, pp. 437–461.

Brown F, Chow C (1973) Lunar-correlated variations in water uptake by bean seeds. *Biological Bulletin*, 145, pp. 265–278.

Brown FA, Jr, Brett WJ, Bennett MF, Barnwell FH (1960) Magnetic response of an organism and its solar relationship. *Biological Bulletin*, 118, pp. 367–381.

Brown FA, Jr, Webb HM, Brett WJ (1960) Magnetic response of an organism and its lunar relationships. *Biological Bulletin*, 118, pp. 382–392.

Burns J (1997) *Cosmic Influences on Humans, Animals and Plants: An Annotated Bibliography*. Scarecrow Press.

Chapman S, Morrell S (2000) Barking mad? Another lunatic hypothesis bites the dust. *British Medical Journal*, 321, pp. 1561–1563.

Cook E (1997) A new assessment of possible solar and lunar forcing of the bidecadal drought rhythm in the western United States. *Journal of Climate*, 10, pp. 1343–1356.

Currie R (1987) Climatically induced cyclic variations in United States corn yield and possible economic implications. *Cycles (Pittsburgh)*, May/June, pp. 78–84.

Currie R, Wyatt T, O'Brian D (1993) Deterministic signals in European fish catches, wine harvests and sea level. *International Journal of Climatology*, 13, pp. 665–687.

De Leon FC-P, Santillan-Doherty AM, Camacho FP et al (2004) Lunar and seasonal rhythms and childhood mortality. *Biological Rhythm Research*, 34, pp. 475–484.

Dichev I, James T (2001) Lunar *Cycle Effects In Stock Returns*. Working paper. University of Michigan Business School.

Dorman LI (2005) Space weather and dangerous phenomena on the earth:

principles of great geomagnetic storms forecasting by online cosmic ray data. *Annales Geophysicae*, 23, 2997–3002.

Edwards L (1998) *The Vortex of Life. Nature's Patterns in Space and Time* (including supplements). Floris books

Endres K, Schad W (2002) *Moon Rhythms in Nature: How Lunar Cycles Affect Living Organisms*. Floris Books.

Eugen J (1968) *New Dimensions in Birth Control* (Cosmobiological Birth Control).

Foster FP 1889 The periodicity and duration of the menstrual flow. New York Medical Journal is 1889, vol 49, 610-611

Foster R, Kreitzman L (2005) *Rhythms of Life: The Biological Clocks that Control the Daily Lives of Every Living Thing*. Profile books

Foster R, Roenneberg T (2008) Human responses to the geophysical daily, annual and lunar cycles. *Current Biology*, 18, pp. 784–794.

Foundation for the Study of Cycles (1989) Annual Conference, 9–12th March, Irvine, California.

Gao Q (2009) Lunar phases effect in Chinese stock returns. Paper presented at the International Conference on Business Intelligence and Financial Engineering, 24–26th July, Beijing.

Garsd A, Shifrine M (1982) Environmental factors affecting seasonal variation in immunity of clinically normal dogs. *International Journal of Biometeorology*, 26, pp. 121–128.

Gunn D, Jenkin P, Gunn A (1937) Menstrual periodicity: statistical observations on a large sample of normal cases. *Journal of Obstetrics and Gynaecology of the British Empire*, 44, pp. 839–79.

Haviland A (1855) *Climate, Weather and Disease*. John Churchill.

Hawke E (2003) *Praise to the Moon: Magic and Myth of the Lunar Cycle*. 2003. Llewellyn Publications.

Hejl Z (1977) Daily, lunar, yearly and menstrual cycles and bacterial or viral infections in man. *Journal of Interdisciplinary Cycle Research*, 8(3–4), pp. 250–-253.

Hicks-Casey W, Potter D (1991) Effect of the full moon on a sample of developmentally delayed, institutionalized women. *Perceptual and Motor Skills*, 3, pp. 1375–1380.

Hisato T, Umemoto T (2004) Regarding lunar cycles and abdominal aortic aneurysm rupture. *Journal of Vascular Surgery*, 40, pp. 1261.

Karnaukhova NA, Sergievich LA, Karnaukhov VA, Karnaukhov VN (2004) Changes in the synthetic activity of lymphocytes under the action of physical factors related to solar activity variation. *Biophysics*, 49(Suppl.1), pp. 552–559.

Klett M (2006) *Principles of Biodynamic Spray and Compost Preparations*. Floris Books.

Kolisko L (1936) *The Moon and the Growth of Plants*. Anthroposophical Agricultural Foundation.

Kolisko L (1947) *Gold and the Sun. The Total Eclipse of the Sun of 20th May 1947*. Anthroposophic Press.

Kolisko E, Kolisko L (1939) *Agriculture of Tomorrow*. John Jennings.

Kollerstrom N (2004) Lunar effect on thoroughbred mare fertility: an analysis of 14 years of data 1986–1999. *Biological Rhythm Research*, 35, pp. 317–327.

Kollerstrom N, Steffert B (2003) Sex difference in response to stress by lunar month: a pilot study of four years' crisis-call frequency. *BMC Psychiatry*, 10th December, p. 20.

Lacey L (1975) *Lunaception: A Feminine Odyssey into Fertility and Contraception*. Coward, McCann & Geoghegan.

Law S (1986) The regulation of menstrual cycle and its relationship to the moon. *Acta Obstetrica et Gynecologica Scandinavica*, 65, pp. 45–48.

Lockley S, Tabandeh H, Skene D, Buttery B, Bird A, Defrace R, Arendt J (1995) Day time naps in blind people. *Lancet*, 346, pp. 1491.

McMinn D (200) *Market Timing By The Moon and The Sun*. Twin Palms Publishing.

Mikulecky M, Rovensky J (2000) Gout attacks and lunar cycle. *Medical Hypotheses*, 55, pp. 24–25.

Miles LEM, Raynal DM, Wilson MA (1977) Blind man goes lunar. *New Scientist*, 1st December, p. 564.

Naish F (1989) *The Lunar Cycle: Astrological Fertility Control*. Prism Press.

Nishimura T, Fukushima M (2009) Why animals respond to the full moon: magnetic hypothesis. *Bioscience Hypotheses*, 2, pp. 399–401.

Ostrander S (1972) *Astrological Birth Control*. Prentice-Hall.

Palmer S, Rycroft M, Cermack M (2006) Solar and geomagnetic activity, extremely low frequency magnetic and electric fields and human health at the earth's surface. *Surveys in Geophysics*, 27, pp. 557– 595.

Payne SR, Deardon DJ, Abercrombie GF, Carlson GL (1989) Urinary retention and the lunisolar cycle: is it a lunatic phenomenon? *BMJ*, 299, pp. 1560–1562.

Peters-Engl C, Frank W, Kerschbaum F, Denison U, Medl M, Sevalda P (2001) Lunar phases and survival of breast cancer patients – a statistical analysis of 3,757 cases. *Breast Cancer Research and Treatment*, 70, pp. 131–135.

Pliny Natural History, Volumes 5–8 (trans. H. Rackham). Loeb Classical Library.

Qazi H, Philip J, Cornford P (2005) The transylvani effect – does the lunar cycle influence emergency urological admissions? *European Urology Supplements*, 4, p. 237.

Raison C, Klein H, Steckler M (1999) The moon and madness reconsidered. *Journal of Affective Disorders*, 53, pp. 99–106.

Robertson J (1832) An inquiry into the natural history of the menstrual function. *Edinburgh Medical and Surgical Journal*, 37, p. 227.

Roe K, Van den Bulck J (2006) Moon and media: lunar cycles and television viewing. *Media Psychology*, 8, pp. 287–299.

Rogers W, Randall W (1972), Multiphasic variations in sunshine and thyroid activity during a year. *International Journal of Biometeorology*, 16, pp. 53–69.

Ruegg S, Hunziker P, Marsch S, Schindler C (2007) Association of environmental factors with the onset of status epilepticus – experience from a tertiary care center intensive care unit. Annual Meeting of American Epilepsy

Society, 1st December, Philadelphia, USA.

Sarton G (1939) Lunar influences on living things. *Isis*, 30, pp. 495–507.

Schneider SH, Miller JR, Crist E, Boston PJ (eds) (1991) *Scientists Debate Gaia*. MIT Press.

Schwenk T (1965) *Sensitive Chaos: The Creation of Flowing Forms in Water and Air*. Steiner Press.

Shifrine M (1982) Seasonal variation in immunity of humans. *Biological Rhythm Research*, 13, pp. 157–165.

Stair JB (1897) A sea worm eaten by the Samoans. *Journal of the Polynesian Society*, 6, pp. 141–144.

Steiner R (1924) Spiritual foundations for the renewal of agriculture. Lectures held at Koberwitz, Silesia, 7–16th June.

Stoupel E (2002) The effect of geomagnetic activity on cardiovascular parameters. *Biomedicine and Pharmacotherapy*, 56(Suppl. 2), pp. 247s–256s.

Stoupel E, Babayev ES, Mustafa F, Abramson E, Israelevich P, Sulkes J (2008) Two groups of acute cardiac events and environmental physical activity. *Russian Journal of Solar–Terrestrial Physics*, 12, pp. 354–359.

Stoupel E, Babayev E, Shustarev P, Abramson E, Israelevich P, Sulkes J (2009) Traffic accidents and environmental physical activity. *International Journal of Biometeorology*, 53, pp. 523–534.

Strestik J, Sitar J, Predeanu I, Botezat-Antonescu L (2001) Variations in the mortality with respect to lunar phases. *Earth, Moon and Planets*, 85–86, pp. 567–572.

Svanes C, Sothern R, Sorhye H (1998) Rhythmic patterns in incidence of peptic ulcer perforation over 5.5 decades in Norway. *Chronobiology International*, 15, pp. 241–264.

Tabandeh H, Lockley SW, Buttery R, Skene DJ, Defrance R, Arendt J, Bird AC (1988) Disturbance of sleep in blindness. *American Journal of Ophthalmology*, 126, pp. 707–712.

Thakur CP, Sharma D (1984) Full moon and crime. *Br Med J (Clin Res Ed)*, 289, pp. 1789–1791.

Tomassen G (1995) Solar imprinting in the geomagnetic world: some biological consequences. *International Journal of Biometeorology*, 38, p. 109.

Treloar R, Boynton R, Behn B, Brown B (1967) Variations of the human menstrual cycle through reproductive life" *International Journal of Fertility*, 12, pp. 77–126.

Ulluwishewa (R (1996) Biodynamic agriculture and traditional farming practices in Sri Lanka: a study of the potential of biodynamic agriculture for alleviating current agricultural problems. Working Paper. School of Geography, University of Leeds.

Valandro L, Zordan M, Polanska M , Puricelli P, Colombo L (2004) Relevance of lunar periodicity in human spontaneous abortions. *Gynecologic and Obstetric Investigation*, 58, pp. 179–182.

Vernadsky VI (1998) *The Biosphere*. Complete Annotated Edition Springer.

Waldin M (2004) *Biodynamic Wines*. Mitchell Beazley.

Weigert M, Kaali S, Kulin S, Feichtinger W (2002) Do lunar cycles influence in vitro fertilization results? *Journal of Assisted Reproduction and Genetics*, 19, pp. 539–540.

Wever R (1986) Characteristics of circadian rhythms in human functions. *Journal of Neural Transmission*, Suppl. 21, pp. 323–373.

Yuana K, Zhenga L, Zhub Q (2006) Are investors moonstruck? Lunar phases and stock returns. *Journal of Empirical Finance*, 13, pp. 1–23.

Zettinig G, Crevenna R, Pirich C, Dudczak R, Waldhoer T (2003) Appointments at a thyroid outpatient clinic and the lunar cycle. *Wiener Klinische Wochenschrifte*, 115, pp. 298–301.

Chapter 4: Magnetism – What's the Attraction all About?

Alberto D, Busso L, Crotti G et al. (2008) Effects of static and low frequency alternating magnetic fields on the ionic electrolytic currents of glutamic acid aqueous solutions. *Electromagnetic Biology and Medicine*, 27, pp. 25–39.

Banik S, Bandyopadhyay S, Ganguly S (2003) Bioeffects of microwave – a brief review. *Bioresource Technology*, 87, 155–159.

Bochu W, Xin C, Zhen W, Qizhong F, Hao Z, Liang R (2003) Biological effect of sound field stimulation on paddy rice seeds. *Colloids and Surfaces B: Biointerfaces*, 32, pp. 29–34.

Brown FA, Jr, Barnwell FH, Webb HM (1964) Adaptation of the magnetoreceptive mechanism of mud-snails to geomagnetic strength. *Biological Bulletin*, 127, pp. 221–231.

Cepeda, M Carr, D Sarquis,T Miranda,Ricardo N Garcia, J Zarate, C Static Magnetic Therapy Does Not Decrease Pain or Opioid Requirements: A Randomized Double-Blind Trial A & A February 2007 vol. 104 no. 2 290-294

Chuanyun D, Bochu W, Chuanren D, Sakanishi A (2003) Low ultrasonic fermentation of riboflavin producing strain *Eremothecium ashbyii. Colloids and Surfaces B: Biointerfaces*, 30, pp. 37–41.

Cook C, Saucier D, Thomas A, Prato F (2009) Changes in human EEG alpha activity following exposure to two different pulsed magnetic field sequences. *Biolectromagnetics*, 30, pp. 9–20 .

Crumpton M (2005) The Bernal lecture 2004: Are low frequency electromagnetic fields a health hazard? *Philosophical Transactions of the Royal Society B: Biological Sciences*, 360, pp. 1223–1230.

Daedalus (1991) Green music. *Nature*, 351, pp. 104.

Davis R, Scott P (2000) Groovy plants: the influence of music on germinating seedlings and seedling growth. *Journal of Experimental Botany*, 51, p. 73.

De Souza A, Garcia D, Sueiro L, Gilart F, Porras E, Licea L (2006) Pre-sowing magnetic treatments of tomato seeds increase the growth and yield of plants. *Bioelectromagnetics*, 27, pp. 247–257.

De Souza A, Sueiro L, Gonzalez L, Licea L, Porras E, Gilart F (2008) Improvement of the growth and yield of lettuce plants by the non-uniform magnetic fields. *Electromagnetic Biology and Medicine*, 27, pp. 173–184.

Du Trémolet de Lacheisserie E, Gignoux D, Schlenker M (2002) *Magnetism: Fundamentals*. Springer.

Elez-Martinez P, Martin-Belloso O (2007) Effects of high intensity pulsed electric field processing conditions on vitamin C and antioxidant capacity of orange juice and gazpacho a cold vegetable soup. *Food Chemistry*, 102, pp. 201–209.

Finegold L, Flamm B (2006) Magnet therapy: extraordinary claims but no proved benefits. *BMJ*, 332, p. 4.

Florez M, Carbonell M, Martinex E (2007) Exposure of maize seeds to stationary magnetic fields: effects on germination and early growth. *Environmental and Experimental Botany*, 59, pp. 68–75.

Gilbert W (1893) *De Magnete* (trans. P. Fleury Motteleay). Facsimile published by Dover Publications.

Harlow T, Greaves C, White A, Brown L, Hart A, Ernst E (2004) Randomised controlled trial of magnetic bracelets for relieving pain in osteoarthritis of the hip and knee. *BMJ*, 329, pp. 1450–1454.

Henry SL, Concannon MJ, Yee GJ (2008) The effect of magnetic fields on wound healing: experimental study and review of the literature. *Eplasty: Journal of Burns and Wounds*, 8, pp. e40.

Hippe P, Uhlmann J (1959) Die Anwendung des Ultraschalls bei schlecht heilenden fracturen. *Zentralblatt für Chirurgie*, 28, pp. 1105–1110.

Huang H, Wang S (2008) The effects of inverted magnetic fields on early seed germination of mung beans. *Bioelectromagnetics*, 29, pp. 649–657.

Iujuan W, Bochu W, Yi J, Defang L, Chuanren D, Xiaocheng Y, Sakanishi A (2003) Effects of sound stimulation on protective enzyme activities and peroxidase isoenzymes of chrysanthemum. *Colloids and Surfaces B: Biointerfaces*, 27, pp. 59–63.

Jiping S, Bochu W, Meisheng L, Hongyang Z, Xin C, Chuanren D (2003) Optimal designs for sound wave stimulation on the growth conditions of chrysanthemum callus. *Colloids and Surfaces B: Biointerfaces*, 30, pp. 93–98.

Kalmijn JA (1971) The electric sense of sharks and rays. *Journal of Experimental Biology*, 55, pp. 371–383.

Kirschvink JL, Winklhofer M, Walker MW (2010) Biophysics of magnetic orientation: strengthening the interface between theory and experimental design.

Journal of the Royal Society Interface, 7(Suppl. 2), pp. S179–S191.

Lambrozo J (2001) Electric and magnetic fields with a frequency of 50–60Hz: assessment of 20 years of research. *Indoor and Built Environment*, 10, pp. 299–305.

Lanchun S, Bochu W, Zhiming L, Chuanren D, Chuanyun D, Sakanishi A (2003) The research into the influence of low-intensity ultrasonic on the growth of *S. cerevisiae*. *Colloids and Surfaces B: Biointerfaces*, 30, pp. 43–49.

Lee SK, Beck NS, Kim HK (1996) Mischievous magnets: unexpected health hazard in children. *Journal of Pediatric Surgery*, 31, pp. 1694–1695.

Liboff AR (2007) Local and holistic electromagnetic therapies. *Electromagnetic Biology and Medicine*, 26, pp. 315–325.

Lissmann HW (1958) The mechanism of object location in *Gymnarchus niloticus* and similar fish. *Journal of Experimental Biology*, 35, pp. 451–486.

Markov M (2007) Therapeutic application of static magnetic fields. *Environmentalist*, 27, pp. 457–463.

Markov M (2007) Expanding use of pulsed electromagnetic field therapies. *Electromagnetic Biology and Medicine*, 26, 257–274.

Markov M (2009) What needs to be known about the therapy with static magnetic fields. *Environmentalist*, 29, pp. 169–176.

Novikov V, Shelman I, Fesenko E (2008) Effect of weak static and low-frequency alternating magnetic fields on the fission and regeneration of the planarian *Dugesia tigrina*. *Bioelectromagnetics*, 29, pp. 387–393.

Novitskaya G, Tserenove O, Kocheshkova T, Novitskii Y (2006) Effect of alternating magnetic field on the composition and level of lipids in radish seedlings. *Russian Journal of Plant Physiology*, 53, pp. 75–84.

Null G (1998) *Healing with Magnets*. Four Walls Eight Windows.

Nyjon K. Eccles. A Critical Review of Randomized Controlled Trials of Static Magnets for Pain Relief. The Journal of Alternative and Complementary Medicine. June 2005, 11(3): 495-509. doi:10.1089/acm.2005.11.495.

Ozel CA, Khawar KM, Arslan O (2008) A comparison of the gelling of isubgol, agar and gelrite on in vitro shoot regeneration and rooting of variety Samsun of tobacco (*Nicotiana tabacum* L.). *Scientia Horticulturae*, 117, pp. 174–181.

Prioreschi P (2001) *A History of Medicine*, vol. 1V. Horatius Press.

Qadri S, Beevi N, Mani A, Leelapriya T, Dhilip K, Narayan P (2006) Sinusoidal magnetic fields and chawki (silkworm) rearing in sericulture. *Electromagnetic Biology and Medicine*, 25, pp. 145–153.

Qin Y, Lee W, Choi Y, Kim T, (2003) Biochemical and physiological changes in plants as a result of different sonic exposures. *Ultrasonics*, 41, pp. 407–411.

Rose DF, Smith PD (1987) Magnetoencephalography and epilepsy research. *Science*, 238, pp. 329–335.

Samad L, Ali M, Ramzi H (1999) Button battery ingestion: hazards of esophageal impaction. *Journal of Pediatric Surgery*, 34, pp. 1527–1531.

Sharma A, Gupta M (2006) Ultrasonic pre-irradiation effect upon aqueous enzymatic oil extraction from almond and apricot seeds. *Ultrasonics Sonochemistry*, 13, pp. 529–534.

Shigemitsu T, Yamazaki K, Nakasono S, Kakikawa M (2007) A review of studies of the biological effects of electromagnetic fields in the intermediate frequency range. *IEEJ Trans*, 2, pp. 405–412.

Subramanian S et al. (1969). A study on the effect of music on the growth and yield of paddy. *Madras Agricultural Journal*, 56, pp. 510–516.

Tallquist, Hj. (1905), KARL SELIM LEMSTRÖM: HIS LIFE AND WORK, Terr. Magn. Atmos. Electr., 10(2), 97–100,

Tkalec M, Malaric K, Pevelak-Kozlina B (2005) Influence of 400, 900 and 1900 MHz electromagnetic fields on *Lemna minor* growth and peroxidase activity. *Biolectromagnetics*, 26, pp. 185–193.

Trebbi G, Borghini F, Lazzarato L, Torrigiana P, Calzoni G, Betti L (2007) Extremely low frequency weak magnetic fields enhance resistance of NN tobacco plants to tobacco mosaic virus and elicit stress-related biochemical activities. *Bioelectromagnetics*, 28, pp. 214–223.

Vaezzadeh M, Noruzifar E, Faezah G, Salehkotahi M, Mehdian R (2006) Excitation of plant growth in dormant temperature by steady magnetic field.

Journal of Magnetism and Magnetic Materials, 302, pp. 105–108.

Vashisth A, Nagarajan S (2008) Exposure of seeds to static magnetic field enhances germination and early growth characteristics in chickpea. *Bioelectromagnetics*, 29, pp. 571–578.

Walther M, Mayer F, Kafka W, Schutze N (2007) Effects of weak, low frequency pulsed electromagnetic fields on gene expression of human mesenchymal stem cells and chondrocytes. *Electromagnetic Biology and Medicine*, 26, pp. 179–190.

Weinberger P, Measures M (1979) Effects of the intensity of audible sound on the growth and development of Rideau winter wheat. *Canadian Journal of Botany*, 57, pp. 1036–1039.

Witzany G (2007) Bio-communication of plants. *Nature Precedings*. Available from: http://hdl.handle.net/10101/npre2007.1429.1

Xiaocheng Y, Bochu W, Chuanren D (2003) Effects of sound stimulation on energy metabolism of *Actinidia chinensis* callus. *Colloids and Surfaces B: Biointerfaces*, 30, pp. 67–72.

Xiujuan W, Bochu W, Yi J, Chuanren D, Sakanishi A (2003) Effect of sound wave on the synthesis of nucleic acid and protein in chrysanthemum. *Colloids and Surfaces B: Biointerfaces*, 29, pp. 99–102.

Yano A, Hidaka E, Fujiwara K, Limoto M (2001) Induction of primary root curvature in radish seedlings in a static magnetic field. *Bioelectromagnetics*, 22, pp. 194–199.

Yano A, Ohashi Y, Hirasaki Y, Fujiwara K (2004) Effects of a 60Hz magnetic field on photosynthetic CO_2 uptake and early growth of radish seedlings. *Bioelectromagnetics*, 25, pp. 572–581.

Yiyao L, Bochu W, Xuefeng L, Chuanren D, Sakanishi A (2002) Effects of sound field on the growth of chrysanthemum callus. *Colloids and Surfaces B: Biointerfaces*, 24, pp. 321–326.

Chapter 5: The Bees and the Birds

Baker CTG 1948 *Understanding the Honey Bee*. Camphill Press.

Balmori A (2009) Electromagnetic pollution from phone masts. Effects on wildlife. *Pathophysiology*, 16(2–3): 191–199.

Balmori A, Hallberg O (2007) The urban decline of the house sparrow: a possible link with electromagnetic radiation. *Electromagnetic Biology and Medicine*, 26, pp. 141–151.

Eskov EK, Sapozhnikov AM (1976) Mechanisms of generation and perception of electric fields by honeybees. *Biophysik*, 21, pp. 1097–1102.

Everaert J, Bauwens D (2007) A possible effect of electromagnetic radiation from mobile phone base stations on the number of breeding house sparrows. *Electromagnetic Biology and Medicine*, 26, pp. 63–72.

Fernie K, Bird D (2000) *Evidence of Oxidative Stress in American Kestrels Exposed to Electromagnetic Fields*. Avian Science and Conservation Centre, McGill University, Canada.

Freeman D, Graham JH, Tracy M, Emlen JM, Alados C (1999) Developmental instability as a means of assessing stress in plant: a case study using electromagnetic fields and soybeans. *International Journal of Plant Sciences*, 160, pp. S157–S166.

Frier H, Edwards E, Smith C, Neale S, Collett T. Magnetic compass cues and visual pattern learning in honeybees. *Journal of Experimental Biology*, 199, pp. 1353–1361.

Garaj-Vrhovac V, Gajski G, Trosic I, Pavicic I (2009) Evaluation of basal DNA damage and oxidative stress in Wistar rat leukocytes after exposure to microwave radiation. *Toxicology*, 259, pp. 107–112.

Gould JL (1986) The locale map of honeybees: Do insects have cognitive maps? Science 1986; 232: pp. 861–863.

Gould J, Towne W (1987) Evolution of the dance language. *American Naturalist*, 130, pp. 317–338.

Gould JL, Kirschvink JL, Deffeyes KS (1978) Bees have magnetic remanence. *Science*, 201, pp. 1026–1028.

Gould JL, Kirschvink JL, Deffeyes KS, Brines ML (1980) Orientation of demagnetized bees. *Journal of Experimental Biology*, 80, pp. 1–8.

Harst W, Kuhn J, Stever H (2006) Can electromagnetic exposure cause a change in behavior? Studying possible non-thermal influences on honeybees – an approach within the framework of educational informatics. http://agbi.uni-landau.de/material_download/IAAS_2006.pdf

Hsu CY, Ko FY, Li CW, Fann K, Leu JT (2007) Magnetoreception system in honey bees (*Apis mellifera*). *Plos One*, 2, pp. e395.

Kavokin KV (2009) The puzzle of magnetic resonance effect on the magnetic compass of migratory birds. *Bioelectromagnetics*, 30, pp. 402–410.

Kirschvink J, Kobayashi A (1991) Is geomagnetic sensitivity real? Replication of the Walker–Bitterman magnetic conditioning experiment in honey bees. *American Zoologist*, 31, pp. 169–185.

Kirschvink JL, Padmanabha S, Boyce CK, Oglesby J (1997) Measurement of the threshold sensitivity of honeybees to weak, extremely low-frequency magnetic fields. *Journal of Experimental Biology*, 200, pp. 1363–1368.

Kuterbach D (1987) *Do Bees Have a Magnetic Sense?* Central Association of Bee-Keepers.

Maori E, Paldi N, Shafir S, Kalev H, Tsur E, Glick E, Sela I (2009) IAPV, a bee-affecting virus associated with colony collapse disorder can be silenced by dsRNA ingestion. *Insect Molecular Biology*, 18, pp. 55–60.

Menzel R, Greggers U, Smith A et al. (2005) Honeybees navigate according to a map-like spatial memory. *PNAS*, 8, 3040–3045.

Naug D (2009) Nutritional stress due to habitat loss may explain recent honeybee collapses. *Biological Conservation*, 142, pp. 2369–2372.

Nichol H, Locke M (1995) Honeybees and magnetoreception. *Science*, 269, pp. 1888–1889.

Panagopoulos D, Karabarbounis A, Margaritis L (2004) Effect of GSM 900 MHz mobile phone radiation on the reproductive capacity of *Drosophila melanogaster*. *Electromagnetic Biology and Medicine*, 23, pp. 29–43.

Schiff H (1991) Modulation of spike frequencies by varying the ambient magnetic field and magnetite candidates in bees (*Apis mellifera*). *Comparative Biochemistry and Physiology A*, 100, pp. 975–985.

Schmitt DE, Esch HE (1993) Magnetic orientation of honeybees in the laboratory. *Naturwissenschaften*, 80, pp. 41–43.

Sharpe R (2009) Honey bee collapse disorder is possibly caused by a dietary pyrethrum deficiency. *Bioscience Hypotheses*, 2, pp. 239–440.

Sherman P, Seeley T, Reeve H (1998) Parasites, pathogens and polyandry in honey bees. *American Society of Naturalists*, 151, pp. 392–396.

Sinha RK (2008) Chronic non-thermal exposure of modulated 2450 MHz microwaves radiation alters thyroid hormones and behaviour of male rats. *International Journal of Radiation Biology*, 84, pp. 505–513.

Towne W (1995) Frequency discrimination in the hearing of honey bees. *Journal of Insect Behaviour* , 8, pp. 281–286.

vanEngelsdorp D, Evans JD, Saegerman C et al. (2009) Entombed pollen: a new condition in honey bee colonies associated with increased risk of colony mortality. *Journal of Invertebrate Pathology*, 101, pp. 147–149.

Walker M (1998) On a wing and a vector. A model for magnetic navigation by homing pigeons. *Journal of Theoretical Biology*, 192, pp. 341–349.

Walker M, Bitterman M (1985) Conditioned responding to magnetic fields by honeybees. *Journal of Comparative Physiology A*,157, pp. 67–71.

Walker M, Bitterman M (1989) Honeybees can be trained to respond to very small changes in geomagnetic field intensity. *Journal of Experimental Biology*, 145, pp. 489–494.

Walker MM, Baird DL, Bitterman ME (1989) Failure of stationary but not for flying honeybees (*Apis mellifera*) to respond to magnetic field stimuli. *Journal of Comparative Physiology*, 103, pp. 62–69.

Walker M, Diebel CE, Pankhurst P, Green C, Hough C, Montgomery J (1997) Structure and function of the vertebrae magnetic sense. *Nature*, 390, pp. 371–376.

Warnke U (1976) Effects of electric charges on honeybees. *Bee World*, 57, pp. 50–56.

Warnke U (2009) *Bees, Birds and Mankind: Destroying Nature by Electrosmog.* Effects of Wireless Communication Techonologies Series. Competence Initiative for the Protection of Humanity, Environment and Democracy.

Wiltschko R, Wiltschko W (2005) Magnetic orientation and magnetoreception in birds and other animals. *Journal of Comparative Physiology A,* 191, pp. 675–693.

Wiltschko R, Wiltschko W (2007) When does bearing magnets affect the size of deflection in clock-shifted homing pigeons? *Behavioural Ecology and Sociobiology,* 61, pp. 493–495.

Chapter 6: Technology –the invisible invader

Agarwal A, Deepinder F, Sharma RK, Ranga G, Li J (2008) Effect of cell phone usage on semen analysis in men attending infertility clinic: an observational study. *Fertility and Sterility,* 89, pp. 124–128.

Belotti M (2007) Endogenous cyclotron ion resonance therapy for keratoconus: preliminary results. *Electromagnetic Biology and Medicine,* 2007, 26, pp. 289–291.

Benvenuto Resolution 2006. *Electromagnetic Biology and Medicine,* 25, pp. 197–2006. Signed by: Fiorella Belpoggi, European Foundation for Oncology and Environmental Sciences; Carl F. Blackman, Raleigh, NC, USA; Martin Blank, Department of Physiology, Columbia University, New York, USA; Natalia Bobkova, Institute of Cell Biophysics, Pushchino, Moscow Region; Francesco Boella, National Institute of Prevention and Worker Safety, Venice, Italy; Zhaojin Cao, National Institute of Environmental Health, Chinese Center for Disease Control, China; Allessandro D. Allessandro, Physician, Mayor of Benevento, Italy, (2001–2006); Enrico D. Emilia, National Institute for Prevention and Worker Safety, Monteporzio, Italy; Emilio Del Giuduice, National Institute for Nuclear Physics, Milan, Italy; Antonella De Ninno, Italian National Agency For Energy, Environment and Technology, Frascati, Italy; Alvaro A. De Salles, Universidade Federal do Rio Grande do Sul, Porto Alegre, Brazil; Livio Giuliani, East Veneto and South Triol, National Institute for Prevention and Worker Safety, Camerino University; Yury Grigoryev, Institute of Biophysics, Chairman, Russian National Committee NIERP; Settimo Grimaldi, Institute of Neurobiology and Molecular Medicine, National Research, Rome, Italy; Lennart Hardell, Department of Oncology, University Hospital, Orebro, Sweden; Magda Havas, Environmental and Resource Studies, Trent University, Ontario, Canada; Gerard Hyland, Warwick University, UK, International Institute of Biophysics, Germany, EM Radiation Trust, UK; Olle Johansson, Experimental Dermatology

Unit, Neuroscience Department, Karolinska Institute, Sweden; Michael Kundi, Head, Institute Environmental Health, Medical University of Vienna, Austria ; Henry C. Lai, Department of Bioengineering, University of Washington, Seattle, USA; Mario Ledda, Institute of Neurobiology and Molecular Medicine, National Council for Research, Rome, Italy; Yi-Ping Lin, Center of Health Risk Assessment and Policy, National Taiwan University, Taiwan; Antonella Lisi, Institute of Neurobiology and Molecular Medicine, National Research Council, Rome, Italy; Fiorenzo Marinelli, Institute of Immunocytology, National Research Council, Bologna, Italy; Elihu Richter, Head, Occupational and Environmental Medicine, Hebrew University-Hadassah, Israel; Emanuela Rosola, Institute of Neurobiology and Molecular Medicine, National Research Council, Rome, Italy; Leif Salford, Chairman, Department of Neurosurgery, Lund University, Sweden; Nesrin Seyhan, Head, Department of Biophysics, Director, Gazi NIRP Center, Ankara, Turkey; Morando Soffritti, Scientific Director, European Foundation for Oncology and Environmental Sciences; B. Ramazzini, Bologna, Italy; Stanislaw Szmigielski, Military Institute of Hygiene and Epidemiology, Warsaw, Poland; Mikhail Zhadin, Institute of Cell Biophysics, Pushchino, Moscow Region.

Campioli GZ (2007) Case study: eosinophilic granuloma. *Electromagnetic Biology and Medicine*, 26, pp. 333–334.

Castellacci P (2007). Case study: peripheric joint disorders. *Electromagnetic Biology and Medicine*, 26, pp. 331.

Ciafaloni A (2007) Cyclotronic ion resonance therapy and arthralgia. *Electromagnetic Biology and Medicine*, 26, pp. 299–303.

Crescentini F (2007) The autistic syndrome and endogenous ion cyclotron resonance: state of the art. *Electromagnetic Biology and Medicine*, 26, pp. 305–309.

D'Andrea P, Maurizio L (2007) Effects of endogenous cyclotronic ionic resonance (ICR) on macular diabetic edema: preliminary results. *Electromagnetic Biology and Medicine*, 26, pp. 293–298.

Fejes I, Závaczki Z, Szállosi J, Koloszár S, Daru J, Kovács L, Pál A (2005) Is there a relationship between cell phone use and semen quality? *Archives of Andrology*, 51, 385–393.

Habash RWY (2008) *Bioeffects and Therapeutic Applications of Electromagnetic Energy*. CRC Press.

Havas M (2006) Electromagnetic hypersensitivity: biological effects of dirty electricity with emphasis on diabetes and multiple sclerosis. *Electromagnetic*

Biology and Medicine, 25, pp. 259–268.

Havas M (2008) Dirty electricity elevates blood sugar among electrically sensitive diabetics and may explain brittle diabetes. *Electromagnetic Biology and Medicine*, 27, pp. 135–146.

Kato M (ed.) (2006) *Electromagnetics in Biology*. Springer.

Leszcynski D, Xu Z (2010) Mobile phone radiation health risk controversy: the reliability and sufficiency of science behind the safety standards. *Health Research Policy and Systems*, 8, p. 2.

Liboff AR (2007) Local and holistic electromagnetic therapies. *Electromagnetic Biology and Medicine*, 26, pp. 315–325.

Liboff AR (2007) 'Local and holistic electromagnetic therapies', pp. 315–325 *Electromagnetic Biology and Medicine*, 26,

Mancuso M, Ghezzi V, Di Fede G (2007) Utilization of extremely low frequency (ELF) magnetic fields in chronic disease; five years experience: three case reports. *Electromagnetic Biology and Medicine*, 26, pp. 311–313.

Mansfield NJ (2005) *Human Response to Vibration*. CRC Press.

Peratta C, Peratta A (2010) *Modelling the Human Body Exposure to ELF Electric Fields*. Topics in Engineering, Vol. 47. WIT Press.

Piccardi G (1962) *The Chemical Basis of Medical Climatology*. Charles C. Thomas.

Rea WJ, Pan Y, Yenyves EJ, Sujisawa I, Suyama H, Samadi N, Ross GH. Electromagnetic field sensitivity. *Journal of Bioelectricity*, 10, 241–256.

Report of an Independent Advisory Group on Non-ionising Radiation (2006) *Power Frequency Electromagnetic Fields, Melatonin and the Risk of Breast Cancer (RCE-1)*. Health Protection Agency.

Roosli M (2008) Radiofrequency electromagnetic field exposure and non specific symptoms of ill health: a systematic review. *Environmental Research*, 107, pp. 277–287.

Rossi E, Corsetti MT, Sukkar S, Poggi C (2007) Extremely low frequency electromagnetic fields prevent chemotherapy induced myelotoxicity. *Electromagnetic Biology and Medicine*, 26, pp. 277–281.

Rubin GJ, Nieto-Hernandez R, Wessely S (2010) Idiopathic environmental intolerance attributed to electromagnetic fields: an updated systematic review of provocation studies. *Bioelectromagnetics*, 31, pp. 1–11.

Santi C, Turco A (2007) Case study: amyotrophic lateral sclerosis. *Electromagnetic Biology and Medicine*, 26, pp. 329–330.

Sher L (2000) The effects of natural and man-made electromagnetic fields on mood and behaviour: the role of sleep disturbances. *Medical Hypotheses*, 54, pp. 630–633.

Stavroulakis P (ed.) (2003) *Biological Effects of Electromagnetic Fields.* Springer.

Vallesi G, Raggi F, Rufini S, Gizzi S, Ercolani E, Rossi R (2007) Effects of cyclotronic ion resonance on human metabolic processes: a clinical trial and one case report. *Electromagnetic Biology and Medicine*, 2007, 26, pp. 283–288.

Walker C, Seitelman L, Mcelhaney J (1982) Effects of high intensity 60Hz fields on bone growth. *Electromagnetic Biology and Medicine*, 1, pp. 339–349.

Wever R (1973) Human circadian rhythms under the influence of weak electric fields and the different aspects of these studies. *International Journal of Biometeorology*, 17, pp. 227–232.

Chapter 7: Sir J.C.Bose

Response in the Living and Non-living, 1902

Plant response as a means of physiological investigation, 1906

Comparative Electro-physiology: A Physico-physiological Study, 1907

Researches on Irritability of Plants, 1913

The physiology of photosynthesis, 1924

The Nervous Mechanisms of Plants, 1926

Plant Autographs and Their Revelations, 1927

J.C.Bose, Collected Physical Papers. 1927

Growth and tropic movements of plants, 1928

Motor mechanism of plants, 1928

Chapter 8: Plants

Bailey-Lloyd C (2003–2004) Classical music therapy. http://ezinearticles. com/?Classical-Music-Therapy&id=43698

Baluska F, Mancuso S (2009) *Signaling in Plants*. Springer.

Begich N, Slade BB (2005–2006) French physicist creates new melodies – plant songs. http://www.rexresearch.com/agro/1strnhm.htm

Berman G, Jonides J, Kaplan S (2008) The cognitive benefits of interacting with nature. *Psychological Science*, 19, pp. 1207–1212.

Booth DT (xxxx) Innovation in wildland shrub establishment. Environmental Geochemistry and Health (1984), volume 6, pp. 111–114

Braam J, Davis RW (1990) Rain induced, wind-induced, and touch-induced expression of calmodulin and calmodulin-related genes in *Arabidopsis*. *Cell*, 60, pp. 357–367.

Braam J, Davis RW (1990) Rain induced, wind-induced and touch-induced expression of calmodulin and calmodulin-related genes in *Arabidopsis*. *Archives of Environmental Contaminaton and Toxicology*, 60, pp. 357–364.

Bringslimark T, Hartig T, Patil G (2009) The psychological benefits of indoor plants: a critical review of the experimental literature. *Journal of Environmental Psychology*, 29, pp. 422–433.

Bruin J, Dicke M (2001) Chemical information transfer between wounded and unwounded plants: backing up the future. *Biochemical Systematics and Ecology*, 29, pp. 1103–1113.

Bruin J, Sabels MW, Dicke M (1995) Do plants tap SOS signals from their infested neighbours? *Trends in Ecology and Evolution*, 10, 167–170.

Caldwell M, Johnston R, McDaniel JG, Warkentin K (2010) Vibrational signalling in the agonistic interactions of red-eyed treefrogs. *Current Biology*, 20, pp.

1012–1017.

Carbonell MV, Martínez E, Díaz JE, Amaya JM, Flórez M (2004) Influence of magnetically treated water on germination of signalgrass seeds. *Seed Science and Technology*, 32, pp. 617–619.

Chang LW, Meier JR, Smith MK (1997) Application of plant and earthworm bioessays to evaluate remediation of a lead contaminated soil. *Archives of Environmental Contaminaton and Toxicology*, 32, pp. 166–171.

Cook CM, Saucier DM, Thomas AW, Prato FS (2009) Changes in human EEG alpha activity following exposure to two different pulsed magnetic field sequences. *Bioelectromagnetics*, 30, pp. 9 –20.

Davies E (2006) Electrical signals in plants: facts and hypothesis. In: Volkov AG (ed.) *Plant Electrophysiology – Theory and Methods*, pp. 407–418. Springer.

Davis R, Scott P (2000) Groovy plants: the influence of music on germinating seedlings and seedling growth. *Journal of Experimental Botany*, 51, p. 73.

Demiray H (2006) Effect of static electric fields in root cells of *Vicia faba*. *Electromagnetic Biology and Medicine*, 25, pp. 53–60.

Dudley S, File A (2007) Kin recognition in an annual plant. *Biology Letters*, 3, pp. 435–438.

Ekici N, Dane F, Mamedova L, Metin I, Huseyinov M (2007) The effects of different musical elements on root growth and mitosis in onion (*Allium cepa*) root apical meristem. Musical and biological experimental study. *Asian Journal of Plant Science*, 6, pp. 369–373.

Faculty of Public Health (2010) *Great Outdoors: How our Natural Health Service Uses Green Space to Improve Wellbeing*. Briefing Statement. Faculty of Public Health.

Fjeld T (2000) The effect of interior planting on health and discomfort among workers and school children. *HortTechnology* , 10, pp. 46–52.

Goldsworthy A (2006) Effects of electrical and electromagnetic fields on plants and related topics. In: Volkov AG (ed.) *Plant Electrophysiology – Theory and Methods*, pp. 247–248. Springer.

Gurcay E, Yuzer S, Eksioglu E, Bal A, Cakci A (2008) Stanger bath therapy for ankylosing spondylitis: illusion or reality? *Clinical Rheumatology*, 27, 913–917.

Hartig T, Mang M, Evans GW (1991) Restorative effects of natural environment experiences. *Environment and Behaviour*, 23, pp. 3–26.

Hou TZ, Mooneyham RE (1999) Applied studies of plant meridian system. I: The effect of agri-wave technology on yield and quality of tomato. *American Journal of Chinese Medicine*, XXVII, pp. 1–10.

Hou TZ, Luan JY, Wang JY, Li MD (1994) Experimental evidence of a plant meridian system. III: The sound characteristics of phylodendron (*Alocasia*) and effects of acupuncture on those properties. *American Journal of Chinese Medicine*, XXII(3–4), pp. 205–214.

Huang H, Wang S (2008) The effects of inverter magnetic fields on early seed germination of mung beans. *Bioelectromagnetics*, 29, pp. 649–657.

Jones D (1991) Green music. *Nature*, 351, p. 104.

Karban R (2008) Plant behaviour and communication. *Ecology Letters*, 11, pp. 727–739.

Konijnendijk C, Nilsson K, Randrup T, Schipperijn J (2005) *Urban Forests and Trees*. Springer.

Kowarik I, Korner S (2005) *Wild Urban Woodlands*. Springer.

Lieberman GA, Hoody LL (1998) *Closing the Achievement Gap: Using the Environment as an Integrating Context for Learning*. State Education and Environment Roundtable, San Diego. Science Wizards.

Lohr VI, Pearson-Mims C, Goodwin GK (1996) Interior plants may improve worker productivity and reduce stress in a windowless environment. *Journal of Environmental Horticulture*, 14, pp. 97–100.

Maller CJ (2004) Nature in the schoolyard: investigations into the potential of 'hands-on' contact with nature in improving the mental health and wellbeing of primary school children. In: Martens B, Keul AG (eds) *Evaluation in Progress – Strategies for Environmental Research and Implementation*. IAPS 18 Conference Proceedings. International Association for People–Environment Studies.

Mancuso S, Shabala S (2007) *Rhythms in Plants*. Springer.

Mancuso S, Shabala S (2010) *Waterlogging Signalling and Tolerance in Plants*.

Springer.

Mencuccinni M, Grace J, Moncrieff J, Mcnaughton KG (2004) *Forests at the Land–Atmosphere Interface*. CABI Publishing.

Milla R, Forero D, Escudero A, Iriondo J (2009) Growing with siblings: a common ground for cooperation or for fiercer competition among plants? *Proceedings of the Royal Society of London B*, 267, pp. 2531–2540.

Mishra NS, Mallick BN, Sopory SK (2001) Electrical signal from root to shoot on sorghum bicolor: induction of leaf opening and evidence for fast extracellular propagation. *Plant Science*, 160, pp. 237–245.

Novitskaya G, Kocheshkova T, Novitskii Y (2006) Magnetically induced root curvature. *Russian Journal of Plant Physiology*, 53, pp, 638–648.

O'Donnell L (1999) Music power: The report. http://users.characterlink.net/odonnell/report.html.

Ravitz LJ (1970) Electromagnetic field monitoring of changing state-function, including hypnotic states. *Journal of the American Society of Psychosomatic Dentistry and Medicine*, 17, pp. 119–27.

Retallack DL (1973) *The Sound of Music and Plants*. DeVorss.

Robards AW, Lucas WJ, Pitts JD, Jongsma HJ, Spray DC (1990) *Parallels in Cell to cell Junctions in Plants and Animals*. NATO ASI series H, Cell Biology, Volume 46. Springer.

Robertson D (1998) About positive music: the plant experiments. http://www.dovesong.com/positive_music/plant_experiments.asp

Rojas E, Herrera LA, Sordo M, Gonsebatt ME, Montero R, Rodriguez R, Ostrosky-Wegman P (1993) Mitotic index and cell proliferation kinetics for identification of antineoplastic activity. *Anticancer Drugs*, 46, pp. 637–640.

Rooke A (1985) Searching for the lost chord: ancient uses and modern trends. http://www.theosophy-nw.org/theosnw/arts/ar-rooke.htm

Schultz J (2002) Biochemical ecology: how plants fight dirty. *Nature*, 416, pp. 267.

Schultz, J, Baldwin I (1983) Rapid changes in tree leaf chemistry induced by damage: evidence for communication between plants. *Science*, 221, pp. 277–279.

Seregin IV, Ivanov VB (2001) Physiological aspects of cadmium and lead toxic effects on higher plants. *Russian Journal of Plant Physiology*, 48, pp. 323–344.

Shabala S (2006) Oscillations in plants. In: Baluska F, Mancuso S, Volkmann D (eds) *Communication in Plants*, pp. 261–275. Springer.

Shang C (1996) The meridian system and the mechanism of acupuncture. 21st,The VXM Network. http://www.vxm.com

Shubin N (2008) *Your Inner Fish*. Pantheon.

Smith A, Pitt M (2009) Sustainable workplaces: improving staff health and well being using plants. *Journal of Corporate Real Estate*, 11, pp. 52–63.

Stankovic B (2006) Electrophysiology of plant gravitropism. In: Volkov AG (ed.) *Plant Electrophysiology – Theory and Methods*, pp. 424–431. Springer.

Subramanian S (1969) A study on the effect of music on the growth and yield of paddy. *Madras Agricultural Journal*, 56, pp. 510–516.

Takabayashi J, Arimura G (2001) Do plants communicate with each other via airborne signals? *AgroBiotechNet* 3: ABN065.

Talbott JA, Stern D, Ross J, Gillen C (1976) Flowering plants as a therapeutic/ environmental agent in a psychiatric hospital. *Hortscience*, 11, pp. 365–366.

Talos (2001) If only corn had ears. *ASPB News*, 286, pp. 8–9.

Taylor A, Kuo F (2009) Children with attention deficits concentrate better after walk in the park. *Journal of Attention Disorders*, 12, pp. 402–409.

Tkalec M, Malaric K, Pevalek-Kozlina B (2005) Influence of 400, 900 and 1900 MHz electromagnetic fields on lemma minor growth and peroxidase activity. *Bioelectromagnetics*, 26, pp. 185–193.

Tompkins P, Bird C (1989) *The Secret Life of Plants*. HarperCollins.

Tompkins P, Bird C (1998) *Secrets of the Soil*. Earthpulse press.

Tudge C (2006) *The Secret Life of Trees*. Penguin.

Turkington R (1989) The growth distribution and neighbour relationships of *Trifolium repens* in a permanent pasture. *Journal of Ecology*, 77, pp. 734–746.

Turkington R, Sackville-Hamilton R, Gliddon C (1991) Within-population variation in localized and integrated responses of *Trifolium repens* to biotically patchy environments. *Oecologia*, 86, pp. 183–192.

Vashisth A, Nagarajan S (2008) Exposure of seeds to static magnetic field enhances germination and early growth characteristics in chickpea. *Bioelectromagnetics*, 29, pp. 571–578.

Volkov A (2006) *Plant Electrophysiology: Theory and Methods*. Springer.

Volkov A, Brown C (2006) Electrochemistry of plant life. In: Volkov AG (ed.) *Plant Electrophysiology – Theory and Methods*, pp. 437–441. Springer.

Wagner E, Lehner L, Veit J, Normann J, Vervliet-Scheebaum M, Albrechtova JTP (2006) Control of plant development by hydro-electrochemical signal transduction: a way for understanding photoperiodic flower induction. In: Volkov AG (ed.) *Plant Electrophysiology - Theory and Methods*, pp. 483-501. Springer.

Weinberger P, Measures M (1979) Effects of the intensity of audible sound on the growth and development of Rideau winter wheat. *Canadian Journal of Botany*, 57, pp. 1036–1039.

Wicke RW (2002) The Mozart effect. *Herbalist Review*, Issue 2002 No. 1. http://www.rmhiherbal.org/review/2002-1.html

Wierzbicka M (1987) Lead translocation and localization in Allium cepa roots. Canadian Journal of Botany, 65, pp. 4008–4026.

Witzany G (2007) Bio-communication of plants. *Nature Precedings*. hdl:10101/npre.2007.1429.1

Wulder M, Franklin S (2003) *Remote Sensing of Forest Environments*. Kluwer Academic.

Wulder M, Franklin S (2007) *Understanding Forest Disturbance and Spatial Pattern*. Taylor & Francis.

ACKNOWLEDGEMENTS

I would like to thank the following people who have
helped me write the book:

Teresa Godbold, Carrie Walker, Rebecca Haywood,
Harriet Venn, Rosalie Silverstone,

Dragos Grosu, Razvan Alexa, Andrei Danila, Lloyd Geddes,
Steve Lodewyke, Paul Price, Victoria Beer.

ABOUT THE AUTHOR

Matthew Silverstone is a serial entrepreneur. He has a degree in economics and a masters degree in international business. He was as one of the youngest executive producers of his generation within the film industry, at aged only 22, whereby he attempted to raise finance for major feature films. He moved on to developing musical talent and helping to develop the careers of budding artists.

Having attempted and failed to make his millions before he was 25 he decided to work within less glamorous sectors of business and developed successful companies within the cleaning, building, property development, childcare and transport sectors. His career came to a halt midway through the launch of a major internet social network site due to the illness of his son, for whom he became a full time carer. It was watching the lack of medical help from the established sectors of science that led him to start questioning everything that he had been told about science.

He comes from a very traditional medical background, both his brother and father are Professors of medicine, so it was not easy for him to shed off his traditional medical ideas and start questioning the very foundation of these concepts. Once he started to do so, and found that the answers to the questions were not what he thought, he started to treat the whole idea as if it were a new business and spent two years researching and developing the ideas behind Blinded By Science. His son has since made a full recovery and this book helps to explain many of the ideas why doctors will never find cures for some of the major illnesses that are affecting society today.